P9-CJH-821

THE SUCCESSFUL DRAGONS

THE SUCCESSFUL DRAGONS

A Natural History of Extinct Reptiles

Christopher McGowan

With Original Illustrations by
Marg Sansom-Markezinis

Samuel Stevens
Toronto and Sarasota
1983

Canadian Cataloguing in Publication Data

McGowan, C., 1942–
The successful dragons

Includes index.
ISBN 0-88866-618-7

1. Dinosaurs. 2. Reptiles, Fossil. I. Title.

QE862.D5M24 567.9'1 C82-095324-5

Samuel Stevens and Company,
64 Alexandra Blvd.
Toronto, Ontario M4R 1L9

Canadian Edition,
ISBN 0-88866-616-7
Printed and Bound in Canada

U.S. Edition,
ISBN 0-89522-022-9

P.O. Box 3899, Sarasota,
Florida 33578

Marsh's illustrations appear on pages 54, 87, 88, 90 and 132. These figures have now been published and appear in Ostrom, J.H. and McIntosh, J.S. 1966. *Marsh's Dinosaurs*, Yale University Press, New Haven. Courtesy of United States Geological Survey and Yale University Press.

For Angela, Claire, and Elizabeth

Acknowledgements

It is with some trepidation that I write my thanks to those who have helped me, for fear of leaving some name unmentioned. I would therefore like to express my sincere thanks and gratitude to everyone who assisted me in making this book possible; from the patient people who read earlier drafts of the manuscript, to those who helped with the final illustrations, and everyone in between.

I thank the National Sciences and Engineering Research Council of Canada, not only for providing a grant towards publication costs of this book, but also for their generous support of my research programme over the years. Thanks also to the Ontario Arts Council for providing a grant.

For reading specific chapters of the manuscript I thank: Profs. C.S. Churcher, P. Dodson, S.J. Gould, R. Johnson, J. Machin, J.S. McIntosh, J.H. Ostrom, L.B. Radinsky, R.E. Sloan, M.P. Winsor, Dr. D.A. Russel and Mr. J. Thomason. For reading the manuscript in its entirety I thank: Mrs. S. Sherwood, Profs. T.S. Parsons and W.E. Swinton, and four anonymous reviewers. For reading parts of the manuscript and for making valuable comments I thank the Meacher family. I am sincerely grateful to each one of you for the time you have invested and the comments you have made.

Marg Sansom-Markezinis' ability to capture Mesozoic reptiles with her brush is much in evidence in the pages which follow. I thank her for her industry, and for her love of her subjects.

The Royal Ontario Museum, where I have learned most of what I know about Mesozoic reptiles, deserves special thanks. Many people in the Museum have helped in some way or another; from proof-reading and photography to discussing ideas, and it would be impossible to thank each one by name without making some inadvertent omissions. I would therefore like to thank everyone who has helped, with particular thanks to the Departments of Photography, Vertebrate Palaeontology, and to the Library. My thanks also for permission to use many of the illustrations which appear in this book.

I am indebted to the late Tom Fairley for editing the manuscript and for giving so much encouragement and valuable advice, a debt I can never repay.

Much midnight oil was burned in writing this manuscript, and countless weekends consumed, which was not very fair to my family. For their support, understanding and long-suffering patience, I thank Angela, Claire and especially Liz, and apologise to them for all the times we missed together.

Contents

THE SUCCESSFUL DRAGONS

1
Setting the Stage

Few of us can gaze up at the skeleton of a dinosaur without being touched with a feeling of wonder. I walk past dinosaurs every day in our museum, but I can never do so without having that same feeling. They were, and still are, magnificent creatures. Just imagine if we could add flesh and blood to those silent bones—just imagine.

The fascination that dinosaurs hold for us probably has a lot to do with their large size, though they were not all giants. Perhaps the fact that they are now all extinct has a certain appeal too, and that they lived and died on the Earth all those millions of years ago, an Earth lush, warm and dominated by reptiles. That is not to say that there were not plenty of other animals living at that time. The major invertebrate groups were all present and flourishing, so too were the mammals and birds, but the reptiles were the major element of the vertebrate fauna. Reptiles flew in the air, reptiles swam in the sea, and reptiles had domain over the land. That is why this particular geological period, the Mesozoic Era, is often referred to as the Age of Reptiles.

Judged in terms of their long tenure on the Earth, a period of some 160 million years, and in terms of their numbers and their diversity, the Mesozoic reptiles were a phenomenal success. This fact flies in the face of the popular practice of epitomising dinosaurs and their reptilian kin with doom and failure. Modern reptiles—the crocodiles, snakes, lizards, turtles, and *Sphenodon* (sole representative of an ancient stock, related to lizards)—though successful in their own right, pale into insignificance in comparison with the reptiles of that former age.

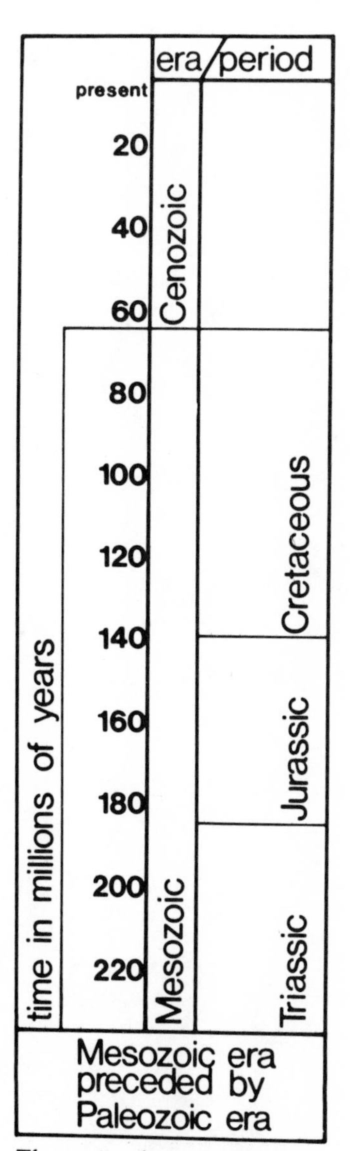

The major divisions of the Mesozoic Era—the Age of Reptiles.

Why were the Mesozoic reptiles so successful? Was there anything special about them? The answer to this last question is probably no—the reptiles probably just happened to be at the right place at the right time. Today it is the turn of the mammals, tomorrow, who knows? Mesozoic reptiles faced similar problems in their world that animals face today, often resolving them in a similar fashion. Some of their solutions, however, were unique, and this is what makes them such a fascinating group to study. Little wonder that so many books have been written about them.

The purpose of this book is to examine the underlying reasons for the success of the Mesozoic reptiles in terms of their adaptations to the environment. No attempt will be made at a comprehensive treatment of all of them—that would require several books. Instead, emphasis will be placed on those groups that illustrate interesting solutions to particular biological problems. The giant sauropod dinosaurs, for example, will be used to illustrate the adaptations that have evolved with increased body size, and the pterosaur *Pteranodon* illustrates some of the intricate modifications that have evolved for high-performance gliding. The ichthyosaurs will figure prominently, not only because they were highly modified for life in the sea, and because they are of particular interest to me, but also because no adequate account of the group has ever been given outside of the technical literature.

We will attempt to treat our subjects as if they were living animals, but the inferences that we can draw are only as robust as the data before us. As most of our knowledge of extinct animals is drawn from the study of their skeletal remains, we have to be very careful not to draw conclusions beyond the limitations of our data. Palaeontologists have a penchant for extrapolation, often rushing in with conclusions where neontologists would fear to tread. To safeguard against this pitfall, constant references will be made to modern animals. Before drawing inferences from the skeletal features of extinct animals we will first determine whether this can be done for the modern animals that we know.

Our interpretations of the biological phenomena we study will be made within the framework of neo-Darwinian evolution, the unifying concept of the biological sciences. While biologists may disagree on certain aspects of the mechanisms of evolution, and while we are revising our ideas on such problems as the evolution of higher taxa (macroevolution), few biologists doubt the fact that evolution has occurred, and continues to occur. Some people, however, deny the fact, arguing that the natural world is more satisfactorily explained in terms of special creation. Many of the criticisms raised by creationists are founded upon misunderstandings and misconceptions of the theory of evolution, and much of this arises from the poor job that we make of teaching the subject of evolution to our high school and university students. My own education was certainly remiss in this regard, and my enquiries lead me to conclude that this is the rule rather than the exception. Fossils are central to most discussions of evolution, and the fossil record has traditionally been used to document the theory. However, as many of us are aware, Darwin found that the fossil record was more of a hindrance than a help.

For all these reasons the second chapter will be devoted to an account of Darwin's work and the fossil record. However, before considering these things, we need to sketch an outline of the Mesozoic world and its inhabitants.

The early part of the Mesozoic Era was a world of evergreens, dominated by pines, firs, and other needle-bearing plants. Ferns were abundant, some of them growing as tall as trees. So, too, were cycads, which looked like palm trees with stunted trunks. Ground cover was provided by various types of mosses, and by horse tails *(Equisetum)*. There were no grasses, shrubs, or other flowering plants. A somewhat similar flora may be seen today in New Zealand, New Guinea, Central and South America, and the Caribbean. It was not until Cretaceous times that flowering plants appeared, and the landscape at that time must have been rather like that of the Gulf coast of North America today. But North America was not in the same geographic position then, and neither were any of the other continents.

The geography of the Mesozoic world was as unusual as its fauna and flora, and this is attributed to the movement of continents. The idea that the continents have drifted apart was first suggested in the 19th century and was formally proposed by Alfred Wegener in 1915 (though he was not first to do so), but did not become generally accepted until about 50 years later. We need not concern ourselves with the details of the theory, there are many excellent texts on the subject.[1] Suffice to say that the evidence that the continents have drifted apart is conclusive, and that the theory provides us with the solutions to some otherwise baffling problems of animal distribution. How, for example, did the flightless birds—the rheas, ostriches, cassowaries, emus, and kiwis—come to be located in South America, Africa, Australia, New Guinea, and New Zealand—lands that are separated by

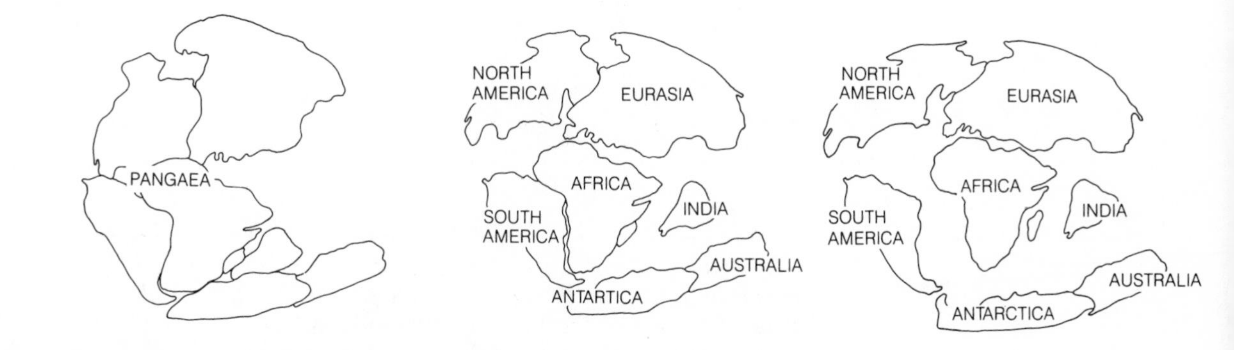

The approximate positions of the continents during the Mesozoic Era. Left to Right: Middle Triassic; Pangea, the universal land mass, begins to break up. Late Jurassic; South America, with Africa still attached has broken off from North America and Eurasia, Antarctica while attached to Australia, has separated from Africa while India drifts towards Eurasia. Late Cretaceous; North America is splitting off from Eurasia with the opening up of the Atlantic Ocean, Africa is almost into its present day position, North and South America are still separate but Australia has not yet separated from Antarctica.

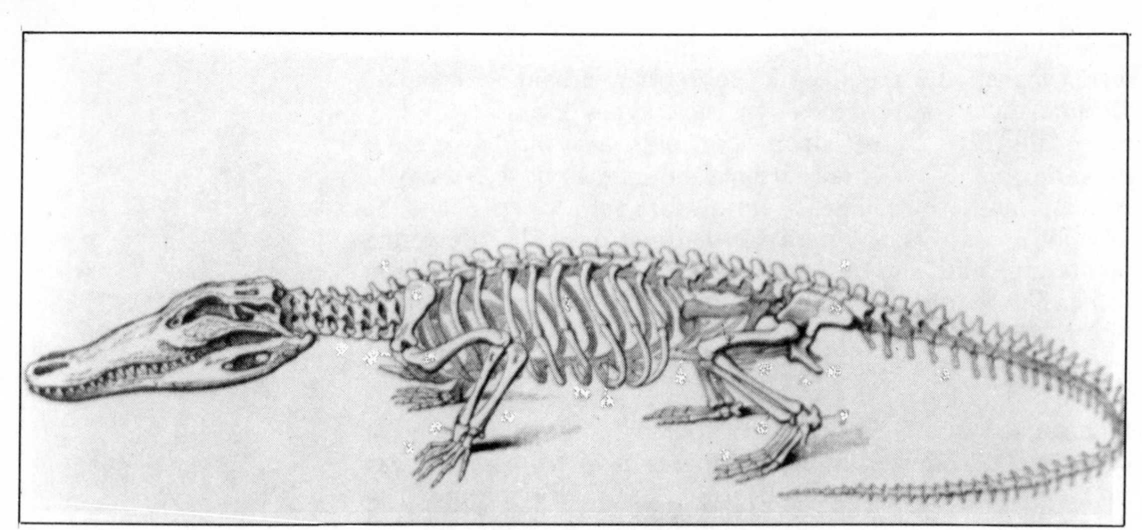

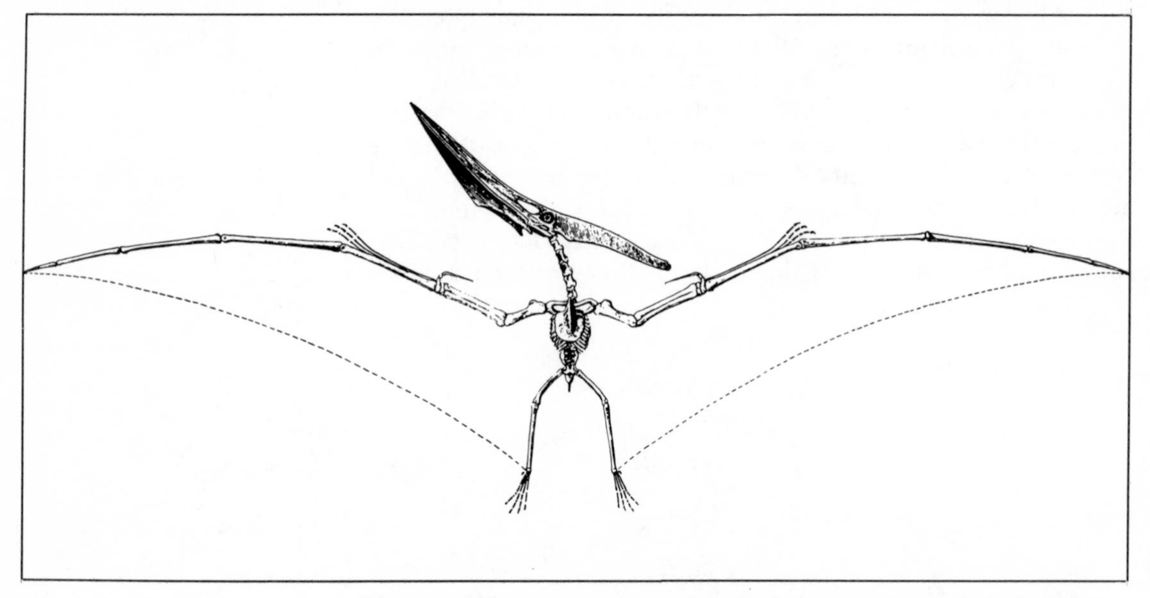

The crocodiles, pterosaurs and thecodonts, are presently included, with the dinosaurs, in the subclass Archosauria. Top left, an alligator skeleton; bottom left, the pterosaur **Pteranodon**; *top right, the thecodont* **Euparkeria**; *bottom right, skull of* **Euparkeria**.

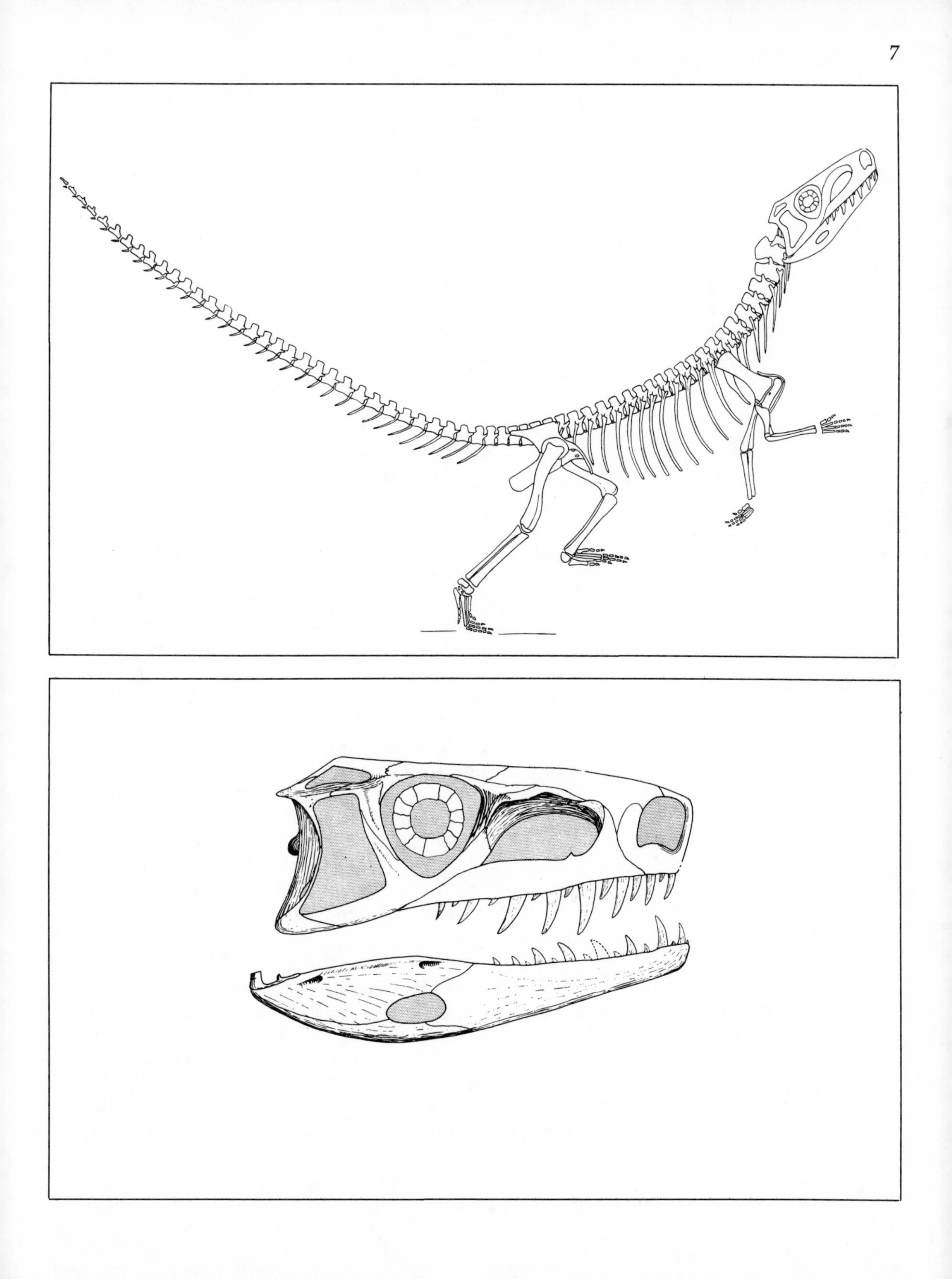

thousands of miles of ocean? They could not fly and presumably were not good swimmers, and it is difficult to visualize a bird the size of an ostrich being rafted out to sea on a mat of twigs! There are many similar distributional anomalies, and these used to be explained by postulating the earlier existence of land bridges. Continental drift not only offers a solution to many problems of animal dispersal, but also explains certain climatic anomalies. Without the concept of drifting continents it would be difficult to explain, for example, why Spitzbergen, within the Arctic Circle, once supported a luxuriant semi-tropical forest.

The major reptilian groups that shared the Mesozoic world with the dinosaurs are depicted on pages 12-13 .

The dinosaurs form two of the five orders of a large subdivision of the reptiles, the subclass Archosauria.[2] The other three orders are the thecodonts, crocodiles and pterosaurs, though there is evidence that the pterosaurs may have more affinity with the lepidosaurs.[3] The thecodonts were a Triassic order that was ancestral to the other archosaurs.

The archosaurs share a number of features, including teeth set in individual sockets along the jaw margins and a skull with two openings in the temple region. The most significant characteristic of the subclass Archosauria is a tendency towards bipedalism, which had far-reaching consequences in the skeleton, especially in the hind legs and pelvic girdle. Man attained a bipedal posture by holding his vertebral column and his pelvic girdle upright. The archosaurs, in contrast, held their backs more or less horizontally, and this could only be achieved with the help of a long tail to balance the body about the hip joint. In most reptiles, including present-day lizards and turtles, the legs are splayed horizontally from the sides of the body, giving an ungainly posture that would presumably be difficult for a large bipedal animal to maintain. The problem was resolved in the archosaurs by the placing of the legs vertically beneath the body. The hind legs carried most or all of the body weight, and were swung fore and aft during locomotion, which put certain demands upon the pelvic girdle.

The reptilian pelvis comprises three paired bones; dorsally there is the ilium, which is attached to the vertebral column, and ventrally there are the pubis and the ischium. Archosaurs have a long ilium that provides a large area of contact with the vertebral column. The pubis and ischium are also extensive and formed large attachment areas for the muscles that drew the hind leg forward and pulled it back again. Many other specializations may be seen in the archosaur skeleton, but they need not concern us here.

What sort of archosaurs were the dinosaurs? First, it should be noted that there are two distinctly different orders of dinosaurs, the Saurischia and the Ornithischia. The characteristic difference between them, reflected in their order names ("lizard-hipped" and "bird-hipped") is the structure of their pelvic girdles. The saurischians have a simple three-pronged pelvis, much like that of their thecodont ancestors, whereas the ornithischian pelvis is complicated by the fact that the pubis has two prongs—an anterior process, which extends forwards, and a posterior process which extends backwards alongside the ischium. There are two types of saurischian dinosaurs: the suborder Theropoda, which were bipedal and mainly carnivorous, and the suborder Sauropoda, which were quadrupedal, herbivorous and often of gigantic size. The ornithischians were probably all herbivorous and were more varied than the saurischians. There are four ornithischian suborders: the unarmoured Ornithopoda, the Ankylosauria, which were armoured with flat bony plates, the Stegosauria, which had a series of vertical plates along the back, and the Ceratopsia, which had horns.

Not all the dinosaurs were large. Some, like *Ornithomimus*, were the size of ostriches, and others were even smaller. But there was a tendency towards gigantism, and most dinosaurs were large animals. Dinosaurs were predominantly, if not completely, terrestrial, and the abundance of fossil remains shows that they formed a major component of the terrestrial fauna.

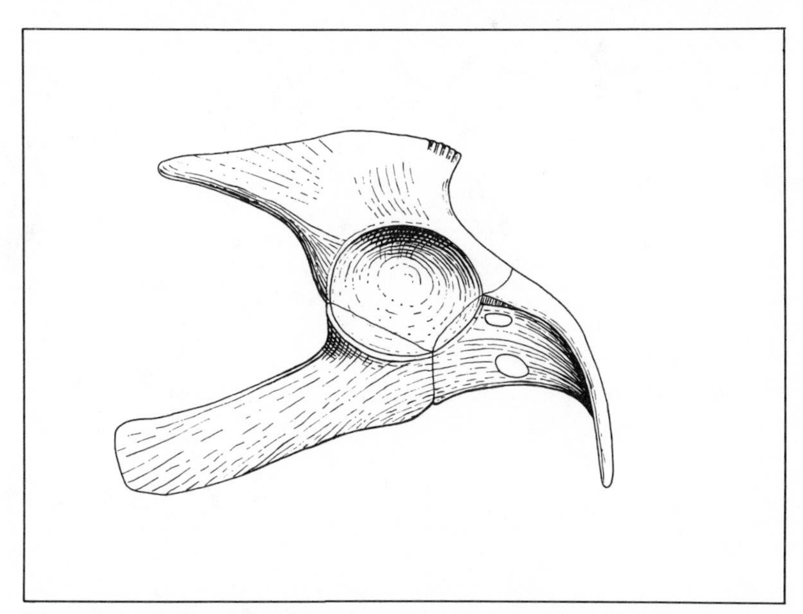

The pelvic girdle of the thecodont **Euparkeria**, *right side. The upper bone, the ilium, attaches to the vertebral column. The anterior bone (at right) is the pubis, the other is the ischium. All three contribute to the round depression, the acetabulum, for reception of the head of the femur.*

The pelvic girdle of a saurischian dinosaur (left) and an ornithischian dinosaur (right), both seen from the right side: 1. ilium, 2. ischium, 3, 4. pubis. Notice that the ornithischian dinosaur has a two-pronged pubis.

There are two types (suborders) of saurischian dinosaurs, the theropods and sauropods, and four suborders of ornithischians, the ornithopods, ankylosaurs, stegosaurs and ceratopsians.

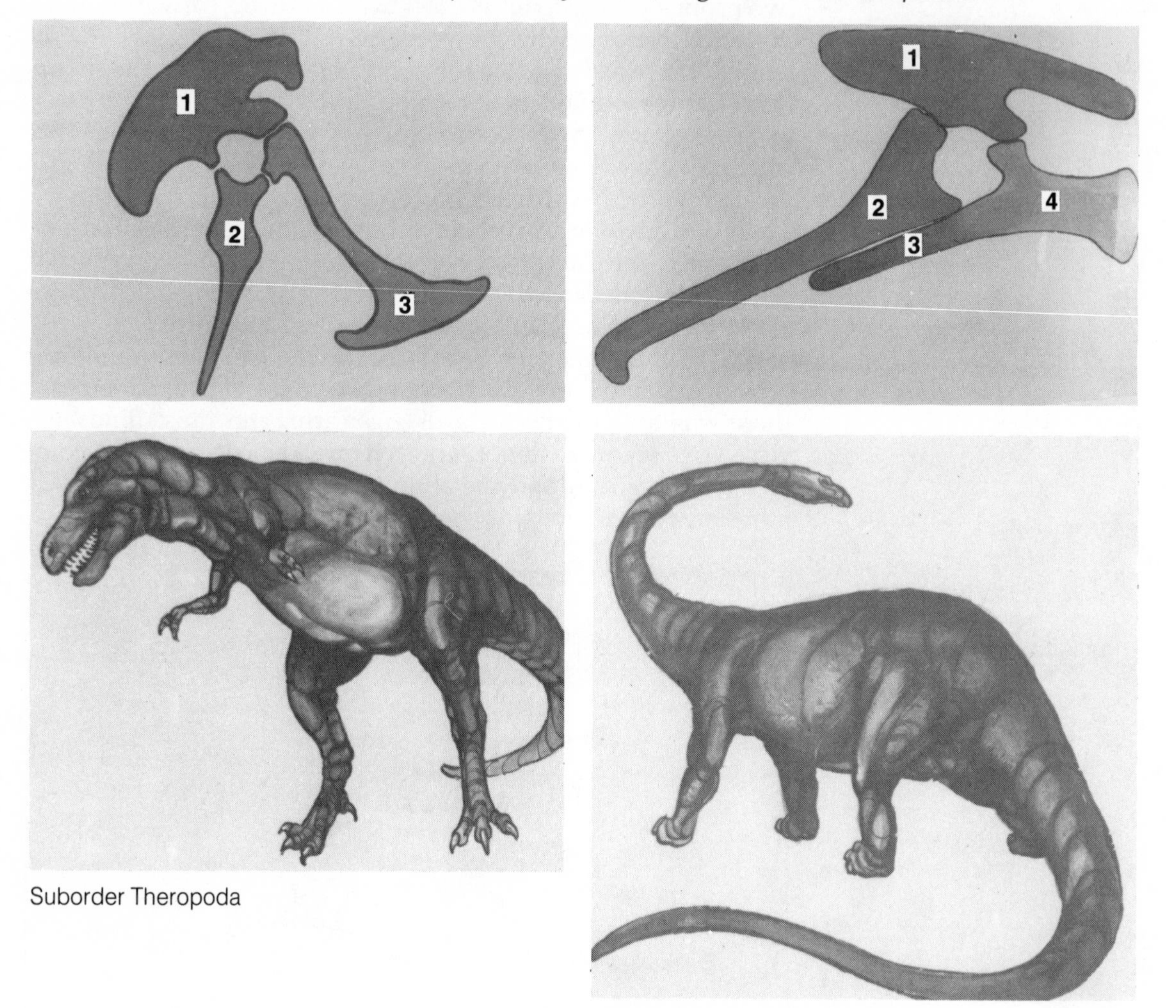

Suborder Theropoda

Suborder Sauropoda

Suborder Ornithopoda

Suborder Ankylosauria

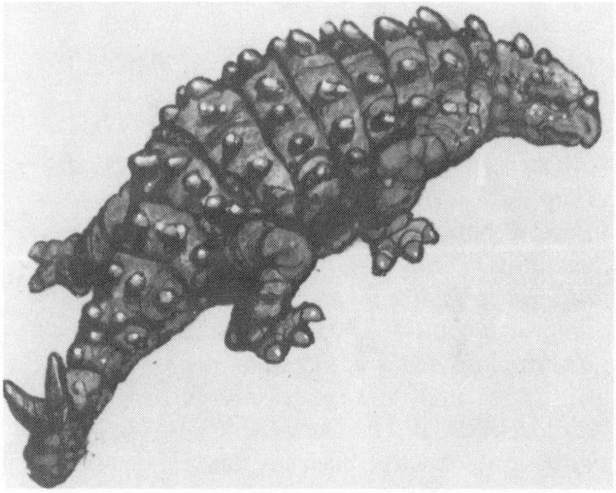

Suborder Stegosauria

Suborder Ceratopsia

Mammal-like reptiles *(Subclass Synapsida)*
These reptiles, which gave rise to the mammals, were still flourishing during the Triassic Period, although they had reached their peak during the preceding Permian Period. Some were herbivores, others carnivores, and they ranged in size from that of a rat to that of a cow. Most of them were large and robust. The primitive synapsids had a sprawling posture, like most other reptiles, but in the advanced types the legs were placed almost vertically beneath the body. They appear not to have been very successful in competition with the dinosaurs, and most of them were extinct by the close of the Triassic Period.

Crocodiles *(Subclass Archosauria, Order Crocodilia)*
Crocodiles and alligators and their relatives, the only surviving reptilian relatives of the dinosaurs, first appeared in the late Triassic Period. Like the chelonians, the crocodiles are a conservative group; they have undergone virtually no change since the Mesozoic Era. Crocodiles spend most of their life in the water, and although their skeletons possess many aquatic features, such as dorsally placed nostrils and eyes, they have undergone little modification from the thecodont stock from which they evolved. All active predators, they are among the largest of the modern reptiles, reaching lengths of about six metres.

Turtles *(Subclass Anapsida, Order Chelonia)*
These familiar shelled reptiles, often referred to as tortoises if they are terrestrial rather than aquatic, flourished throughout the Mesozoic Era and survive to the present day. They are a conservative group, having undergone virtually no change since the early Mesozoic Era. They are also the most modified reptilian group, having the most specialized skeleton. The body is completely encased in a shell, formed of a series of fused plates, and most of the vertebral column and the limb girdles are fused or firmly attached to the inside of the shell. Teeth are absent, their function being performed by a horny sheath attached to the jaw margins. Many chelonians are herbivores, while others are predatory, feeding on a wide range of animals, from fishes to snails and beetles. By present-day standards some chelonians are very large—the leatherback turtle reaches almost two meters in length—while some Cretaceous turtles were about four metres in length.

Rhynchocephalians *(Subclass Lepidosauria, Order Rhynchocephalia)*
These lizard-like reptiles appeared in the Triassic Period and were long believed to have become extinct by the close of the Mesozoic Era—until a living representative, **Sphenodon** *was discovered in New Zealand.* **Sphenodon**,*is very similar in structure to its Mesozoic relatives, providing another example of a group that has undergone no major change since the Mesozoic Era.*

Lizards and snakes *(Subclass Lepidosauria, Order Squamata)*
Lizards and snakes, which are closely related, are the most numerous of modern reptiles. The lizards appeared in the late Triassic Period, but the snakes did not appear until the Cretaceous Period. Almost all lizards and snakes are predatory. Most are terrestrial, and they are usually of only moderate size. The largest modern lizard, the Komodo Dragon, reaches a length of about three metres, and the largest snake, the anaconda, may reach a length of about 10 metres. Lizards and snakes are characterized by their lightly constructed skulls, some segments of which are able to move relative to others, facilitating the capture and manipulation of wriggling prey.

Plesiosaurs *(Subclass Euryapsida, Order Sauropterygia)*
These swimming reptiles appeared at the beginning of the Jurassic Period and shared the marine environment with the ichthyosaurs. While plesiosaurs and mosasaurs are frequently found together in the same beds, mosasaurs appear not to occur with ichthyosaurs, and these two groups may have been mutually exclusive.[2] *Plesiosaurs have been described as looking like snakes threaded through the bodies of turtles. Some, called elasmosaurs, had a small head and a long neck, while others, the pliosaurs, had a large head and short neck. They ranged in length from a few metres to over 10 metres, and were probably all carnivorous.*

Pterosaurs *(Subclass Archosauria, Order Pterosauria)*
The flying reptiles appeared towards the end of the Triassic Period, and flourished throughout the rest of the Mesozoic Era. (Birds did not appear until towards the end of the Jurassic Period.) The earliest pterosaurs were about the size of starlings, but some of the later ones were gigantic; the largest species had an estimated wingspan of about 14 metres. Pterosaurs were probably predatory.

Mosasaurs *(Subclass Lepidosauria, Order Squamata)*
These large lizards, closely related to modern monitors, appeared and disappeared again in the Upper Cretaceous Period. They lived in the sea, and had very long and deep (from top to bottom) tails that were used for swimming. Their fore and hind limbs were probably webbed and used for steering, and perhaps also for propelling them when moving slowly.

Mosasaurs were large animals, and the largest species reached lengths of more than 10 metres.

Ichthyosaurs *(Subclass Euryapsida, Order Ichthyosauria)*
Appearing during the early Triassic, the ichthyosaurs lived throughout the Mesozoic Era. They were highly modified for swimming and their fish-like appearance has earned them the name of fish-lizard. Ichthyosaurs were active predators, and they ranged in size from about one to 15 metres.

2
Darwin and the Fossil Record

After two unsuccessful attempts to weather the December gales blowing hard from the southwest, H.M.S. *Beagle*, a well-built barque of 234 tons, finally beat her way clear of Devonport and into the English Channel. The year was 1831. On the other side of the Channel lay a troubled France, torn apart by political conspiracies and civil unrest, and now in the grip of a cholera epidemic. England herself tottered on the brink of social disorder. The wealth of the Industrial Revolution lay in the pockets of the few, and the enormous gulf between rich and poor was widening. H.M.S. *Beagle* set a south-southwesterly course, leaving England and her troubles and the grey winter far behind. Her master, Captain Robert FitzRoy (1805–1865),was charged and directed by His Majesty King William IV to complete a survey of Patagonia and Tierra del Fuego, to survey the shores of Chile, Peru, and certain Pacific islands, and to conduct a series of chronometrical measurements around the world. Charles Darwin (1809–1882), a quiet young man of 22, had been appointed as naturalist, and he shared a cramped day cabin with FitzRoy. The expedition, which lasted for five years and took him right around the world, was to change Darwin's life, and one day bring about a revolution in man's view of the living world. But what were man's views of the living world at that time?

Fossils were central to most discussion of natural history, and much progress had been made in palaeontology since the early writings of the 16th century.[1] It was widely accepted among naturalists that fossils were the remains of organisms that had once lived, and largely through the efforts of the French anatomist Georges Cuvier (1769–1832), it was generally believed that many of those organisms had become extinct. Extinction, however, was unacceptable to some people because of their religious beliefs: God had created all species, and to suggest that some had become extinct was to question the perfection of the Creation and the Creator.

Cuvier's case supporting the idea of extinction was founded upon a careful comparative study of modern and fossil vertebrates. Cuvier demonstrated, for example, that the two species of modern elephants (African and Indian) were distinguishable on the basis of skeletal anatomy, and since both differed from the fossil remains of the mammoth, he concluded that the latter must have belonged to a different species. Discarding the possibility that a terrestrial animal as large as a mammoth could have passed unnoticed in the wild, he concluded, reasonably, that this elephant species had become extinct. Cuvier also believed that

Charles Darwin from a photograph taken in 1874.

Fossil molluscs from the Jurassic, drawn by J. Phillips for his monograph, The Geology of Yorkshire.

species were stable entities, that is, that they did not undergo change with the passage of time.

Cuvier's fellow countryman Jean-Baptiste Lamarck (1744–1829) discounted both the idea of the stability of species, and the concept that some species had become extinct. He believed, instead, that species were continuously changing and that with the passage of time species represented by fossil remains had become transformed into modern species. Several other authors had discussed similar evolutionary concepts, including Darwin's own grandfather, Erasmus Darwin (1731–1802), but Lamarck's treatment was the most thorough.

Lamarck believed that animals "strove" to become better adapted to their environments, and that features they acquired in that way were passed on to their offspring, which would make further improvements. Ancestors of the giraffe, for example, were said to have had short necks, but their constant straining to reach higher into the trees caused their necks to stretch—a trend which, continued over many generations, eventually resulted in the modern giraffe.[2]

Cuvier and Lamarck both held Professorships at the Museum National d'Histoire Naturelle in Paris, and when their institution acquired a collection of embalmed animals from an Egyptian tomb they were given a rare opportunity to test their respective hypotheses on the stability of species. The remains, which were several thousand years old, could be recognized as those of species still in existence. The question was, were there any detectable differences between them and modern representatives of the same species? Admittedly, the time interval was not a very long one, but, since it was then believed that the age of the Earth was to be counted in thousands rather than millions of years, the interval seemed significant. There were no differences. Lamarck was apparently proved wrong and Cuvier's belief in the stability of species was strengthened.

By studying the stratification of rocks, Cuvier had been able to demonstrate that different groups of organisms became extinct at different times. He was also able to recognize particular rock layers by the fossils they contained, and these layers could be traced over considerable distances. This fundamental principle of stratigraphy, however, was not new, and had been documented by earlier authorities. Cuvier attributed extinctions to changes in the physical world—floods, climatic changes, and the like—which he referred to as revolutions but which are frequently called catastrophes. He believed that such events were localized and that they occurred fairly frequently. His work had a great influence on other scientists, and his ideas were sometimes distorted to support other causes.

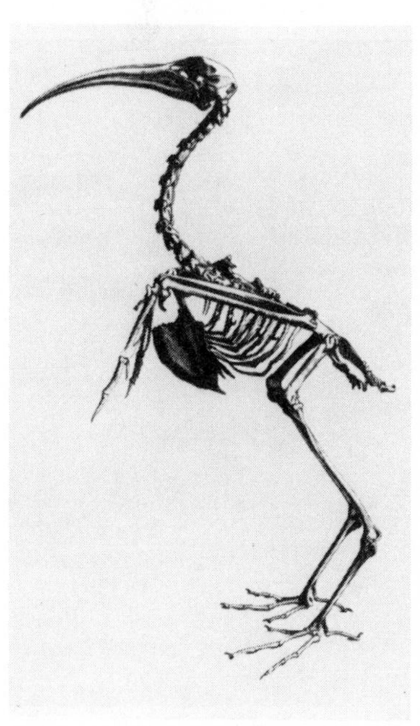

Cuvier's drawing of an Ibis skeleton from an Egyptian tomb.

A British geologist, the Reverend William Buckland (1784–1856), identified Cuvier's last "revolution" with the Great

Flood of Noah. Claiming this as scientific validation of the Bible, he spent much of his life propagating the old diluvial theory, which attempted to account for various historical events in terms of the Great Flood. However, the theory could not stand up to the scathing attacks of such men as Charles Lyell (1797–1875), one of Buckland's former pupils.

Lyell is best known for his *Principles of Geology* (published during the years 1830–33), in which he set out his ideas on the principle of uniformity. According to this principle, changes that have occurred in the Earth's crust can be explained in terms of processes that can be observed in the modern world. The cutting back of a river bank by the scouring action of the water, for example, can actually be observed. It is a slow process, but extrapolated over thousands of years, it can account for the carving out of huge river valleys. Darwin took a copy of the first volume of Lyell's *Principles of Geology* with him on the *Beagle* and was much influenced by the principle of uniformity. In later years, he applied this principle of interpreting the past by reference to the present in his work on the origin of species.

The fossil record was far less complete when Darwin was a young man than it is today, but it was adequate to show that there was something of a succession of groups or organisms through geological time. There was, for example, a period that was dominated by reptiles, followed by a period when mammals predominated. This strongly suggested that new species had appeared sequentially throughout the history of the Earth, not just at the beginning, as told in the Bible. Cuvier, however, believed that this succession was due to the migration of animals from elsewhere. He did not see any need to suggest that new species had evolved or been newly created.

Darwin's love of biology and geology had been reinforced during his three years at Christ's College, Cambridge, where he received the degree of Bachelor of Arts. At Cambridge he became well acquainted with J.S. Henslow (1796–1861), Professor of Botany. They used to take long walks together, discussing natural history, and Henslow's intense powers of observation rubbed off onto Darwin, who earned the epithet, "the man who walks with Henslow." In the summer of 1831 Darwin accompanied Professor Adam Sedgwick (1785–1873) on a geological excursion to North Wales that gave him invaluable experience in interpreting the geological record. It was on his return from this trip that he found a letter from Henslow informing him that Captain FitzRoy was seeking a naturalist to be a companion for him on a voyage around the world. This was an opportunity no young man could afford to miss.

FitzRoy was a religious man and believed that the voyage would provide an excellent opportunity to substantiate the book of Genesis. Darwin also had religious convictions and had once contemplated entering the church.

> Whilst on board the *Beagle* I was quite orthodox, [in religion] and I remember being heartily laughed at by several of the officers (though themselves orthodox) for quoting the Bible as an unanswerable authority on some point of morality.[3]

He was well aware of Lamarck's evolutionary theory, and of the evolutionary speculations of his grandfather, Erasmus Darwin, but these had made no impression upon him. Like Cuvier, Lyell, and many others, he was convinced of the permanence of species.[4] The interview with FitzRoy was successful, and Darwin was offered the post.

Darwin, a meticulous observer and an avid collector, soon filled his cabin with bottles of specimens preserved in spirit. Many of the animals and plants he described in his notebook were new to science, and he sent specimens back to Henslow in England whenever he had an opportunity. He was fascinated by the myriad of specializations in animals and plants, and was constantly aware of a struggle for survival. He was much impressed by the way in which different species replace one

The Beagle visited Buenos Aires in September 1833, and Darwin made an overland excursion to Santa Fé.

another from region to region. During an overland excursion from Buenos Aires to Santa Fé he wrote:

> I was surprised to observe how great a change of climate a difference of only three degrees of latitude . . . had caused. This was evident from the dress and complexion of the men—from the increased size of the ombu-trees—the number of new cacti and other plants—and especially from the birds. In the course of an hour I remarked half-a-dozen of the latter, which I had never seen at Buenos Aires. Considering that there is no natural boundary between the two places, and that the character of the country is nearly similar, the difference was much greater than I should have expected.[5]

He recorded the facts of his journey with the same care and attention to detail with which he made his observations, and his knowledge of the natural world grew steadily. He was as enthusiastic about geology as he was about biology, and made several excursions in search of fossils. At Punta Alta, in the Argentinian Pampas, some 640 km south of Buenos Aires, he found the fossil remains of a variety of giant land mammals, including some giant ground sloths. He wrote: "It is a remarkable circumstance that so many different species should be found together; and it proves how numerous in kind the ancient inhabitants of this country must have been. The remains . . . were associated . . . with shells of existing species."[6]

The following year, 1834, found Darwin geologizing along the Patagonian coast of Argentina, where he found similar giant

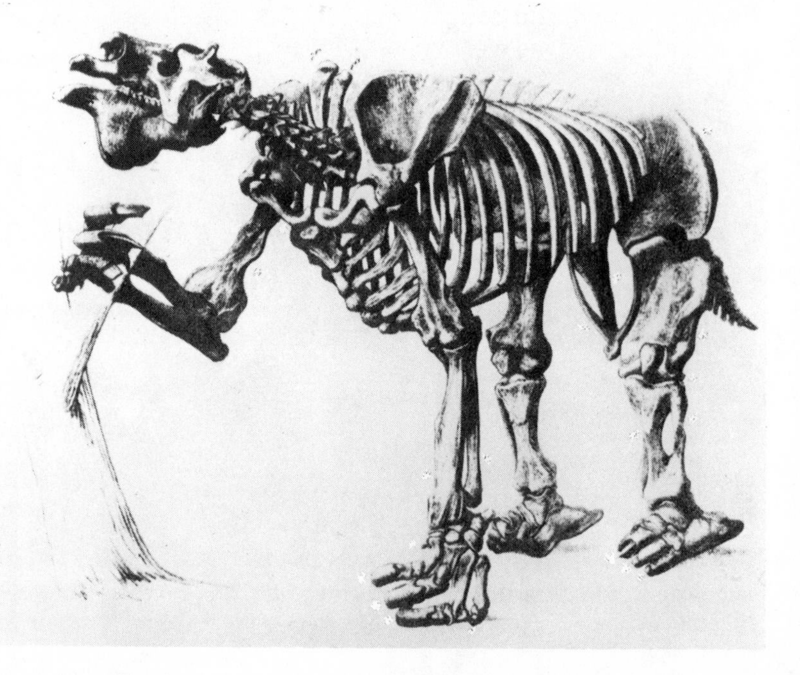

Darwin found remains of the giant ground sloth **Megatherium** *in Patagonia, and sent them to Richard Owen for study. Owen's reconstruction of the complete skeleton as published in 1856.*

Hunting the guanaco (llama) in Patagonia.

fossil mammals, including an animal "allied to the guanaco or llama, but fully as large as the true camel."[7] He recognized the close similarity between these extinct forms and their diminutive living relatives, and concluded that the climate and conditions during their lifetime were much like those of the present day.

> It is impossible to reflect without the deepest astonishment, on the changed state of this continent. Formerly it must have swarmed with great monsters. . . but now we find only the tapir, guanaco [llama], armadillo, and capybara; mere pigmies compared to the antecedent races. The greater number, if not all, of these extinct quadrupeds lived at a very recent period; and many of them were contemporaries of the existing molluscs. Since their loss, no very great physical changes can have taken place in the nature of the country. What then has exterminated so many living creatures? In the Pampas, the great sepulchre of such remains, there are no signs of violence, but on the contrary, of the most quiet and scarcely sensible changes.[8]

Here we see Darwin questioning the widely held catastrophic interpretation of extinction, which had been developed by Cuvier, and modified by Buckland to substantiate the Bible.

Of all the places he visited during his five-year odyssey the Galapagos Islands were to have the greatest impact.

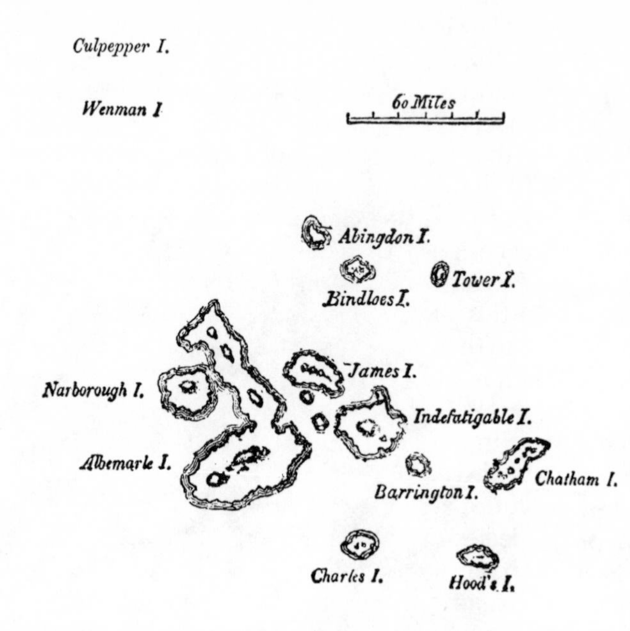

The Galapagos Archipelago lies 1100 km off the coast of Ecuador.

The Galapagos Archipelago is a group of volcanic islands lying on the equator about 1100 km off the coast of Ecuador. A party from the *Beagle* landed on Chatham Island on the morning of September 17, 1835. Darwin wrote:

> Nothing could be less inviting than the first appearance. A broken field of black basaltic lava is every where covered by astunted brushwood, which shows little signs of life. The dry and parched surface, having been heated by the noonday sun, gave the air a close and sultry feeling, like that from a stove: we fancied even the bushes smelt unpleasantly.[9]

Darwin spent his first night on Chatham Island in an area where volcanic cones were particularly numerous. He likened what he saw to parts of Staffordshire, where great iron foundries fragmented the skyline. The next day he had his first encounter with the giant tortoises for which the islands were named (galapago is Spanish for tortoise). "One was eating a piece of cactus, and when I approached, it looked at me, and then quietly walked away: the other gave a deep hiss and drew in its head."[10]

From Chatham Island they moved to Charles Island, and then they sailed on to Albemarle Island, the biggest of the group. After spending some days there, Darwin and a small party were landed at James Island for a week while the *Beagle* went off for fresh water. One of the most abundant animals there was the marine iguana, *Amblyrhynchus cristatus*. "It is a hideous-looking creature, of a dirty black colour, stupid and sluggish in its movements. . . . This lizard is extremely common on all the islands throughout the Archipelago. It lives exclusively on the rocky sea-beaches, and is never found, at least I never saw one, even ten yards inshore."[11] The marine iguana, which is endemic to the Galapagos (that is, occuring only there), is quite unlike any other reptile in that it feeds exclusively on seaweed, swimming some distance from shore to graze on the sea bed. Closely related to the marine iguana is the terrestrial iguana, *Amblyrhynchus demarlii*, which they found on four of the islands. "It would appear as if this species had been created in the centre of the Archipelago, and thence had been dispersed only to a certain distance."[12] (Darwin may have been using "creation" in a general sense, without necessarily implying creation by God, because he used the same word in the same sentence in the second edition of his journal of the voyage, which was written after he had developed his evolutionary theory.)

The idea that species evolved, rather than having been created, appears to have formed during the latter part of the voyage. We may visualize the young Darwin testing his embryonic ideas on FitzRoy, who would have made a perfect foil. Years later, after the publication of *The Origin of Species*, FitzRoy, now Admiral FitzRoy, recalled that he had often remonstrated with Darwin during the voyage for entertaining views that were contrary to the first chapter of Genesis.[13]

On October 20, 1835, H.M.S. *Beagle* left the Galapagos and set a course for Tahiti, more than 5,000 km away. Many more places were visited after Tahiti, but the closer they got to England, the more homesick they all became. In a letter to Henslow written from St. Helena on July 9, 1836, Darwin lamented, "Oh, the degree to which I long to be once again living quietly with not one single novel object near me! No one can imagine it till he has been whirled round the world during five long years in a ten-gun-brig."[14]

The *Beagle* returned to England on October 2, 1836, and Darwin made all haste to return to his family in Shrewsbury. There was much to be done. He set to work arranging for various specialists to work on the specimens he had brought back, retaining the geological and mineralogical specimens for himself. At this time in his career he was very interested in geology, and read several papers to the Geological Society of London. He was elected secretary of the society in 1838, and served for three years. He also started writing an account of his voyage, and in July of the next year he started his first notebook on the origin of species.

His visit to the Galapagos had a considerable influence on him, and this influence increased with time. Referring to the islands in the first edition of his account of the voyage (1839), he wrote:

> . . . the organic beings found on this archipelago are peculiar to it; and yet that their general form strongly partakes of an American character. It would be impossible for any one accustomed to the birds of Chile and La Plata to be placed on these islands, and not to feel convinced that he was . . . on American ground. This similarity in type, between distant islands and continents, while the species are distinct, has scarcely been sufficiently noticed. The circumstances would be explained, according to the views of some authors, by saying that the creative power had acted according to the same law over a wide area.[15]

Into the second edition (1845), he injected a cautious hint of what was crystallizing in his mind:

> Most of the organic productions are aboriginal creations, found nowhere else; there is even a difference between the inhabitants of the different islands; yet all show a marked relationship with those of America, though separated from that continent by an open space of ocean. . . . The archipelago is a little world within itself, or rather a satellite attached to America, whence it has derived a few stray colonists, and has received the general character of its indigenous productions. Considering the small size of these islands, we feel the more astonished at the number of their aboriginal beings, and at their confined range. . . . Hence, both in space and time, we seem to be brought somewhat near to that great fact—that mystery of mysteries—the first appearance of new beings on this earth.[16]

He observed 13 different species of finches that were similar to, but distinct from, those of the mainland. "The most curious fact is the perfect gradation in the size of the beaks."[17] Some species had short bills and fed on seeds, others, with long slender bills, fed on the flowers of the cactus, while still others used twigs to extract insects from the crevices of trees.

The year 1839 must have been a particularly satisfying one for Darwin. Not only did he see the publication of the first edition of his *Journal of Researches*, but he also got married, to his cousin, Emma Wedgewood, of the famous family of fine china and porcelain manufacturers. The newlyweds lived first in London, but in 1842 purchased a large house in the countryside of Kent, near the village of Downe, and settled into a rural life. That same year, Darwin sketched an essay on his ideas on the origin of species. This sketch, which was never intended for publication, was written in pencil on heavy vellum, and parts of it are difficult to read. Nevertheless it is an interesting manuscript because it contains the essentials of Darwin's theory.

The steps that led Darwin to his theory are outlined in his autobiography, which he wrote in his 67th year. He recalls four

A distinctive feature of certain Galapagos finches, called Darwin's finches, is the shape of their bill. Top left, Large Ground Finch (**Geospiza magnirostris**)*; top right, Medium Ground Finch* (**Geospiza fortis**)*; bottom left, Small Tree Finch* (**Camarhynchus parvulus**)*; bottom right, Warbler Finch* (**Certhidea olivacea**).

observations he made during his voyage on the *Beagle* that deeply impressed him: the discovery of large fossil mammals in South America resembling certain smaller mammals still living there; the way in which closely allied South American animals replace one another as the latitude increases; the South American character of the species on the Galapagos Islands; and, lastly, the way that each of these islands has its own endemic species. These facts could only be explained by recognizing that species had become modified. The Lamarckian theory of the modification of species by the inheritance of acquired characters was unacceptable, consequently Darwin had to seek an alternative mechanism.

Following Lyell's principle that present processes could be used to explain the past, he channelled his energies into investigating the modifications that species have undergone during their domestication. He began to collect every relevant piece of information on plant and animal breeding, and soon saw what a powerful force selective breeding had been in the modification of species. One has only to think of the great variety of dogs that has been produced from the original wild stock, or the improvements in meat yield that have been obtained by the selective breeding of cattle, to realize this. If man could produce such great modifications by selective breeding within such a short time (the selective breeding of farm animals dates to the work of Robert Bakewell in the 18th century), then surely even greater modifications could be produced in nature over the course of many thousands of years. The problem was—how?

The answer came to Darwin towards the end of 1838, just 15 months after he had started his work on the species problem. "I happened to read for amusement 'Malthus on Population', and being well prepared to appreciate the struggle for existence which everywhere goes on from long-continued observation of the habits of animals and plants, it at once struck me that under these circumstances favourable variations would tend to be preserved, and unfavourable ones to be destroyed."[18]

Darwin's theory is elegant in its simplicity. Offspring are similar to, but not identical with, their parents. Therefore no two individuals are exactly alike. Each species produces far more offspring than can possibly survive, and as the offspring are not exactly alike it follows that some individuals will have features that give them an advantage over others. These advantages, however slight, give the individual a better chance of surviving. He termed this process—the process of the selection of advantaged individuals—natural selection. As advantaged individuals have a better chance of survival, they tend to leave more offspring, and since these offspring inherit some of their parents' favourable features, they too tend to have improved chances of survival. The action of natural selection, operating over a long period, would therefore bring about a modification of the species, causing it to become better adapted to the environment.

Darwin believed that the environment was slowly changing, for he had observed such changes in the geological record. In the process of continuously adapting itself to the changing environment, a species would eventually become so changed that it would be a new species.

In 1844, Darwin expanded the sketch he had started in 1842 into an essay of some length, and divided it into nine chapters. In contrast to the sketch, the essay was carefully written and obviously suitable for publication. But Darwin never published it. He must have been fully aware of the impact his theory would have had on the world, and it may have been this that held him back. He was only 35 years old but did not enjoy good health, and the thought of a premature death was probably never far

The study at Down House.

from his mind. It was for this reason that he placed his essay into safe keeping, and instructed his wife that, in the event of his death, she was to set aside a sum of £400 to have it published. He included a list of names of suitable editors: Lyell, Forbes, Henslow, Hooker, and Strickland—men of science whose council he had frequently sought, and whom he respected. As it turned out, he lived to 73.

Darwin devoted eight of the following twelve years to a study of barnacles; work on the species problem proceeded slowly. In a letter to Lyell on November 10, 1856, he wrote: "I am working very steadily at my big book; I have found it quite impossible to publish any preliminary essay or sketch; but am doing my work as completely as my present materials allow without waiting to perfect them. And this much acceleration I owe to you."[19] (Lyell had prompted Darwin to publish his findings because he feared he might be anticipated.)

Notwithstanding his poor health, his time passed quietly and pleasantly. His dutiful wife Emma bore him 10 children, seven of whom survived, and he enjoyed them to the full. But this delightfully untroubled way of life came to an abrupt end on a June morning in 1858. A letter arrived from the Malay Archipelago, from the naturalist Alfred Russel Wallace (1823–1913), with whom he had corresponded during the previous year. The letter contained an essay that Wallace asked him to read, and if he thought it had any merit, to convey to Lyell. The essay was entitled, "On the tendency of varieties to depart indefinitely from the original type." Darwin probably read it over and over again. He was shattered. Here was exactly the same theory for the origin of species as his own.

With characteristic magnanimity he wrote a warm letter of recommendation and transmitted Wallace's essay to Lyell, pointing out, balefully, that he had been anticipated. Lyell consulted Hooker, and the two men agreed that Wallace and Darwin should receive equal recognition for their work. Wallace's essay, together with an abstract of Darwin's 1844 essay, were sent to the Linnaean Society with a letter of explanation, and the two papers were published together.

Darwin now busied himself with his book, and within a year published *The Origin of Species*. The first edition of 1,250 copies was sold out on the day of publication. Over the next few years five more editions appeared, each with improvements and emendations. In its essentials, Darwin's theory is accepted by the majority of modern biologists, a fitting tribute to the insight of its author. This is all the more remarkable when we consider how little was known of the living world at the time the book was written. Nothing was known about the mechanism of heredity, fertilization, or cell division, little was known about cell structure, and the fossil record was fragmentary. One major discrepancy between Darwin's work and current concepts is in the details of the mechanism of speciation, and, as this has a considerable bearing on the interpretation of the fossil record, it is of particular concern to us here.

While Darwin recognized that some species remain unchanged over considerable periods of time, and also that a new species might split off from an existing one, most of his discussions on speciation centred upon the transformation of one species into another. For Darwin, each species was being modified continuously by the action of natural selection, and so becoming better adapted to its environment. The accumulation of these slight modifications over long periods of time, Darwin held, eventually leads to the transformation of the original species into a new species. Thus, if we were able to follow the geological history of a given species, we would expect to find gradual changes from the original species at the base of the sequence (the oldest layer) to the new species at the top. This gentle transformation has been termed "phyletic gradualism",[20] and it is a concept that pervades most textbooks in palaeontology.

Does the fossil record provide evidence for the gradual transformation of one species into another? Darwin could not find a single case and wrote: "Geology assuredly does not reveal any such finely graduated organic chain; and this, perhaps, is the most obvious and gravest objection which can be urged against my theory."[21] Darwin attributed the dilemma largely to the imperfections of the fossil record, and devoted a whole chapter to the problem.

The Jurassic oyster, **Gryphaea**.

Palaeontologists searched the rocks for supporting evidence, but instead of finding finely graded sequences they found only interrupted series. Forty years after the publication of *The Origin of Species,* an English palaeontologist, A.W. Rowe, described a finely graded sequence for a Cretaceous sea urchin, *Micraster,* which occurs in chalk deposits in England.[22] This became one of the classic pieces of evidence for the gradual transformation of species. Some years later a similar series was described for a Jurassic oyster, *Gryphaea.*[23] Several other sequences have been described, but most of them have been demonstrated to be erroneous, and it seems that the transformation of one species into another is exceedingly rare.[24] The majority of fossil species, then, remain unchanged for long periods of time.[25] Indeed, if this were not true we would be unable to use fossil species as indicators for specific geological horizons.

Does this mean that Darwin was wrong? Before we can answer this question we have to consider the modern view of the species, and how new species may arise.

The species is viewed as an aggregate of interbreeding populations which is reproductively isolated from other species. The yardstick of whether two groups of animals are members of the same species, then, is whether they freely interbreed when they come into contact. This is the biological species concept. The environment must provide the individual with all its needs—food, shelter, opportunities to breed and the like—and since these needs are usually highly specific for each species it follows that most species are restricted to a circumscribed segment of the environment. This is the species range. Environmental conditions outside this range are unsuitable for survival, and the periphery of the range is a transitional zone between survival and failure.

Some species have very large ranges. The house sparrow, for

example, a native of Europe, has been successfully introduced into North America and has a very wide geographical distribution. Because of the great extent of the sparrow's range, it is not possible for an individual sparrow to move throughout the entire extent of that range. Individual sparrows tend to be restricted to local populations, and the same is true of most other species. Conditions vary slightly from one part of the range to another and, due to the action of natural selection, populations become adapted to local conditions. Darwin was well aware of this and pointed out that species with larger geographic ranges tend to exhibit greater degrees of geographic variation. The greatest extremes in local adaptations occur, logically, at the periphery of the species range, where conditions are transitional. Consequently, there are significant differences between individuals living in the central portion of the range and individuals living at the periphery. However, peripheral populations do not diverge very far from adjacent populations because they are not subjected to widely differing conditions, and because they continue to interbreed freely. There are gradations, but no distinct breaks, between the populations of a species.

Darwin, drawing on his knowledge of animal husbandry, noted that animal breeders prevent interbreeding between a variety they are trying to perfect, and other varieties. If they did not, the differences would soon be lost. Similarly, most evolutionists now believe that speciation occurs only when interbreeding ceases, and this is most likely to occur when a peripheral population becomes physically isolated from the rest of the species. As the environment of the isolated population is different from that of the remainder of the species, it will be subjected to different pressures of natural selection. The resulting changes effected by natural selection will accumulate rather than being lost by interbreeding, and the isolated population will diverge from the rest of the species. This concept of speciation is called the allopatric model. It is not the only model, but is the one that is most widely accepted.

We have reason to believe that speciation events probably occur rapidly, that is, in terms of geological time. We have examples of rapid speciation events in Lake Nabugabo, a small lake in Tanzania that is separated from Lake Victoria by a sand bar.[26] The sand bar is known to have formed about 3,500 years ago. The fish populations in Lake Nabugabo have therefore been isolated from those of Lake Victoria only for a few thousand years, but in that time they have undergone speciation, and five of the species are endemic. While a few thousand years is a considerable time in terms of human experience, it is only a moment in the geological scale.

According to the allopatric model of speciation, then, a new species arises from a small population at the periphery of the species range, and it seems that the event is relatively rapid.

What, then, are the chances of our being able to see the event in the fossil record? The first point which must be made, one that cannot be overstated, is that the chances of a dead animal becoming preserved are remote. We shall see why this is so in the next chapter. It therefore follows that large populations have a better chance of leaving a fossil record than small ones by virtue of the greater number of dead individuals available for preservation. Second, even when a fossil has been found there is still a probability that the section of rock enclosing it will be destroyed. Consider, for example, how rapidly sea cliffs are cut back by the oceans. The efficacy of erosion is reflected in the variations in thickness of specific geological strata from one region to another. Sediments that are several hundreds of metres thick at one locality may have a thickness of only a few metres elsewhere or be entirely wanting. For example, there are almost no Mesozoic rocks in the whole of Ontario or the Canadian Shield, whereas such rocks reach great thicknesses in western Canada. A third point, which is seldom considered, is that a fossil that has survived to the present day will never be found unless it has been exposed by the elements. Furthermore, if the rock exposure is not in an accessible location, its contained fossils will still fail to be discovered—good fossil localities are few and far between.

Given these facts, what is the probability of finding a series of fossils in a specific geographical location where a particular speciation event occured? The probability must be close to zero, and is reduced even further by the likelihood that the speciation event occurred rapidly. This is because rapid speciation would involve fewer generations than a protracted speciation event, and this in turn would contribute fewer individuals for possible fossilisation. Darwin, as we have seen, believed that speciation occurred slowly:

> In order to get a perfect gradation between two forms in the upper and lower parts of the same formation, the deposit must have gone on accumulating for a very long period, in order to have given sufficient time for the slow process of variation; hence the deposit will generally have to be a very thick one; and the species undergoing modification will have had to live on the same area throughout this whole time.[27]

Aside from this aspect, Darwin's solution to the problem of why we do not find intermediates between species has a remarkably modern ring to it:

> there is reason to suspect . . . that . . . varieties are generally at first local; and that such local varieties do not spread widely and supplant their parent-forms. . . . the chance of discovering in a formation in any one country all the early stages of transition between any two forms, is small.[28]

Many palaeontologists still argue that gradual transformations of one species to another did occur, but others, probably a majority, believe that speciation events occurred rapidly and that, for the vast majority of species, stasis was the rule rather than the exception.[29] This concept is called "punctuated equilibrium."

Even if a speciation event were recorded in the fossil record we have absolutely no way of recognizing it, simply because we cannot determine when interbreeding between two groups has ceased. Palaeontologists have long recognized that the species they study in the rocks are not necessarily equivalent to living species, simply because the yardstick of interbreeding cannot be applied, but the distinction is often forgotten. Two fossils may look very similar but this does not necessarily mean that they were once capable of interbreeding and therefore members of the same (biological) species. There are examples today of species which look identical to one another but which do not interbreed and which therefore belong to separate species (called sibling species). We must also remember that fossils usually comprise only hard parts, and although many living species can be (and frequently are), identified on skeletal features alone (molluscs, for example on shell features, mammals on tooth characters) many other species can only be distinguished from one another on features that cannot be fossilised (birds, for example, are usually identified on plumage). When we look at the fossil record we often forget that we are only looking at a chronicle of the evolutionary changes that have occurred in the skeleton. Imagine all the other changes for which we have no record. Quite clearly the fossil record lacks the fine resolution required to document the actual origins of new species. Nevertheless it does provide a fairly good record of the major features of evolution. If Darwin had used the fossil record just to show that evolution had occurred, rather than attempting to use it to document the origin of new species, it would not have been such an embarrassment to him.

3
What are Fossils?

Fossils are common, and most of us have encountered them at one time or another. They turn up on beaches, in quarries, and in gravel pits; farmers sometimes strike them with the plough, and construction workers often find them during excavations. Fossils find their way into children's pockets, seaside shops, living rooms, auction rooms, and museums large and small. What are they?

The word "fossil" comes from the Latin *fossilis*, meaning "dug up." It is used for any remains or evidence of animals or plants taken from the ground. Fossils, which were known to the Greeks, were the subject of published works as early as the 16th century. Their stony appearance naturally led many to believe that they were inorganic, like minerals, and various explanations were offered for their formation in the ground. By the late 17th century, their organic origin was quite widely accepted, at least among intellectuals, but the common man often attributed them to the supernatural, and this is reflected in names like "devil's toenail" for a common fossil shell found in England.

Most fossils are the remains of hard parts of animals and plants, bones, teeth, shells, corals, and wood being the most common; but soft parts are sometimes preserved as impressions in rock or as natural casts. We have fossils of soft-bodied animals such a worms and jellyfish, natural casts of brains, skin impressions, feather impressions, footprints—and more besides. Detailed studies of fossils, especially of bones and teeth, reveal evidence of diseases and injuries sustained during life, and chemical analysis can sometimes indicate the state of decomposition of the body just before its burial. The remains of plant and animal material in body cavities give valuable dietary information, and the rare occurrence of embryos inside some animals enables us to unequivocally identify some specimens as females. Fossils can therefore yield more information than the size and shape of the organisms they came from and we will be looking at some of the more exciting pieces of evidence that have been gleaned. Our main concern, however, will be with the nature of fossils and how they were formed.

Anyone who has handled a fossil knows that it is usually not exactly like its modern counterpart, and the most obvious difference is that it is often much heavier. Fossil bone and wood, in particular, often have the quality of stone rather than of organic material, which has led to the term petrification, with the implication that living material has been changed into stone. This interpretation is erroneous, as we shall see, and fossils are sometimes remarkably similar in composition to present-day materials. As most of the fossils that have been studied by vertebrate palaeontologists are of bone we now know a great deal about its structure, and most of our account will therefore be devoted to a study of fossil bone. Before we can understand the changes that bone undergoes during fossilization, however, we need to know something about bone itself.

Bone is both hard and resilient, properties that are imparted by its two main components: the mineral apatite and the protein collagen. The nature of each of these components may be demonstrated by removing one or other of them from a sample of fresh bone. If bone is left for a couple of days in an oven set at 150°C, the collagen is broken down, leaving behind the apatite. Apart from being discoloured and somewhat lighter, the bone looks just as it did before treatment, but handling reveals that it has undergone significant changes. While it is still hard to the touch, it is no longer resilient. Indeed, it is so brittle that it can be chipped with a fingernail and will be shattered if it is dropped on a hard floor. If a second bone is soaked in acid, the mineral apatite is dissolved, leaving the collagen. A 10% solution of a strong acid such as nitric acid will complete the job in a few hours; vinegar also works, though it takes several days. Collagen is a rubbery substance, and the treated bone can be tied in a knot. The combination of resilient protein and hard mineral is comparable to reinforced concrete, which combines the resilience of steel rods with the hardness of concrete. The collagen exists as very fine fibrils around which are cemented microcrystals of apatite. The collagen fibrils have a diameter of about 0.3–0.5 micrometres (1/1000 mm), and the apatite crystals are about 4 x 2–3 x .25–.50 micrometres.[1] Both components are too small to be seen with a light microscope.

Few animal structures look as stable and lifeless as a bone, but bone is actually a dynamic living tissue that undergoes frequent remodelling throughout life. The forces acting upon bones are continuously being monitored, and if they should change, corresponding changes occur in the bones. If an office worker, for example, were to take up manual work, those bones subjected to increased stress would become more robust. Conversely a reduction in stress results in bone thinning. The response to changing stress takes days rather than weeks and can actually be measured by a simple experiment. The clavicle (collar bone) lies close to the surface, and an approximate measure of its diameter can be obtained using calipers. One of my students sportingly let me measure his clavicle before and after taking up weight training. Over the period of the Christmas vacation his clavicle increased in diameter by 4.6 mm, an increase of more than 25%.

The non-living fabric of bone, that is, the collagen fibrils and apatite crystals, is produced by cells called osteoblasts. Once their job is done and they have become surrounded by bone material they undergo change and become osteocytes. The osteocyte, which lies inside a small cavity in the bone matrix called a lacuna, is smaller and flatter than an osteoblast, and has a spidery appearance because of the fine threads of cytoplasm that project from the cell body. The role of osteocytes is somewhat unclear, but they appear to be involved in the exchange of materials between the tissue fluids and bone matrix, and they may also have some limited capacity for bone manufacture. They receive their nutrients from the blood, and most tetrapods have highly vascular bone. The life span of osteocytes may extend over many decades, and it seems that when they die the bone around them undergoes breakdown. Empty lacunae, and lacunae containing remnants of dead osteocytes, are often seen in the bones of old individuals.

Most bones are porous, and this is usually obvious even without a microscope. The size of the pores varies from one region of the body to another and from bone to bone. The outermost layer of a bone has relatively small pores, and is described as compact bone, while the spongier bone towards the centre is called cancellous bone. Long bones, that is, the bones of the limbs, usually have a marrow-filled central cavity, and, in mammals, this is where red blood cells are manufactured. The marrow extends into the pore spaces of the cancellous bone. The marrow usually becomes less productive in older animals, and becomes converted into a yellow fat (once used as tallow in candles). In mammals, birds, dinosaurs, and some other vertebrates, the bone matrix is arranged in concentric layers about numerous central blood vessels, giving a distinctive microscopic appearance described as Haversian bone. This structure is most easily seen in the compact bone.

To understand the changes that take place during fossilization, it is necessary to consider the fate of a body after death. When an animal dies, its body is usually broken down by the action of scavenging animals, large and small, and by the putrifying action of bacteria. The rate of breakdown is determined by a number of factors including temperature, humidity, and the types of scavengers. Decomposition occurs much more rapidly in warm moist conditions than in cold dry conditions. Explorers in the Antarctic sometimes come across the desiccated remains of penguins that may have been dead for hundreds of years, whereas tropical rain forests destroy their dead rapidly.

The efficiency of large scavengers is documented by some observations on a population of orangutans in the tropical rain forests of central Borneo.[2] During a five-and-one-half year period of fieldwork, involving 8,000 hours of direct observation,

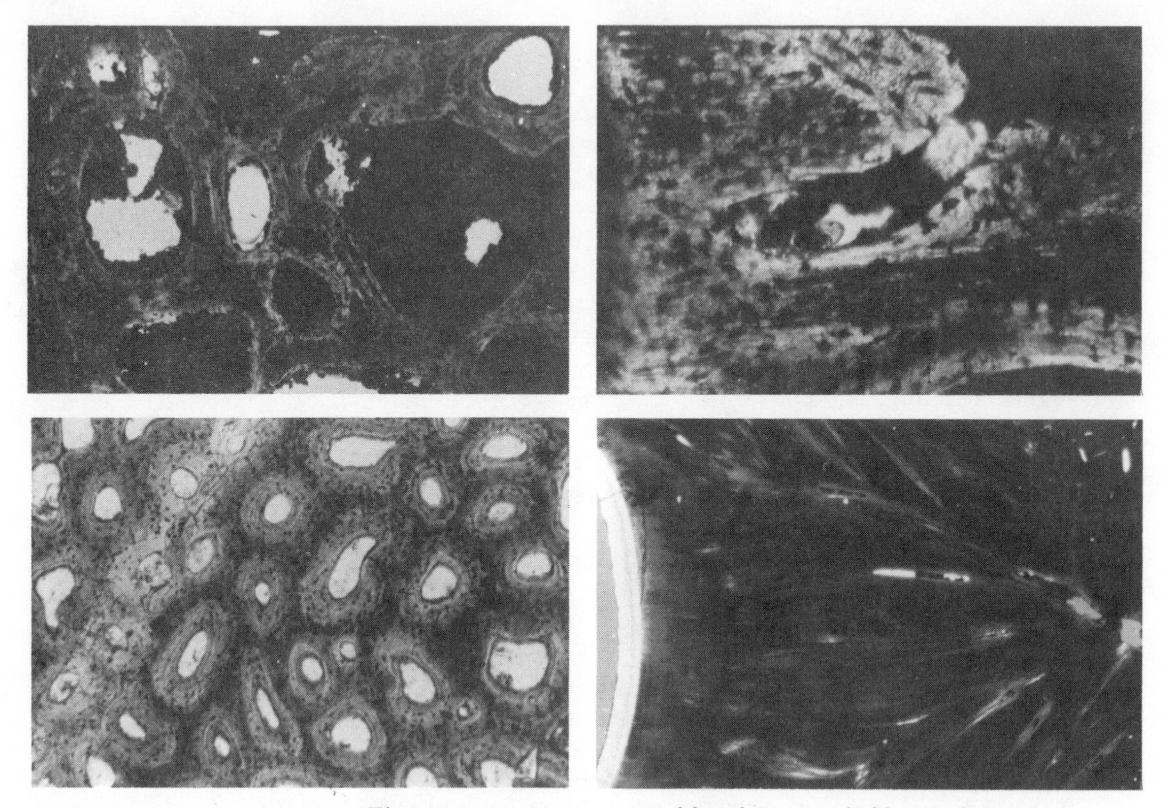

The microscopic structure of fossils is revealed by studying thin sections. **Top row**, *left to right: Transverse section through the vertebra of a hadrosaurian dinosaur (Upper Cretaceous); the black areas are pores which have been filled with minerals. At higher magnification small dark bodies can be seen—the lacunae—once housing the living bone cells (osteocytes). The concentric arrangement of lacunae in the third slide (archaeological human material) is characteristic of Haversian bone. Fossil bone often has all of its pores filled with mineral, as in the fourth slide, from the vertebra of the ornithopod dinosaur* **Camptosaurus** *(Upper Jurassic); photographed under polarised light the mineral crystals (calcite) appear patterned.*
Second row, *left to right: Transverse section through the vertebra of an ichthyosaur (Lower Jurassic); notice that the pores are almost devoid of minerals. The next three slides are transverse sections through the tooth of a hadrosaur. The white layer on the left of the first slide is the enamel, beneath it is the dentine, and at the far right is the pulp cavity. At higher magnification (last two slides) blood vessels can be seen radiating through the dentine from the pulp cavity. Notice the dark granules in the blood vessels, and in the pulp cavity.*

the remains of dead orangutans were only found on two occasions. On the first occasion an old male was found, probably less

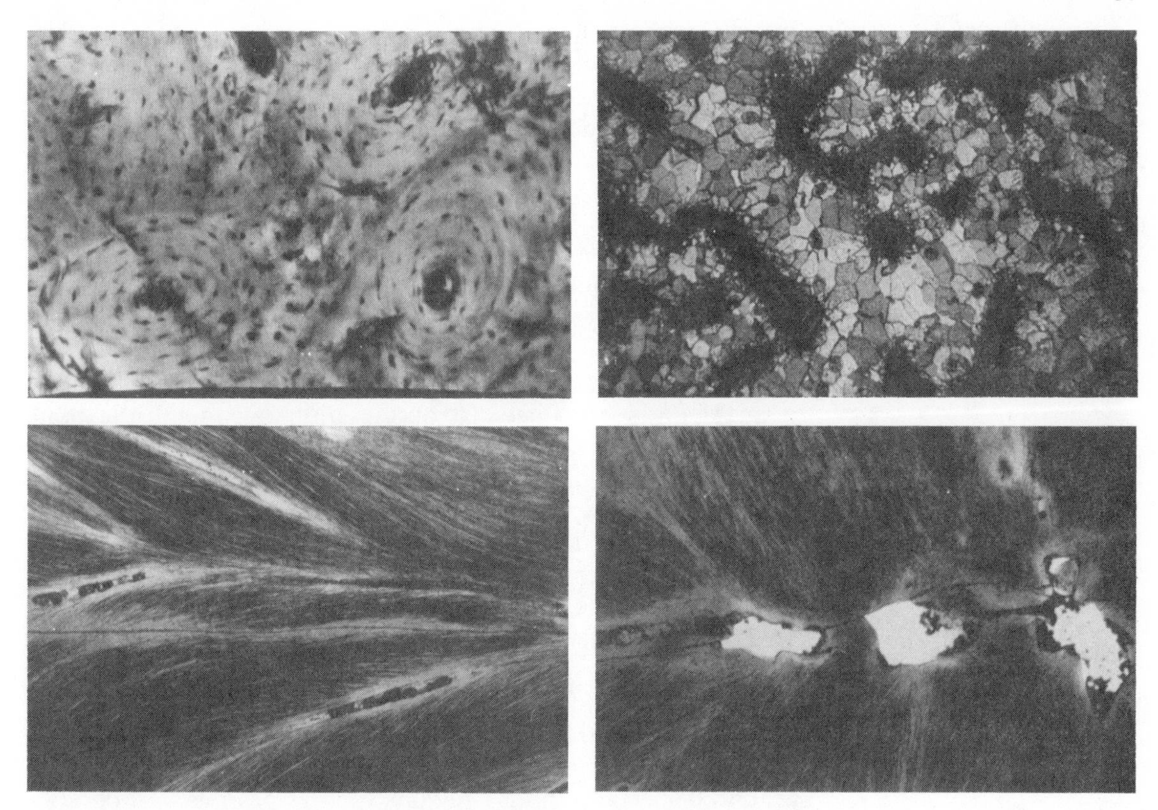

than 12 hours after his death. Wild pigs had already started work on the corpse. The entire contents of the body cavity had been devoured, many ribs were missing, and the shoulders and hips had been largely stripped of flesh. Much-trodden ground surrounded the carcass, and patches of bare earth and small clumps of orangutan hair showed that the body had been dragged back and forth many times. While the observer was examining the carcass one pig returned, moved cautiously towards the remains, and then began to drag it around with such vigour that bones were wrenched out of their sockets and some were removed from the body. On the second occasion, only a fragment of the skull was discovered, and a thorough search of the surrounding area failed to reveal even the smallest scrap of bone. Little wonder that the fossil record of man and his relatives is so fragmentary: the early phase of our evolutionary history was passed in warm forests.

To stand any chance of preservation, a skeleton has to be spared from the ravages of scavengers. Rapid burial offers one solution, entombment in caves and fissures another, and some of our best-preserved fossils are from cave deposits. Rapid burial can occur on land as a result of dust and sand storms, and in natural catastrophes such as landslides and volcanic eruptions, but the greatest chances of rapid interment occur in water. Sea, lake, and river beds receive a continuous rain of particles from the water above. These sediments consist of the bodies of microscopic animals and plants (plankton), fragments of larger organisms, and solids washed down from the land. The rate at which sediments accumulate varies with the location, and is generally highest in estuaries and in coastal waters where there is much run-off from the land. Some of our best-preserved Mesozoic fossils, including the ichthyosaurs, pterosaurs, and the earliest bird, are from deposits that were formed in shallow seas close to the land.

Assuming that a bone escapes the attention of scavengers, what changes are likely to occur, and how might the bone become transformed into a fossil? The least resistant constituent of bone is collagen, which breaks down into its component amino acids fairly readily. This process is accelerated by increased temperature, and is probably encouraged by bacteria. As the bone loses collagen it comes less resilient and progressively more brittle, as we have seen. Brittle bones, if left uncovered, are particularly vulnerable to the weathering action of the elements, wind, rain, frost, and sun all taking their toll. Surface cracks appear and deepen, and the usual outcome is that the bone disintegrates.

Bones are sometimes seen weathering out on the surface of the ground, especially in arid regions such as prairies and deserts. They are light compared with fresh bones because they have lost much of their collagen, not to mention their fluid, and are brittle and easily broken. Unless buried or otherwise protected from the elements, they will eventually break up and disappear. Burial not only protects bones from scavengers and the elements, but also provides a suitable environment for an exchange of materials between the soil and the bone.

Fossil bone differs from fresh bone in having little or none of its original collagen, and it usually has additional mineral material that has been deposited in its pores from the surrounding sediments. The bone mineral itself is virtually unaltered. Some fossil bones have all of their spaces filled in with foreign minerals, while others have taken up little or nothing from their surroundings. Probably all of the minerals deposited within the pores have been taken up, in solution, by the action of water percolating through the bone. The degree of mineralization appears to be determined by the nature of the environment in which the bone was deposited and not by the antiquity of the bone. For example, the black fossil bones and teeth of various animals that are common in many parts of Florida are heavily mineralized but date back only 20,000 years or so, whereas the dinosaur bones of western Canada, which are at least 65 million years old, are scarcely in-filled at all. Under optimum conditions, the process of mineralization probably takes only thousands rather than millions of years.

As sediments accumulate on top of a skeleton, the mounting pressure usually results in compression and consequent distortion of the bones. Sometimes, however, there is little or no distortion. The hardness of the sediments, the rate at which they become consolidated, and the degree of mineralization of the bones may all affect the amount of distortion that occurs.

There is a wide variation in the amount of organic material in fossils, which is often related not so much to the age of the fossil as to the conditions of burial. Collagen is usually found only in small quantities, most of it having been degraded to its component amino acids. Some fossils, including many dinosaurs, contain relatively large quantities of amino acids, and these have even been detected in Devonian fossils that are some 350 million years old. These very old fossils contain much smaller amounts of amino acids than younger fossils, but the relative quantities of the different types of amino acids are similar to those of fresh bone. Most fossils, therefore, have undergone less change than you might expect, and this is reflected in the fact that their fine structure, as revealed by the microscope, is usually little changed. Indeed, it is sometimes virtually impossible to distinguish between modern bone and fossil bone by microscopic examination.

The considerable progress that has been made in analytical techniques has made it possible to make precise measurements of the amino acids and elements present in fossil bones. The quantities of the materials being analysed are usually small, so great care has to be taken to prevent contamination. This is particularly important when analysing bone samples for amino acids, and samples have to be inspected to ensure that they are not contaminated by moulds, lichens, bacteria, or other foreign proteins. The remarkably well preserved fossils of Pleistocene age which have been collected in their thousands from the famous Rancho La Brea locality of Los Angeles are especially suitable for these analytical techniques. Many thousands of years ago this area of California, now within the city limits of Los Angeles, was a tar seep, and animals became mired in the soft tar when they came to drink the water that collected there. The specimens include sabre-toothed cats, bison, camels, horses, bears, dire wolves, and small mammals such as gophers, and many of them are similar to fresh bone in the amounts of amino acids they contain. Others contain considerably smaller amounts. The bones of one bison, for example, contained 227.4 milligrams of amino acids per gram of bone, which is similar to the amount found in fresh bison bone, whereas the remains of one of the gophers contained only 6.8 milligrams per gram.[3] The gopher bones, presumably, had already lost much of their original collagen prior to burial, whereas the bison had probably been buried soon after death. Even though the gopher retained only about 5% of its original organic content, the proportions of the various amino acids it contained were similar to those of the bison. Collagen has an amino acid content that is quite different from that of bacteria. Some fossil bones, however, have an amino acid composition that is intermediate between those of collagen and bacteria. In some cases, such bones occur in the same beds as bones that have amino acid compositions that are typical of collagen. As all the bones were exposed to similar soil environments, we can infer that the carcass that yielded bacterial amino acids underwent more bacterial decomposition prior to burial than the others. When fossil bones are analysed for elements, besides large quantities of calcium and phosphorus it is usual to find measurable amounts of other elements, including iron, strontium, barium, yttrium, and manganese. Manganese is responsible for the black coloration of many fossils. Some bones also contain traces of radioactive elements. Some of the elements may have been present in the animals at the time of their death, while others have leached into the bone from the surrounding sediments. We cannot be sure in which direction a particular element has migrated, and can therefore only take an educated guess at its origin.

The bones of living animals contain large quantities of blood and are surrounded by muscles that also contain much blood. Blood contains the red pigment haemoglobin, which is rich in iron, so it is possible that the iron invariably found in fossil bones is from this source. Most of the dinosaur skeletons in the Royal Ontario Museum that I have analysed contain large quantities of iron. All of these dinosaurs were collected from sandstone beds of Upper Cretaceous age, and the sandstone in the immediate vicinity of the bone frequently has a brown discoloration. Analysis shows that this discoloration is rich in iron. The iron concentration decreases with the distance from the bone, suggesting that it was derived from the bone and was not a natural component of the sandstone. It therefore seems reasonable to suggest that the iron originated from the blood in the bone and in the investing muscles.

A very useful tool for analysing elemental composition is the electron probe. Samples of bone, or matrix, are cut and polished and placed inside the instrument, which is essentially a modified electron microscope. A very fine beam of electrons is directed at the sample and an image of the specimen is displayed on a screen. When the electrons strike an atom they cause it to become excited, that is, to radiate energy, and each element emits a characteristic type of energy, that is, a particular wavelength of radiation. By measuring the quality and quantity of the emitted radiation each element can be identified and its relative abundance assessed. When the electron probe was used to analyse samples of dinosaur bone that were rich in iron, it was found that the iron was located in the in-filling material that occupied the pores of the bone. A tooth was also sectioned and examined, and a similar in-filling material was found inside the very fine blood vessels that radiate from the pulp cavity. This lends support to the suggestion that the iron was derived from the blood, but it is still possible that the iron was leached into the skeleton from the surrounding sandstone, becoming deposited in the blood vessels during the passage of time.[4]

Yttrium, which is often found in small quantities in dinosaurs and other fossils, is a rare element, found in nature only in small amounts. If yttrium is administered to living animals, it is taken up by the skeleton at those sites where bone is being absorbed.[5] Bone absorption is carried out by specialized cells called osteoclasts that actively erode bone surfaces. Bone absorption goes on hand-in-hand with bone growth because increases in size are accompanied by changes in shape, requiring parts of the bone to be eroded. The process of bone absorption is most active in young animals because of their rapid rate of growth. It is therefore possible that fossil bones containing yttrium are from individuals that had absorbed the element from their diet during periods of rapid growth. However, it is equally possible that the yttrium was not present at the time of death at all, but rather leached in from the surrounding matrix.[6]

As we can never be sure of the origins of elements in fossils, any conclusions drawn from elemental analysis are speculative. An example of this is provided by the interpretations that have been placed on strontium/calcium ratios. Strontium is a metal belonging to the same chemical family as calcium. It occurs naturally in the environment in relatively low concentrations, compared with calcium (the extensive atmospheric testing of nuclear weapons during the 1950's released into the environment quantities of the radioactive isotope strontium 90, which began turning up in human bones and teeth. There is, therefore, an extensive literature on the absorption of strontium by animals.) When plants containing strontium taken up from the soil are eaten by herbivores, some of the element is absorbed by the bones even though living things select calcium in preference to strontium. Here it takes the place of calcium in the apatite crystal, becoming permanently "locked in." The bones of herbivores consequently tend to contain small quantities of strontium. Carnivores, feeding on the flesh of herbivores, consume relatively less strontium in their diet, and their bones therefore contain smaller amounts of strontium, compared with calcium. It has therefore been suggested that the ratio of strontium to calcium can be used as an index to diets, the value being greater in herbivores than in carnivores.[7] While this appears to be a promising tool for palaeontologists, it does not always give meaningful results, as the following example will show.

Ornithomimus, the small ostrich-like dinosaur from the Upper Cretaceous period of North America, is without teeth, and there has been some speculation about its diet. Was it mainly herbivorous, like its present-day analogue, the ostrich, or did it feed on insects, small lizards, and the occasional mammal? The hands are particularly well developed, with long, grasping fingers, and it has been suggested that these may have been used for sneaking eggs from the nests of other dinosaurs. The entire skeleton is lightly built, and the long, slender hind legs suggest an ability to run fast, which would be a decided advantage in such a hazardous occupation. In Mongolia, the remains of an ornithomimid dinosaur were found amongst a nest of fossil eggs apparently belonging to another dinosaur. The skull had been badly crushed, almost as if an irate parent had caught the intruder going about its nefarious business.[8] This is entirely speculative, but it makes a good story!

In an attempt to cast some light on the problem, I set about measuring strontium/calcium ratios. Bone samples were taken from *Ornithomimus*, and, for comparison from the carnivorous dinosaur, *Albertosaurus*, and the herbivore, *Corythosaurus*—all three from the Upper Cretaceous of Alberta. Whereas the strontium/calcium ratio should have been highest in *Corythosaurus* and lowest in *Albertosaurus*, the reverse was true, which makes little sense. The results suggest that the strontium/calcium ratios may have changed since death, perhaps because of exchanges of strontium between the bone and the surrounding sediments. As we can never be sure of the extent of exchange between a bone and the surrounding sediments, I suspect that elemental analyses of skeletons will never yield reliable information.

Palaeontology is the ultimate expression of escaping into the past, and life in the Mesozoic looks progressively more idyllic as life in the 20th century becomes more complex and less certain. But dinosaurs and their contemporaries were not immune to pain and suffering, and we have direct evidence of disease and injury preserved in their bones. Abnormalities in fossil bones and teeth are not unusual, and have been noticed since the early days of palaeontology. A significant amount of information has accumulated, and the publication of a major work on the subject in 1923 may be taken as the birth of a new branch of palaeontology called palaeopathology.[9] Considerable attention has been focused on human diseases, and the last few years have witnessed many autopsies on Egyptian mummies. The study of

This ostrich-sized dinosaur **Ornithomimus**, *which lived in the late Cretaceous period, is depicted here stealing eggs from another dinosaur.*

ancient diseases is an intriguing subject, but we will do little more here than whet the appetite with a few examples from the Mesozoic.

Healed bone fractures are not uncommon in dinosaur skeletons, and are revealed by bony swellings, called callosities, at the site of the injury. When a bone is broken the fractured ends become cemented together by a fairly coarse network of bone, the callosity thus formed serving a first aid role. As the fracture is consolidated from the inside, the callosity is reduced in size, but, as anyone who has had a broken bone will know, it never completely disappears. Some indication of the amount of healing that has occurred since the injury can, therefore, be obtained from the size of the callosity. If the two broken ends are not

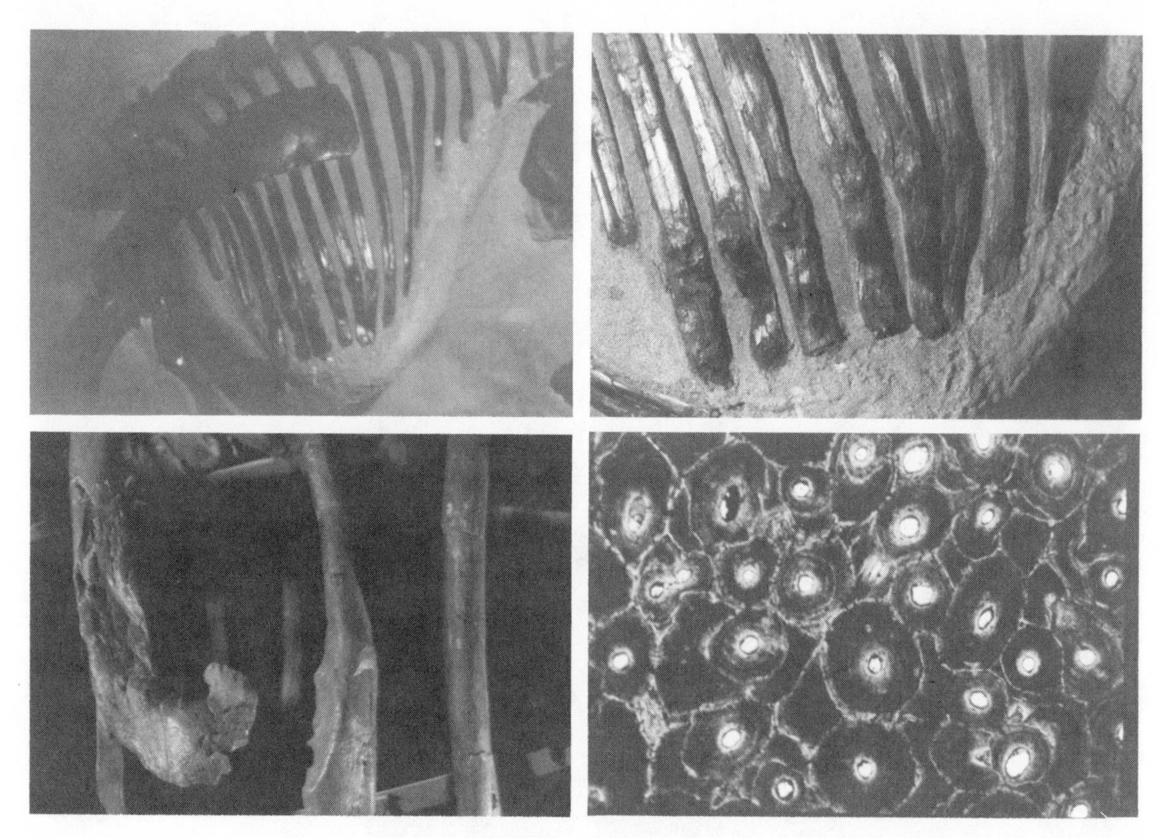

Evidence of bone damage and disease is revealed by studying skeletons and thin sections of bone. **Top row**, *left to right: Sometime in life this hadrosaur received a blow to the left side that broke six ribs. A close inspection shows the bony callosities formed at the sites of repair. Viewed from the right this horned dinosaur* **Chasmosaurus** *looks normal. From the left side, however, a deformed rib can be seen.*

Bottom row, *left to right: Close inspection reveals a bony outgrowth, and some abnormality in the adjacent rib. A thin section cut from the shaft of the deformed rib has the normal appearance of Haversian bone. The second section, taken from the outgrowth, shows abnormal bone. Bony outgrowths from other parts of the skeleton, including some toes, are indicative of a chronic bone disease.*

displaced during repair, the bone will heal neatly, but this is not always the case, and repaired bones are sometimes joined together by extensive callosities, as in the *Albertosaurus* specimen in the Royal Ontario Museum which has a badly healed fracture of its right leg (fibula bone).

Some injuries are so severe that fractured bones puncture the skin, exposing them to bacterial invasion. Infections contracted in that way may spread throughout the skeleton, and a probable

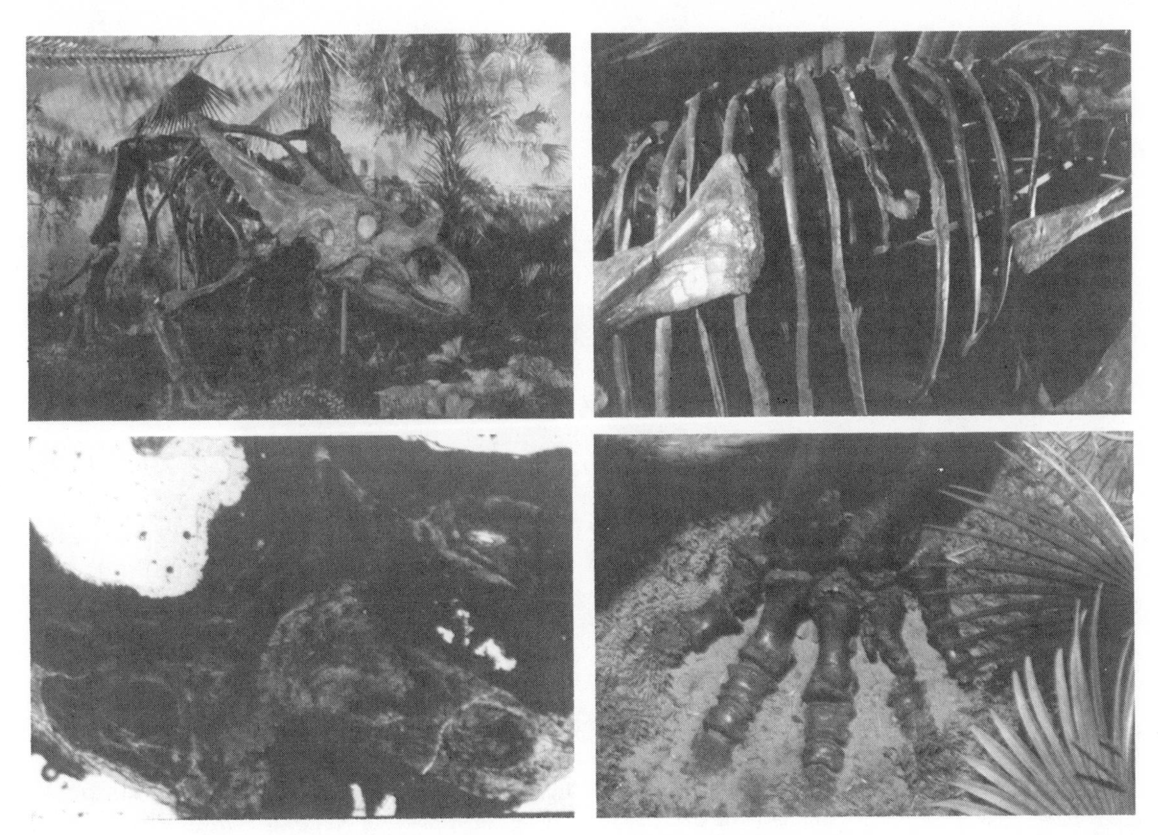

instance of such a chronic disease is provided by a specimen of a horned dinosaur that is on display at the Royal Ontario Museum. Viewed from the right side, the skeleton looks normal, but a cursory inspection of the other side reveals an odd deformation of one of the ribs. The rib in question is about half the length of the others, and ends in an expanded and roughened bony outgrowth. A bone sample was removed from this outgrowth and compared with a sample taken from the normal portion of the rib. Instead of the orderly appearance of Haversian systems seen in the normal rib section, the sample from the outgrowth has a disarranged appearance, and the bone cells, judged from the size of their lacunae, are about twice the normal size. This is typical of bone that has been formed in response to a fracture, but a close examination of other parts of the skeleton reveal other abnormalities suggesting something more than a simple injury. Many of the toe bones have been eroded and are roughened by bony outgrowths. Similar outgrowths occur on many of the vertebrae. Perhaps the injury sustained by the rib, which never healed properly, broke the surface of the skin, introducing bacteria that spread throughout the skeleton. The disease may have contributed to the animal's death.

Most dinosaurs have long tails, and these seem to have been particularly vulnerable to injury. Sometimes tails are found in which two or more vertebrae have become fused together, which suggests that their adjacent articular surfaces were damaged at one time. Back problems are sometimes alleviated in our own species by surgically fusing two vertebrae. This is effected by damaging their adjacent articular surfaces.

Most of the vertebrate fossils that have been found are the remains of hard parts, usually bones and teeth, but evidence of soft parts is occasionally preserved. The most frequently encountered evidence of the soft anatomy is impressions in the sediments, and footprints are the most common of these. Dinosaur trackways have been discovered in many parts of the world, and they provide us with a fascinating link with the past. To place one's feet in depressions left in the mud millions of years ago and measure one's stride against that of a dinosaur is a thought-provoking experience. Fossil trackways hold more than fascination, as we shall see in a later chapter, because they provide useful information about posture and locomotion in dinosaurs.

Far less common than trackways are impressions of skin—usually of dinosaurs—made when they lay down. The weight of their bodies pressing down on the ground left natural impressions of their skin. These impressions were subsequently filled in with sediments, which became consolidated into a hard natural cast of the skin.

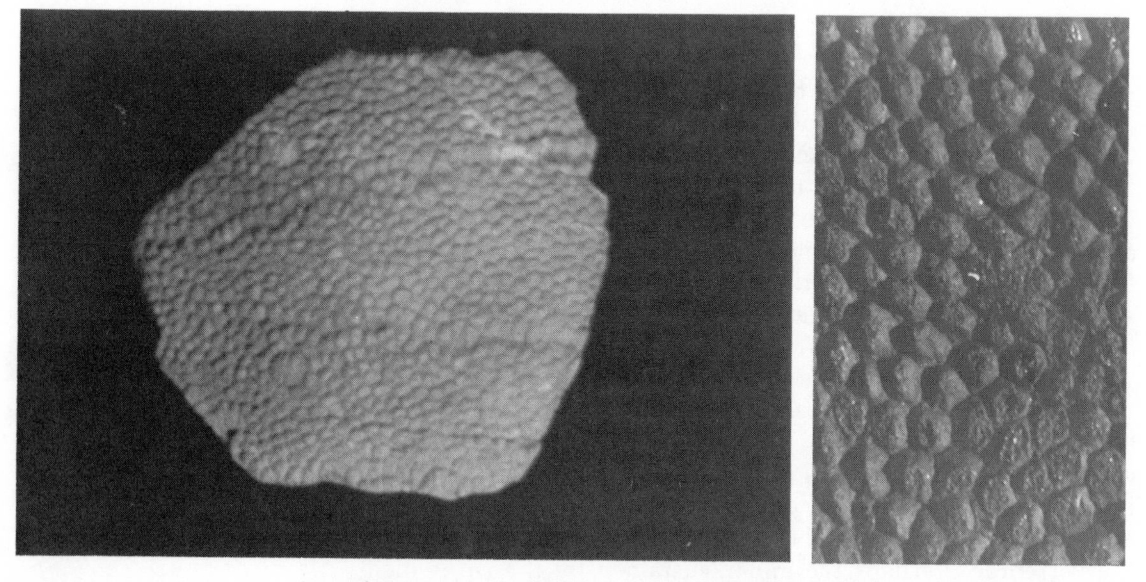

A natural cast of the skin of a hadrosaurian dinosaur, preserved in sandstone. The skin had a pebbled structure, clearly seen in the close-up, and appears to have been devoid of scales.

There are some instances of natural skin casts being found in association with skeletal remains, which permits identification of the dinosaur. Hadrosaurs appear to have lacked scales, and their pebbled skin was probably much like that of an elephant.

Skin impressions are not confined to dinosaurs, and the most finely preserved impressions have been found in marine sediments. Most notable of these are from the Lower Jurassic shales of Holzmaden in southern Germany. Holzmaden is renowned for its ichthyosaurs, and a number of these have the body outline preserved as a carbonaceous film. But for the discovery of such perfectly preserved material, we would not know that ichthyosaurs had a dorsal fin, nor would we know anything about the shape of the tail flukes. Equally remarkable was the discovery of small pterosaurs, together with well-preserved impressions of their delicate wing membranes.

Casts and impressions of internal organs have also been found, and casts of the brain are probably the most instructive of these. The brain is a very soft organ that lies protected within the skull. After death, it probably decomposes fairly rapidly, and the bony cranium that once housed it often becomes filled with earthy particles. If the particles become consolidated, a natural cast is formed, called an endocast. In birds and mammals, the inside walls of the cranium conform closely with the contours of the brain, so that the endocast is a faithful replica of the original brain. The conformation is less precise in reptiles, whose endocasts give only an approximate idea of the size and shape of the original brains. The material forming the endocast is often more resistant to weathering than the surrounding bone, so it sometimes happens that the skull is destroyed, leaving a replica of the brain. This appears to have been the case with the British Museum specimen of *Archaeopteryx*, the oldest known bird, and the endocast provides valuable information on the possible behavioral potentials of this important animal.

When evidence of the soft anatomy is preserved, it is not the original material that remains, but a stony replica. As a consequence, the fine detail of the structure is usually lost. We can learn nothing, for example, about the structure of the brain cells by studying natural endocasts, any more than we can learn about the structure of the skin cells by studying casts of dinosaur skin. There are some remarkable exceptions, however, as in the well-preserved fine structure of the body muscles of a fish that lived during the Jurassic.[10] The muscles in this unusual specimen appear as blocks of material attached to the vertebrae, and a microscopic examination reveals numerous fibres that compare in size with those of modern animal muscles. Modern muscle fibres, or cells, are each made up of a large number of fibrils. Within each fibril is a repeating series of interdigitating filaments, and, because these are in register in adjacent fibrils, the whole muscle fibre has a finely striated appearance when viewed under high magnification. (It is for this reason that skeletal muscle is usually called striated muscle.) When small pieces of the fossilized fish muscle were examined under high magnification, the investigator was amazed to discover that the fibres were striated, and that the stripes corresponded in width with those of modern muscles. How is this remarkable preservation explained? What we are looking at is not the original material of the muscle, which has long since disappeared, but a high-resolution replica of it formed in mineral. We do not know under what conditions preservation occurred, but suspect that burial must have been rapid. Replication may have occurred by a process similar to that used by botanists in the acetate peel technique, which is used in studying plant cells. If nail varnish is coated lightly on the surface of a leaf, allowed to dry, and then peeled off and examined under a microscope, all of the details of the skin cells can be seen. In the fish specimens minerals presumably crystallized onto the surface of the muscle soon after death, and certainly before the muscles decomposed, which may have occurred within a few days.

With the advent of the electron microscope it has become possible to study fossils under very high magnifications revealing the minutest details. At such magnifications, the fine tubules radiating throughout the dentine of teeth appear as large channels. Small particles are often found within the tubules, and these have been tentatively identified as bacteria.[11] Whether these structures actually represent high-fidelity mineral casts of bacteria is questionable at the present, and more work has to be done to see if they are always associated with bones and teeth that have evidence of disease. We still have some intriguing things to learn about fossils and the process of their preservation.

4
Interpreting a Skeleton

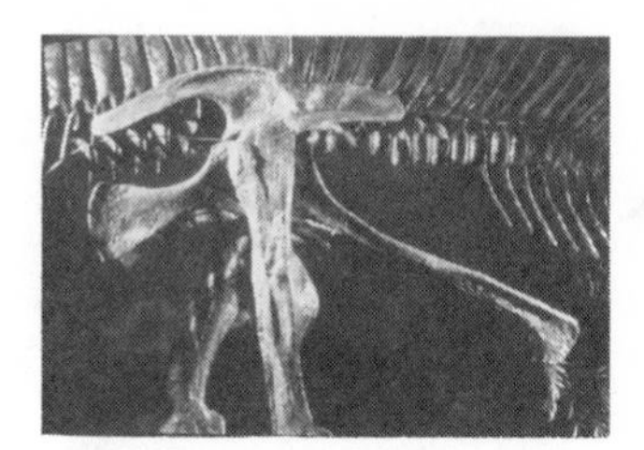

Palaeontologists are famous, or infamous, for being able to tell us everything about an animal from the smallest scrap of information. Complete animals have been reconstructed from isolated bones, and I have even read a discussion of the possible diet of an animal that was represented only by its footprints. Baron Cuvier, generally regarded as the father of vertebrate palaeontology, was not averse to producing bold reconstructions on the most tenuous evidence, and palaeontologists of lesser personage can hardly be criticized for emulating the master. We might forgive our forefathers for their transgressions, but unfortunately their bad habits have been handed down, and the practice of drawing conclusions beyond the limitations of the data is as prevalent today as it was last century. The discourse on the food preferences of the animal that has left only its footprints was published in a reputable palaeontological journal in 1977. The best safeguard against falling into this trap is to make constant reference to present-day animals. If it is not possible to reconstruct a particular feature from the skeleton of a modern animal, then it will not be possible in the case of a fossil one.

A wealth of information can be drawn from the detailed study of fossils, but there are also many things we cannot learn from them. At very best we have a complete skeleton to study, but even this is only part of the animal. We have none of the soft parts (though we may sometimes have clues to these in the form of skin impressions, muscle-insertion scars on bones, endocranial casts of the brain, and the like); we cannot watch the animal move, observe its behaviour, measure its temperature, record its heart rate, or measure any of its other body functions. We seldom know its sex, we can rarely determine how old it was when it died, and often we have no way of knowing whether it was an adult or juvenile. If we have a number of similar skeletons to study, we can probably never be sure whether they belonged to the same species because, as we saw in an earlier chapter, we have no way of recognizing a biological species. There are, therefore, definite limitations to what we can learn from fossils and we must constantly be aware of these. Forewarned of the pitfalls, we can proceed to examine a dinosaur skeleton and see what it can tell us about the animal that once gave it life.

Dinosaurs appear to have been predominantly terrestrial, and they were confronted with the same problems of supporting and moving their bodies against the force of gravity as present-day land animals. Most dinosaurs were herbivores, like many living vertebrates, and some of them provided a food source for the carnivores. The skeletal adaptations of these two life styles were quite distinct, and we usually have no more difficulty in distinguishing between herbivorous and carnivorous dinosaurs than we do in distinguishing between a lion and an antelope. Most carnivorous dinosaurs conformed to the same general pattern throughout the Mesozoic Era, and the greatest diversity was seen among the herbivores. One very successful group of herbivores was the hadrosaurs, which appeared towards the end of the Cretaceous. Hadrosaurs have been found in many parts of the world, from Europe to the Far East and are particularly well represented in North America.[1] Many well-preserved hadrosaur skeletons have been collected from western Canada and the United States, and they are the commonest Canadian dinosaurs. Because they are so well known, they are a logical group for us to examine here, both to learn about dinosaurs and to find out how skeletons can be interpreted. Most of our account will therefore be based upon hadrosaurs, but we will also be referring to other types of dinosaurs.

By dinosaur standards, most hadrosaurs were not particularly large. They were about the size of the Indian elephant (some giant hadrosaurs, however, have been reported from Baja California with an estimated length of 15 m[2]). Many species are recognized, distinguished mainly by differences in the skull. Some species have elaborate crests on the head, varying from fairly low structures, as in *Lambeosaurus lambei*, through fairly extensive helmet-shaped crests, as in *Corythosaurus casuarius*, to the enormous backward-projecting crest of *Parasaurolophus walkeri*. Before investigating these curious head structures further, we will examine the skeleton to find out what we can about posture and locomotion.

Most museum collections of dinosaurs were acquired during the latter part of the last century and early part of the present one, and a great deal has been learned about them since those days. It is not surprising, then, that we have to question the postures in which some dinosaur skeletons have been mounted. In the dinosaur gallery at the Royal Ontario Museum, for example, there is a fine skeleton of *Corythosaurus casuarius* that was mounted in the 1920s in an upright posture. At that time many palaeontologists thought that hadrosaurs walked in that way, while others, impressed by the position in which most hadrosaurs have been found, believed that they walked on all fours with the tail curving gently to the ground. Close examination of the upright *Corythosaurus* skeleton reveals that the head of the femur articulates with the pelvis at the point where two bones (the pubis and the ilium) join together, which is a point of weakness. It is therefore unlikely that the body could have been

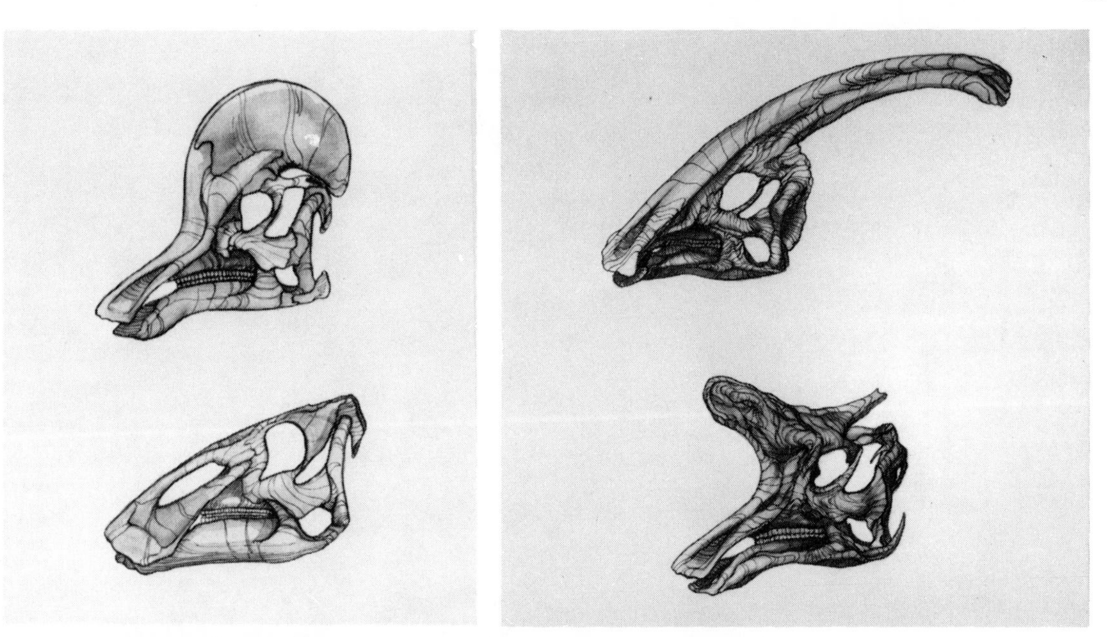

The main differences between the various hadrosaur species is in their skulls. **Top left, Corythosaurus casuarius**, *with its extensive semicircular crest; bottom left, the crestless* **Edmontosaurus regalis**; *top right,* **Parasaurolophus walkeri** *with its extensive tubular crest; bottom right,* **Lambeosaurus lambei** *with an anterior hollow crest and a small solid crest inclined backwards. All four from the Upper Cretaceous of western Canada, drawn from specimens in the Royal Ontario Museum.*

held in an upright position. However, we cannot be emphatic about this because we do not always draw correct conclusions from the study of skeletons. The skeleton of the elephant, for example, is adapted for supporting a large body mass, and a bipedal posture is inconceivable. But elephants have been observed to stand on their hind legs in the wild, in order to reach up into trees. Perhaps hadrosaurs could stand, but not walk, with a semi-erect posture. Since the hind legs are considerably larger than the front legs, both in length and relative thickness, it is reasonable to conclude that they carried most of the weight, and this is probably why hadrosaurs have often been shown as having a bipedal posture. We are bipedal, but we are rather unusual because we hold our vertebral column vertically. Other bipedal animals, which includes birds and kangaroos, have an essentially horizontal vertebra column, and it is now believed that hadrosaurs, similarly, held their backs horizontally during locomotion.[3] The hadrosaur tail, rather than curving to the ground, was probably held stiff and straight, counter-balancing

The upright posture in which this hadrosaur skeleton (**Corythosaurus casuarius**) *was mounted is now believed incorrect. Close inspection of the pelvis shows that the head of the femur abuts against the joint between the pubis and ilium, which was probably an area of weakness.*

the weight of the front of the body about the pivot formed between the femur and the pelvis.

The vertebral column comprises a large number of vertebrae. Each vertebra consists of a short cylinder of bone, the centrum, surmounted by an arch and spine through which the spinal cord passed from the brain. Adjacent vertebrae articulate with one another by paired processes called zygapophyses that face upwards and inwards, articulating with the downwards and outward-facing surfaces of the posterior zygapophyses of the vertebra in front. The anterior and posterior surfaces of the centra also articulate, and there is sometimes a ball-and-socket joint between them.

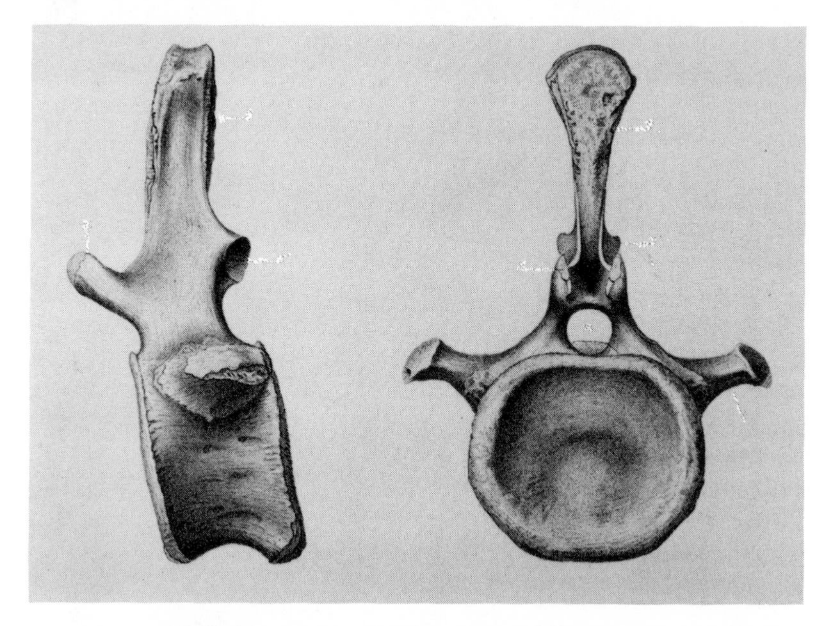

A caudal vertebra from the sauropod dinosaur **Camarasaurus grandis**, *from the left side, and from the front, showing the typical structure of a vertebra. See text for details.*

In some dinosaurs, such as *Deinonychus*, the prezygapophysis of the tail are enormously elongated and form an overlapping bony sheath around the tail, which was kept absolutely straight. The hadrosaurs lacked elongated prezygapophyses and probably maintained the shape of the tail by muscular action. The ossified tendons that run along the length of the tail probably also served a stiffening role. (Ossified tendons are found in some modern animals—those stiff white splints in the leg muscles of the turkey are ossified tendons, but they are not used for stiffening the leg, they serve to transmit the pull of muscles to bones.) The neural spines are relatively long, as are the chevron bones, which project down from each centrum, and consequently the tail is very deep.

The counterbalancing mechanism of the hadrosaur skeleton was beautifully demonstrated when we were mounting a skeleton of *Lambeosaurus lambei* for our dinosaur gallery at the Royal Ontario Museum. The method now used to mount a skeleton is to drill out the bones and thread them onto a steel framework so that the skeleton will stand on its own legs as it did in life. The vertebrae are strung onto a horizontal rod welded to the vertical rods in the legs. During the construction of *Lambeosaurus*, the tail vertebrae were the first to be strung on, and the leverage generated by the tail was so great that a large concrete block had to be attached at the other end. Once the other vertebrae and the skull had been added, the skeleton became so well balanced that the touch of a finger was enough to make it rock up and down.

Similar counterbalancing may be seen in birds, especially the large flightless ones. During a visit to Australia I had an opportunity to watch some emus in a conservation area. Emus are naturally inquisitive, and one of them approached me and was quite happy to let me rub him under the chin. This slight movement was enough to cause his body to rock up and down about the hip joint, just like our hadrosaur.

The problem of deciding on an appropriate walking pose for our skeleton of *Lambeosaurus* was simplified by the fact that we had a set of tracks in which to mount the skeleton. The trackway had not been made by *Lambeosaurus*, because it was from a geologically older horizon, but it had obviously been made by a similar dinosaur. The impressions of the toes were broad and blunt, with no indication of claws, and the bony foot of *Lambeosaurus* corresponded quite closely with the impression. The trackway was made by a dinosaur walking on all fours, and the imprints of the hind feet were considerably larger and deeper than those of the forefeet, confirming that most of the weight was carried on the hind legs. The length of the stride, that is, the distance between the footprint and the next print made by the same foot, was just under 2 m, which is quite modest compared with the length of the skeleton (8 m). The short stride indicates that the animal was walking fairly slowly at the time, because the length of the stride increases with speed.

When I am walking slowly, my stride is a little less than 1 m, but it increases to 5 m when I am running. The direct relationship between stride length and speed may be demonstrated by changing speed while walking on snow and then going back and examining one's trackway. (It may also be demonstrated on a dry day by wetting one's shoes in a shallow bowl of water before walking and then running along a dry sidewalk, but this method usually elicits comment from neighbours.)

This contemporary mount of the hadrosaur **Lambeosaurus lambei** *has been given a horizontal vertebral column. Notice that the feet, which are set in a trackway, have the heel raised from the ground in the digitigrade pattern of walking. Hadrosaurs are believed to have run on their hind legs with forelegs clear of the ground. The animal was walking rather slowly. The artist's restoration shows a group of lambeosaurs being disturbed and taking flight.*

The fact that in our trackway the front feet were also making contact with the ground is further evidence of slow progression, because it is believed that the animal held its front legs off the ground during running. It has been claimed that the speed of a dinosaur can be calculated from its stride, but the methodology is unsound and the results therefore questionable.[4] The track width, that is, the distance between the centre of a left footprint and the centre of a right footprint, measured across the track, was only 20 cm. The footprints were therefore not far off from being in a straight line, the feet being placed well beneath the body during the locomotion. One has only to look at trackways left in the snow to realize that this is very common among tetrapods. During locomotion, some of a tetrapod's feet are off the ground, stability being sacrificed for forward motion. If the feet were placed well to the side, the body would constantly be toppling towards the unsupported side, and muscular energy would have to be wasted in corrective movements.

The hadrosaur foot has three large toes, all pointing forwards, and all ending in a small hoof. Instead of walking on the entire foot, the hadrosaur raised its heels clear off the ground, so that it walked on its toes. This method of walking is called digitigrade. When we walk we place the sole of the foot on the ground, which is called plantigrade walking, but we become essentially digitigrade when we sprint. The digitigrade pattern adds another segment to the leg and, as we shall see, this is a strategy for increasing speed. The part of the foot that is held clear of the ground is called the metatarsus, and it is fairly long in hadrosaurs. Only the tips of the toes can be discerned in footprints, and it seems likely that an extensive pad of connective tissue cushioned the hind foot, as in the elephant. The front foot is much smaller and more slender than the hind one, and the digits do not spread out. Impressions of skin that have been found show that the hadrosaur's fingers were connected by a web of skin.

When we look at the massive hind leg of a hadrosaur, we are looking at the structure that not only supported most of the body weight but also supplied most of the power for thrusting the body forward. The power was provided by muscles, and while these have long since disappeared they have left traces on the surfaces of the bones. If we examine the skeleton of a modern animal we can detect areas where muscles once attached to the bones. These muscle attachment areas have various forms, from ridges and depressions to roughened areas. The general plan of muscles is fairly conservative within the vertebrates, and consequently we can get some idea of the muscle arrangement of a dinosaur by comparing their muscle attachment areas with those of a modern reptile. However, this approach gives us only a very approximate idea of the muscle arrangement, and we need to do far more work on modern animals in order to test its limitations. A study of the limb muscles of the kiwi, for example, showed that relatively few of the surface features on the bones can be correlated with specific muscles, and it was impossible even to attempt to reconstruct the musculature from a study of the skeleton.[5] The majority of the detailed muscle reconstructions that have been published for extinct animals are probably of doubtful value.

Most of a hadrosaur's muscular energy was used in pulling the leg backwards (retraction) against the resistance of the ground, and the extensive muscles that performed this task originated largely from the posterior half of the pelvis and from the root of the tail, and were inserted onto the back edge of the femur. Pulling the leg forward (protraction) was accomplished by muscles that originated from the anterior half of the pelvis and inserted onto the anterior edge of the femur. The protractor muscles did not have to work against the resistance of the ground, only against the inertia of the leg, that is, the tendency of the leg to remain where it was. The inertia of an object increases with its weight, as anyone who has tried to push a heavy car will know, and the weight of a leg is made up of the bone and muscles attaching to it. The femur was sheathed in muscles, most of which were concerned with extending (straightening) and flexing (bending) the lower leg segment on the femur. Muscles were also present on the calf and shin, for moving the foot about the ankle joint and also for moving the toes. The action of these muscles was probably transmitted to the feet by long tendons and there were probably few muscles in the foot.

The bulk of the leg muscles must therefore have been concentrated proximally (close to the centre of the body), and this is a strategy for reducing the inertia of the leg. R.T. Bakker, of Johns Hopkins University, challenged this argument,[6] citing several papers to support his view that the proximal placement of muscles does not significantly decrease the amount of energy expended during locomotion. While these papers did show that rheas (birds that have proximally placed leg muscles) expend relatively similar amounts of energy during locomotion as man (who does not have his leg muscles concentrated proximally), this does not prove Bakker's case, because rheas differ from man in far more ways than in the placement of their leg muscles. One way to test Bakker's case would be to run tests with a man (or rhea) before and after having the position of the leg muscles altered. This is obviously an impossible experiment, but it is one that can be simulated. Anyone who doubts that the relative position of a mass along the length of a leg has a great effect on the amount of energy expended in locomotion should try running with a bag of lead shot strapped to each ankle! I found that I could run about twice as fast with bags of shot attached to my thighs as I could with the bags attached to my ankles, and it was also far less tiring. The principle of reducing the inertia of a moving limb by concentrating the weight close to the pivot is illustrated every time a skater does a fast pirouette. The spin starts with the arms outstretched, which gives the body the greatest inertia, and when the arms are tucked in close to the body the sudden decrease in inertia causes a rapid increase in velocity. During the recovery stroke, a running animal tucks the leg in close to the body, thereby reducing its inertia, which increases its speed and reduces the amount of energy it must use to get into position for the next stride.

The speed of an animal is determined by the length and speed of its stride, and both may be increased by increasing the length of the lower leg segment (below the knee). The horse, for example, is a fast runner and it has a lower leg that is considerably longer than the upper leg; the ratio of the two segments is about 2.5:1. In the elephant, which is not specialized for running, the lower leg is much shorter than the upper leg, and the ratio is only 0.7:1. In *Lambeosaurus* the ratio of the lower leg to the upper leg is 1.5:1, which suggests that it may have been capable of running fairly fast. Being digitigrade effectively added another segment to the lower leg. This not only increased the length of the stride, but also the speed, because the speed of the stride is the sum of the speeds of the individual segments. Increased speed cannot be accomplished by increasing the length of the upper leg segment, because this would increase the distance through which the powerful retractor and protractor muscles would have to move, thus decreasing the speed of the stride; the inertia of the leg would also be considerably increased.

From the time of their discovery, hadrosaurs were interpreted as having been aquatic, and this was largely because of their tails, which are long and deep and were believed to have been used for swimming. When evidence was found for a web of skin joining the fingers it was naturally taken as further evidence for an aquatic way of life. However these two features, are not necessarily adaptations for swimming. While it is true that crocodiles, marine iguanas, and other aquatic reptiles have deep tails that are used for swimming, there are many terrestrial reptiles, including *Sphenodon* and many lizards, that have similar tails but never venture into the water. The tails of carnivorous dinosaurs, horned dinosaurs, and plated dinosaurs are also fairly deep, but few palaeontologists would consider that they were aquatic. Possession of webbed hands would probably have been of little assistance to a swimming hadrosaur because the

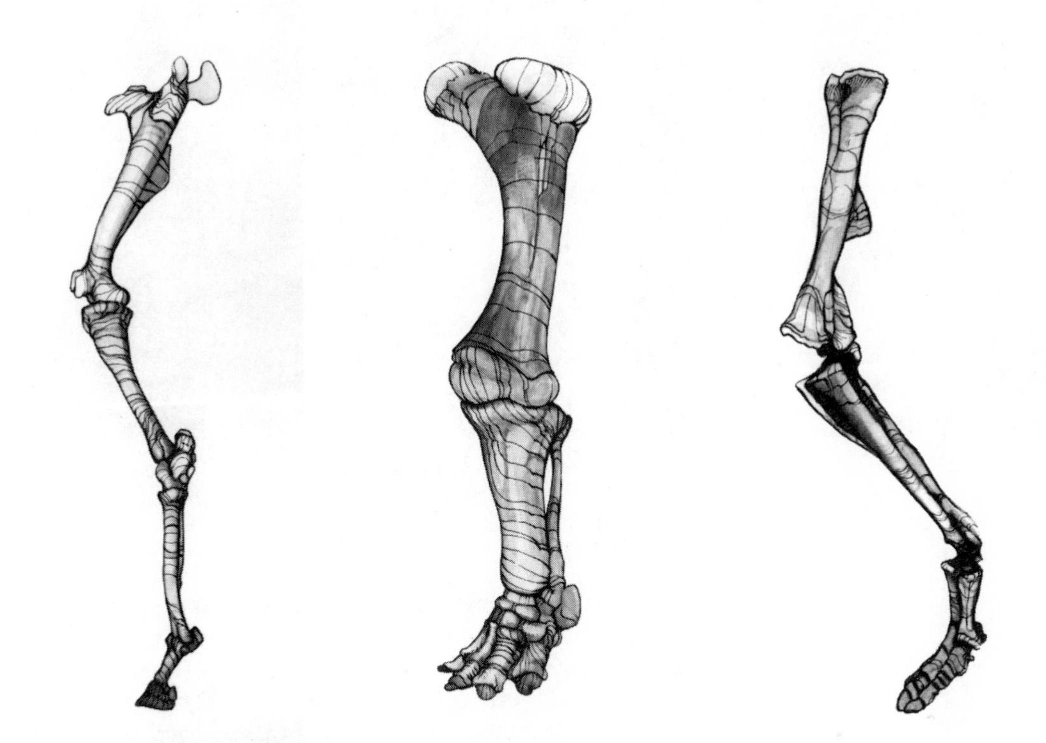

The relative lengths of the upper (above the knee) and lower leg segments can give some indication of running potentials. In the horse (left) a fast runner, the lower segment is more than twice the length of the upper one. The elephant (middle), which can neither trot nor gallop, has a lower segment that is shorter than the upper one. In **Lambeosaurus** *(right) the lower segment is about one and a half times longer than the upper segment, which suggests an ability to run fast.*

hands were small compared with the relatively large body. The hand of the kangaroo has the fingers united by a sheath of skin, but this is clearly not an aquatic adaptation. Kangaroos use their front limbs to prop themselves when moving slowly or when stopping to feed, and it seems likely that hadrosaurs, similarly, used their front limbs during slow locomotion. The skeletal adaptations of hadrosaurs therefore do not necessarily imply an aquatic life style, and we will soon see that some independent evidence about their food preferences supports the idea that they were terrestrial. This does not mean that hadrosaurs were not capable of swimming or that they never entered the water, merely that they may have spent most of their time on the land.

The skull, and in particular the teeth, provides us with most of our information on the possible feeding habits of extinct animals. Hadrosaurs have between 200 and 250 teeth packed into

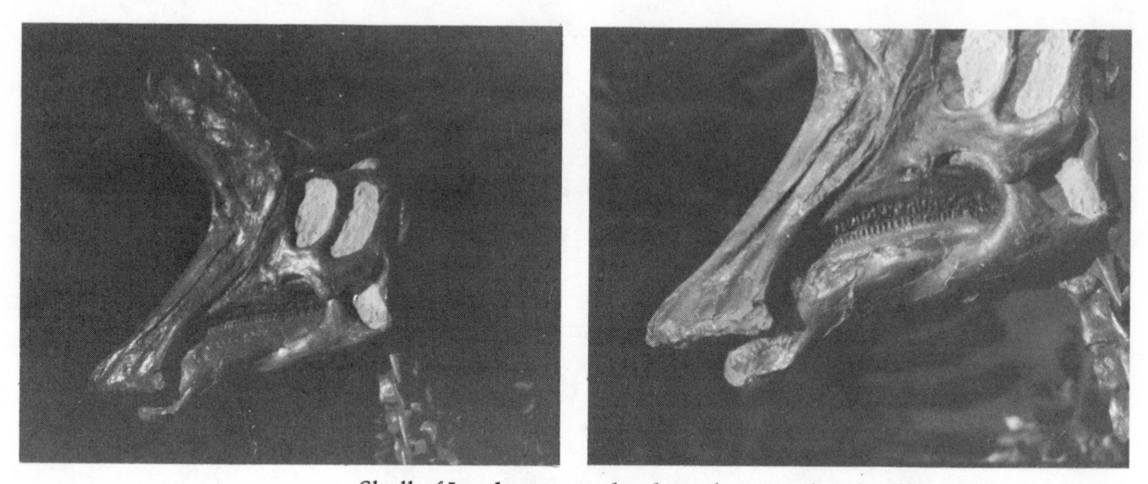

Skull of **Lambeosaurus lambei***, showing details of the teeth. Far right: Inside surface of the dental batteries; the individual teeth are diamond shaped, and the arrow marks the upper edge of the lower dental battery.*

each half of each jaw. The teeth are arranged in four dental batteries, two upper and two lower, and each battery has about 40 vertical series with between three and six teeth in each series. The individual teeth are only a few centimetres long and have a diamond-shaped cross section. Only those teeth that are at the free edge of each dental battery have worn surfaces, which shows that they alone were in use. Reptiles, unlike mammals, continually replace their teeth throughout life, and as the hadrosaur wore away its teeth, new ones took their places from lower down in the vertical series. The batteries were arranged so that the lower ones cut inside the upper ones, and the two sets of grinding surfaces thus formed were extensive. Whenever we see extensive grinding surfaces, whether it be in sheep, horses, or elephants, we can be fairly sure that we are dealing with a herbivore, because plants need much chewing. Animals do not possess digestive enzymes for breaking down the cellulose cell walls of plants, this function being performed by bacteria that live in the gut, and in order to assist this process food must be ground thoroughly before it is swallowed. Compared with meat, plants are relatively low in nutrients and they must therefore be consumed in much larger quantities. Hence the herbivore's need for extensive grinding surfaces. In spite of their soft appearance, many plants are abrasive, causing teeth to wear down rapidly. Horses resolve this problem by having high-crowned teeth that take a lifetime to wear down. The strategy of the hadrosaurs was to continuously replace their worn-out teeth.

When food is being chewed it is important that the grinding surfaces remain parallel to one another. If the jaw joint is at the same level as the grinding surfaces the jaws will close like the

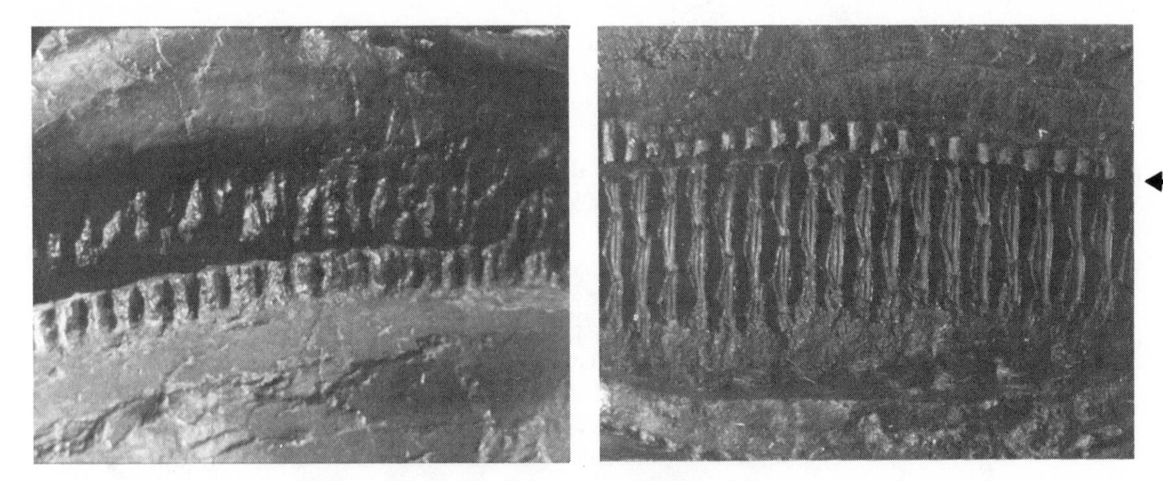

blades of a pair of scissors, the upper and lower back teeth coming into contact before those at the front. The jaw joint in the hadrosaurs is located below the level of the teeth. Consequently, when the jaws were closed the upper and lower teeth came together as one. (In mammals the jaw joint is located above the level of the teeth, having the same effect.) The jaw joint is formed between the quadrate, a stout, rod-shaped bone that extends vertically downwards from the back of the skull, and a shallow depression in the mandible into which the end of the quadrate fits. The depression is large compared with the end of the quadrate, and it is elongated in the direction of the lower jaw, or mandible, which suggests that the mandible was capable of being moved backwards and forwards as well as up and down. If the mandible was moved backwards and forwards while the teeth were clenched, an effective grinding action would be produced, and this is confirmed by evidence from the teeth. Examination of a number of hadrosaur skulls shows that the upper dental batteries are not of the same length as the lower ones, but the wear patterns are the same on both.[7] This could have occurred only if the mandible moved backwards and forwards, thus causing the lower batteries to grind along the length of the upper ones. Further support for this mechanism is provided by the evidence of muscle scars on the bones, which suggests that the hadrosaurs possessed muscles that brought about a fore-and-aft movement of the mandible. The dental batteries occupy most of the upper and lower jaw margins, but do not extend along their entire length. We might suppose that it would have been more advantageous for the dental batteries to extend along the entire length of the jaw margins, but this is not so. Effective grinding requires not only that the food be abraded between the teeth, but that the abrading take place under pressure. The muscles that provide this pressure are located at the back of the skull, just in front of the jaw joint, and run from the skull to the mandible. The teeth closest to the jaw joint experience a more powerful bite than those farther away, and we know this from our own experience: nuts are cracked more easily between the back teeth than between the front ones. The pressure on the teeth at the front of the dental batteries was probably quite low compared with that at the back, consequently there may have been no advantage in extending them any farther forward.

The hadrosaur's popular name of "duck-bill dinosaur" comes from the fact that its upper and lower jaws are expanded into broad bills. The occlusal (contact) edges of the upper and lower bills correspond with one another quite closely, and there is evidence that they may have been covered with horny sheaths, similar to the beak of a bird. Natural moulds of an upper sheath have been preserved in a few specimens, and it seems that the original structure was thin and probably horny, with a fluted internal margin. This has suggested that the upper bill may have functioned as a filtering device, like the fluted upper bill of ducks, and it has been used to support the aquatic interpretation for hadrosaurs.[8] Hadrosaurs may have used their bills for dabbling in the water for small plants and animals, just like most ducks, but there is no reason to suppose that their bills were unsuitable for cropping plants. Because of the prevalence of the belief that hadrosaurs were aquatic, it has been argued that the bill was capable only of cropping soft aquatic plants, but the considerable wear on the teeth shows that the hadrosaurs were feeding on fairly tough material. Direct evidence for the food preference of at least one hadrosaur came in 1922 with the discovery of the remains of the stomach contents in a particularly well-preserved skeleton, now in the Senckenberg Museum in Frankfurt.[9] All of the identifiable remains are of land plants, and conifer needles of the species *Cunninghamites elegans* are particularly abundant. At the time of this discovery, the aquatic interpretation for hadrosaurs was so deeply entrenched that the author (R. Krausel) was somewhat hesitant to accept his findings for what they were and made the point that the evidence only indicated that hadrosaurs *could* feed on land plants. The subjugation of evidence that is contrary to currently accepted principles has occurred time and again in the history of science.

We have said that plant material is relatively low in nutrients, and must therefore be eaten in large quantities, and that it is digested by bacterial action, a slow process. As a consequence, herbivores have a much longer digestive tract than carnivores, and this is normally filled with slowly decomposing food. Herbivores therefore tend to have relatively wider bodies than carnivores; horses and cows, for example, are broad across the back, while lions and tigers are narrow. In the hadrosaurs and other ornithischian dinosaurs, the large gap between the posteriorly directed pubes and ischia of the pelvis and the end of the rib cage would have been occupied by a large gut.

While the skull has provided most of the evidence of the probable feeding habits, it has also furnished other information. The striking feature of most hadrosaur skulls is the development of a crest, and many explanations have been given for its possible function.

There are two types of crests, hollow and solid, and some hadrosaurs have no crests at all. The solid crests are relatively small and may have the form of a small knob on top of the skull, as in *Prosaurolophus*, or a fairly prominent horn extending backwards and upwards from the top of the head, as in *Saurolophus*. The hollow crests are relatively large, but are flattened from side to side, especially towards the top. The nostrils, or nares, are large openings on either side of the snout which continue into bony canals conducting air towards the trachea. In the region corresponding to the forehead, the two bony canals open out into a single chamber, which is the hollow of the crest. This chamber carried the inspired air down to the trachea and eventually into the lungs. The hollow crest therefore formed part of a fairly complex duct system that carried air from the nares to the trachea. Some hadrosaurs, including *Lambeosaurus lambei*, have both a hollow crest and a small solid crest, that extends back from the top of the skull. The details of the duct system vary from species to species. In *Parasaurolophus walkeri*, which has a large backward-projecting crest, the two bony canals from each naris do not open out into a single chamber but, instead, continue back to the end of the crest, double back on themselves, and then pass forward again towards the throat. As an added complication, two blind-ending

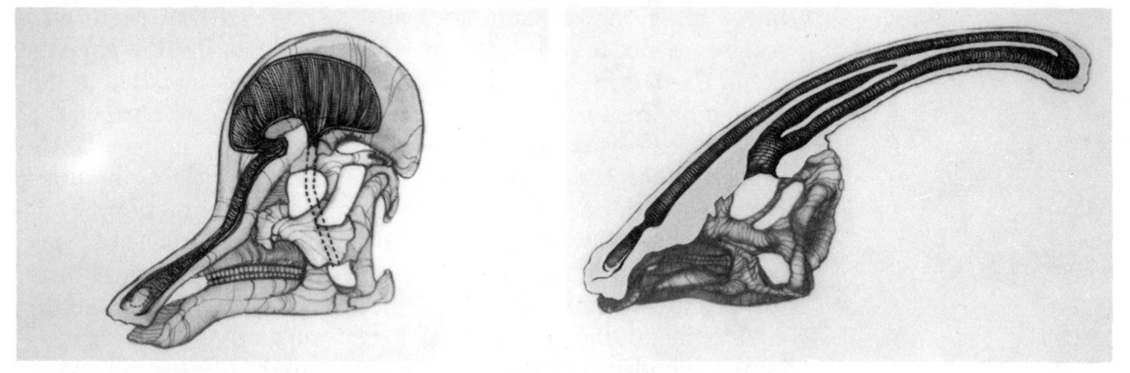

The hollow crests of hadrosaur skulls conducted air from the paired nares to the throat. The air passages are relatively simple in **Corythosaurus** *(left), but are doubled back upon themselves in* **Parasaurolophus** *(right). See text for details.*

tubes connect up with this looped system in the region where the inhaled air passed down to the throat.

Speculation on the possible function of the crests covers a wide spectrum, from the plausible to the ridiculous. The long infatuation of palaeontologists with the aquatic interpretation for hadrosaurs naturally led to a number of aquatic solutions to this problem. Some have suggested that the chamber functioned as a reserve supply of air that could be drawn upon during submergence. Notwithstanding the relatively small volume of the crest,[10] it is inconceivable that this air could have been taken into the lungs when the animal was under water. Others have suggested that air may have been taken in at the top of the crest, which thus functioned as a snorkel, but there is no evidence of an opening in any hadrosaur skull.

Baron Franz Nopcsa, a Hungarian palaeontologist, proposed that all of the crested hadrosaurs were males, and non-crested ones females. Apart from the fact that there are other skeletal characteristics that distinguish crested from non-crested hadrosaurs, there is the problem that the two types are seldom found together in the same geological horizons. Yet another suggestion was that the crests were weapons of defence, but the very thin walls of the hollow crests make this unlikely.

Professor John Ostrom of Yale University approached this problem by considering which of the several functions of the nasal passages of modern animals best fit the pattern of elaboration seen in hadrosaurs.[11] The narial passages function to remove particles, to humidify, and, in the case of warm-blooded animals, to warm the inhaled air before it passes to the lungs. The passages also provide for the sense of smell (olfaction). There is no reason why the hadrosaur crest should not have served several or all of these functions. Ostrom concluded that the most likely function was olfaction, and he showed that there was some evidence that the olfactory bulbs of the brain (the parts of the brain that interpret the sense of smell) were upturned in the crested hadrosaurs to project into the crest area, whereas in the flat-headed forms the bulbs were not upturned. This evidence suggests that the main function of the crest was olfaction. However, it does not mean that this was the sole function.

Since the hollow crest communicated with the trachea, it has been suggested that it may have served as a resonating chamber for producing loud sounds. Little imagination is required to equate the double-armed tube of *Parasaurolophus* with a trombone.[12] If hadrosaurs did produce loud sounds, these sounds may have been used to communicate danger to others or perhaps to attract potential breeding partners. Living animals employ various techniques for attracting mates, a role usually played by the

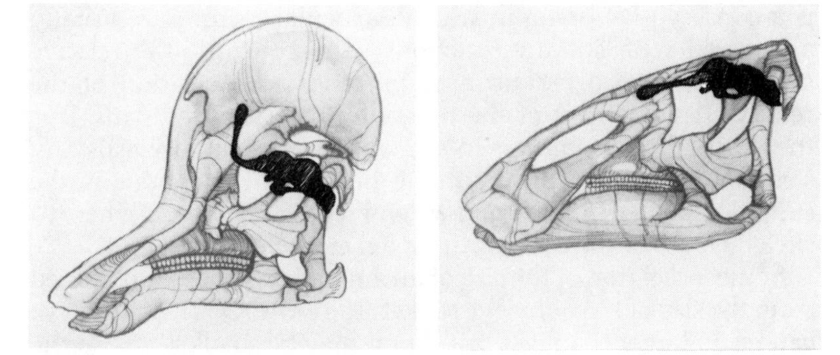

There is some evidence that the olfactory bulbs of the brain were upturned into the air spaces in the crested hadrosaurs (left) but not in the crestless ones (right). This suggests an olfactory function for the crests.

male of the species. Birds sing and display their colourful plumage, frogs croak, and amorous mammals often display their prowess to females in contests of strength with other males.

Closely related species often look alike, and it is important for individuals to be able to recognize their own kind, to prevent matings between individuals of different species. Some palaeontologists believe that species recognition was the main function of the crests, and this suggestion has particular merit because, apart from their cranial differences, hadrosaurs are skeletally very similar.[13] The solid crests could not have fulfilled olfactory or sound-producing functions, and species recognition seems to be their most likely role. *Lambeosaurus lambei*, as already seen, had a hollow crest and a solid crest, and the whole complex probably served more than one function. This may have been true of most crests, and perhaps their roles were not the same in all species.

Enough of the crest and its possible functions! We will now search the skull for clues to the sensory and nervous responses of hadrosaurs. But before attempting to assess the sensory potentials of animals that lived tens of millions of years ago, we have to be familiar with present-day animals. Specifically, we need to know whether there are features of the skull that can be used as reliable clues to sensory function. An animal's sensory awareness (of sight, sound, smell, taste, or touch) requires both the possession of the relevant sensory organ (eyes, ears, olfactory organs, taste buds, touch receptors) and the development of the particular region of the brain that converts impulses from these organs into sensations. Therefore, we are interested not only in sensory organs but also in brain structure. The vertebrate brain is a conservative organ in which particular regions are usually associated with specific functions. Consequently, the relative development of a certain area provides an indication of the relative development of the function it is associated with. It is therefore of great interest to see whether the skull reveals any structural information about the brain. However, this is the subject of a later chapter, and we will restrict our concern here to skeletal clues of the sensory organs themselves.

Some indication of the size of an animal's eye may be obtained from the size of the bony eye socket, the orbit. Obviously an eye can be no larger than its orbit, but it may be smaller, and so the orbital size only indicates the maximum possible size. Most birds have large eyes, sight being their predominant sense, and they have correspondingly large orbits. Birds of prey have particularly acute vision, and their eyes and orbits are correspondingly large. The kiwi, on the other hand, is a nocturnal bird that forages for worms and insects with a long bill, and so its eyes play a minor role in its life; the eye and the orbit are both small. Most mammals have a good sense of sight; so do some reptiles, but others rely more on their sense of smell. Many reptiles and birds have a series of bony plates embedded in the white of the eye, presumably functioning to maintain its shape, and these are usually joined together to form a sclerotic ring. Sclerotic rings have been preserved in many dinosaurs, pterosaurs, and ichthyosaurs, and give a good indication of the actual size of the eye. Large eyes have more light receptor cells than smaller eyes, and are therefore more sensitive, but a large eye sees no more of the world than a small one. The eye of a dog, for example, is much larger than that of a mouse, but the dog probably sees no more of its surroundings. However, a dog can probably see more detail than a mouse in poor light conditions, because its eyes, being larger, can gather more light. Large eyes are often correlated with the nocturnal habit, and this is well illustrated in owls.

In most vertebrates, the visual angle of the eye (essentially the maximum angle of the arc, or more accurately of the cone, through which light can enter the eye) is about 170 degrees.[14] In many animals the eyes are directed forward so that the two fields of view overlap, giving a binocular vision. This permits depth perception, of particular importance to hunting animals and others that have to judge distances. The greater the degree of overlap of the two fields, the more complete is the binocular vision, but the total field of view is correspondingly reduced. In animals that are hunted, the eyes are on the side of the head. There is little overlap of visual fields, and the total field is close to twice that of a single eye, that is, nearly 360°. Binocular vision is diminished, but their all-round vision enables these animals to

The eyes of the hunter face forwards, giving binocular vision, hence good depth perception. Those of the hunted face laterally, giving poor depth perception but a good all-round field of view.

detect predators from whatever direction they may approach. In predators, from polar bears to hawks, the eyes are directed forward, and the placement of the eyes can therefore give some clue to habits. Many reptilian predators, however, have only a limited field of binocular vision, including the alligator (24°), the monitor lizard (32°) and the boa constrictor (34°). The sense of smell is probably extremely important in these animals.

The hadrosaur orbit is relatively large and the sclerotic ring has been preserved in some specimens, giving us a good indication of the size of the eye. In our mounted skeleton of *Lambeosaurus lambei*, the sclerotic ring has an outside diameter of approximately 70 mm, which indicates an eye of about the same size as a cow's. Evidence from endocranial casts for flat-headed hadrosaurs is incomplete in the region of the optic lobes, but the cerebral hemispheres, which were probably concerned with sight among other functions, were fairly large. The evidence suggests that sight was probably well developed. Although the skulls have probably undergone some lateral compression, it is evident that the eyes were placed on the side of the head rather than in a forward-looking position. This suggests that hadrosaurs probably had wide-field rather than binocular vision, which is an adaptation of the hunted.

So far nothing has been said of the sense of hearing but the amount of information we have for hadrosaurs, or indeed for any other dinosaur, is small. Our own ear, like that of all mammals but unlike that of fishes, amphibians, reptiles, and birds, has three parts—outer, middle, and inner. The outer ear consists of an ear-flap, the pinna, which leads into a canal that is closed at the bottom by the eardrum. On the other side of the eardrum is the middle ear cavity, inside which is an articulating series of three small bones. The outer bone, the malleus, is attached to the ear drum. The inner bone, the stapes, is attached to a smaller membrane stretched across a small opening that leads to the inner ear. The middle bone of the series is the incus. The three bones serve to transmit vibrations from the eardrum to the inner ear.

All vertebrates have an inner ear but there is much variation in its development. It is essentially a small, fluid-filled, and membraneous sac (ours is only about 3 cm high) embedded in the bone or cartilage at the back of the skull. The membraneous sac, or labyrinth, is separated from the surrounding bone by a thin layer of liquid that serves to transmit vibrations from the stapes. The upper portion of the membranous labyrinth is concerned with balance and has three semicircular canals at right angles to one another. Whenever the head is moved the fluid in the canals is swirled, causing excitation of the sensory cells within. Depending on which way the head is moved, the fluid in one of the three canals will be swirled more violently than in the other two, and the impulses travelling to the brain give an awareness of position. When we spin around on the spot, the fluid in the three canals becomes so swirled, and the sensory cells so confused, that we become dizzy and are no longer capable of balancing. The hearing function of the membranous labyrinth is conducted in a small coiled tube, the cochlea, which is lined by cells that are sensitive to the sound waves falling upon them. Reptiles do not have a coiled cochlea, having instead an uncoiled tube, the cochlear duct, which is perhaps less sensitive to sound than the mammalian cochlea. The pinna, and the canal leading to the eardrum, are only found in mammals. In amphibians, reptiles, and birds, the eardrum is on the surface of the head, behind the eye, though in some reptiles and birds it lies at the bottom of a shallow depression or short canal. Fishes have no eardrum at all. Furthermore, whereas mammals have three bones for transmitting the vibrations to the inner ear, amphibians, reptiles, and birds have only one, the stapes. Since the membranous labyrinth is encased in bone, it is sometimes possible to obtain a cast of it, similar to those that have been obtained for the brain, and these can give an indication of the relative development of hearing. Little is known of the ear structure in hadrosaurs, aside from what can be learned from casts of the membranous labyrinth of *Anatosaurus* and *Lophorhothon*.[15] The typical reptilian pattern of semicircular canals was present, and there was evidence of a well-developed cochlear duct.

The shape and position of the stapes can provide clues to hearing ability. A stapes has been found in at least two hadrosaurs (*Anatosaurus* and *Corythosaurus casuarius*) and it appears to have been in its natural position in one of these.[16] The stapes was long and slender, and projected from the lateral wall of the cranium to the area behind the quadrate, suggesting the possession of a fairly large eardrum. The evidence is not extensive, but does suggest that *Anatosaurus* and *Corythosaurus* were probably able to hear well, perhaps all the better to detect the approach of the carnivorous dinosaurs that were an ever-present threat to them.

Several species of carnivorous dinosaurs (collectively called carnosaurs) were contemporaneous with the hadrosaurs, but they were fewer in numbers, just as present-day carnivores are outnumbered by their prey species. We might choose to study any one of these carnivores because, with a few notable exceptions, they were all very much alike. As we have an almost complete mounted skeleton of *Albertosaurus libratus* in the dinosaur gallery of the Royal Ontario Museum, this is an obvious choice.

Albertosaurus libratus, close relative of *Tyrannosaurus rex* (both members of the family Tyrannosauridae and usually referred to as the tyrannosaurs) is found in Alberta, in western Canada, for which it was named. *Tyrannosaurus rex*, which reached a maximum length of about 14 m, has been found in the western United States, but only scraps have been found in Canada. Both species were large, among the largest carnivores ever to have walked the Earth, and the differences between them are minor. Our specimen of *Albertosaurus libratus* has a total length of just over 6 m, which is about 20% smaller than most hadrosaurs, but it was not fully grown, and an adult individual would be of hadrosaur size. *Albertosaurus* is much more slender than a hadrosaur and the individual bones of the skeleton are generally relatively thinner. The ilium, for example, is less than 1 cm thick, compared with more than 2 cm in *Lambeosaurus*.

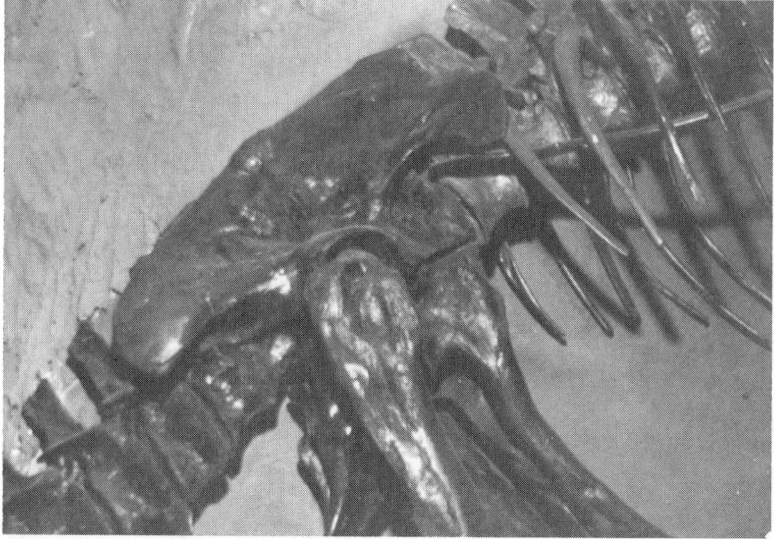

Although this skeleton of the carnosaur **Albertosaurus** *is mounted in a semi-upright position, close inspection reveals that the head of the femur does not abut against the joint between the pubis and ilium. This is because the ilium is far deeper here than it is in hadrosaurs, and we believe carnosaurs were capable of a more upright posture, as depicted in the restoration. Carnivorous features of* **Albertosaurus** *include the sharp, serrated teeth, short neck, and clawed hands and feet.*

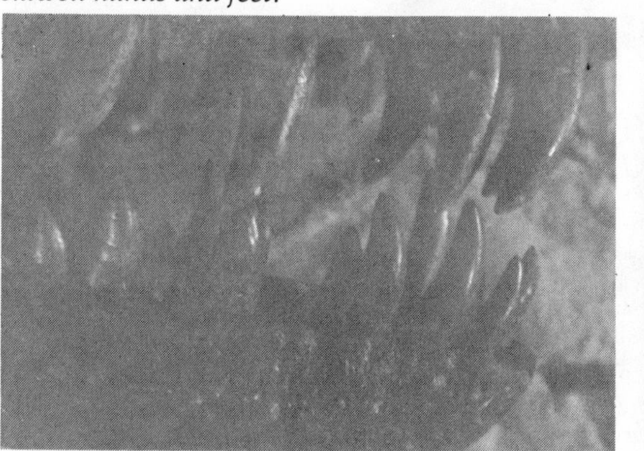

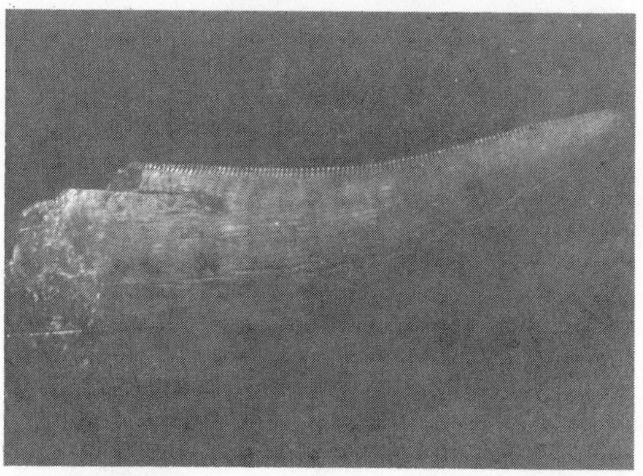

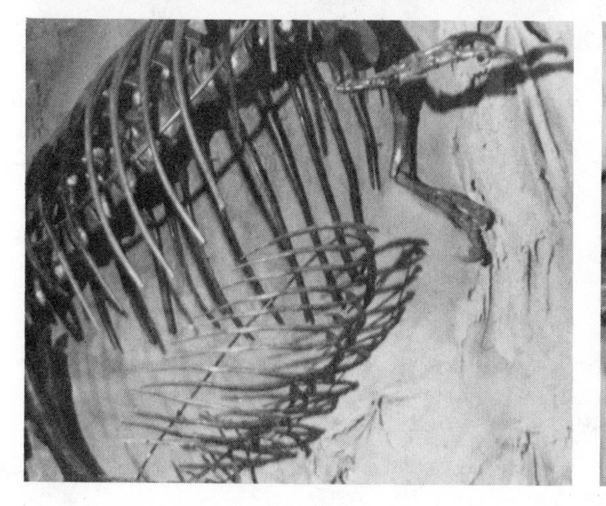

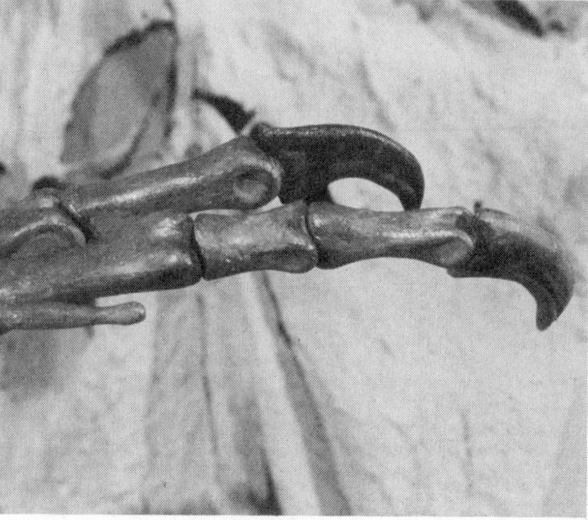

Our skeleton of *Albertosaurus* was mounted in the 1920s and given an upright posture similar to that of the hadrosaur *Corythosaurus casuarius*, discussed at the beginning of the chapter. We saw that such an upright posture was implausible for the hadrosaurs, but it probably was not for the carnosaurs. If we look at the pelvis of *Albertosaurus libratus* we find that the hip joint is quite different from that of the hadrosaur. The head of the femur, instead of being braced against a weak point, abuts against a bony buttress of the ilium. This is because the ilium makes a larger contribution to the anterior rim of the acetabulum than it does in the hadrosaur, and the weak point is consequently farther down. The pelvis, and therefore the vertebral column to which it is attached, is able to tilt up to about 60° from the horizontal before the head of the femur abuts against the weak point, whereas in the hadrosaurs this angle is only about 20°. On the evidence of the pelvis, then, it appears that *Albertosaurus* may have been able to stand in a semi-erect posture, perhaps to look around for prey, but we believe that the vertebral column was probably held horizontally during locomotion, as in other dinosaurs.

The carnivorous habits of *Albertosaurus* and its relatives are immediately betrayed by the structure of the skull. The sharp teeth have the appearance of daggers, and closer inspection reveals small serrations on their front and back edges, similar to those of a steak knife. Their efficiency in puncturing and slicing through flesh is in no doubt, and they have retained their cutting edges to the present day. The teeth are set in deep sockets, with about as much of the tooth below the jaw line as there is above it, consequently, both jaws are deep. If the teeth had not been firmly rooted they might have been ripped out in struggles with captured prey. Teeth were lost from time to time, as in the hadrosaurs, and they were continually being replaced. Tooth replacement was alternate—a strategy for preventing adjacent teeth from being replaced at the same time, which would have resulted in gaps.[17] The sequential nature of tooth replacement in *Albertosaurus* and other reptiles may be seen by marking alternative teeth along the length of a jaw margin. A line drawn through the tips of the marked teeth reveals a regular size gradation. Each tooth starts as a small bud that pushes its way into the pulp cavity of an existing tooth as it grows. Eventually the old tooth is expelled, and the new one takes its place.

The front teeth in the upper jaw are smaller than the others, and instead of being flattened from side to side they are flattened from front to back and are analogous to the chisel-shaped incisors of mammals. Presumably the front teeth were used for tearing meat and tendons from bone in much the same way as a dog uses its incisors on a meaty bone. When considering chewing in hadrosaurs, we found that the jaw joint permitted a considerable amount of backward and forward movement, but in the carnosaurs the joint is so constructed that only a hinge-like up-and-down movement is permitted. The quadrate has an elongate and rounded articular surface set at right angles to the length of the skull, and this fits into a corresponding groove in the mandible. Carnivores use their teeth primarily for cutting and slicing and the importance of restricting the joint to an up-and-down movement is immediately obvious to anyone who has tried cutting anything with scissors that have a loose joint. A similarly restricted jaw joint can be seen in present-day mammalian carnivores. The carnosaur skull is relatively larger than that of most herbivores, and is set on a short thick neck. The long skull provided a wide gape for seizing and killing, and for slicing large pieces of flesh. The weight of the massive head was reduced by large openings in the skull in addition to the orbit, the naris, and the temporal openings for the muscles, a strategy also found in the giant sauropods as we will see in the next chapter. The bones of the carnosaur skull are also remarkably thin, in contrast to those of the hadrosaurs, which are quite robust. The bones of the mandible of our specimen of *Albertosaurus* for example, are only about 0.5 cm thick, compared with more than 2.0 cm in *Lambeosaurus*. The mandible of *Albertosaurus*, being restricted to up and down movements, was not exposed to strong lateral forces and had only to resist the strong vertical forces generated by the powerful bite. *Lambeosaurus*, on the other hand, probably moved its mandibles from side to side, as well as up and down and back and forth, when chewing, and would therefore have experienced larger lateral forces. These differences in forces are reflected in the differences in thickness of their mandibles.

We have seen that predators possess binocular vision, but if we compare frontal views of a hadrosaur and a carnosaur we do not see such a striking difference in orbital placement as we do when comparing, say, a rabbit and a fox. Does this negate our impression of the carnosaurs as active predators? Might they instead have been scavengers, feeding on carrion, as some palaeontologists have suggested? We will never know the answer to this question but can gain some insight by looking at modern animals. There are some animals, such as the ostrich and its flightless relatives, in which the orbits are essentially lateral, but the eyes face forwards. These birds have well-developed binocular vision, but the skull bears no evidence of this. Furthermore, many predatory reptiles, as we have seen, have laterally placed eyes but still have some degree of binocular vision. It is therefore entirely possible that the carnosaurs had at least some degree of binocular vision. Perhaps olfaction played an important role;

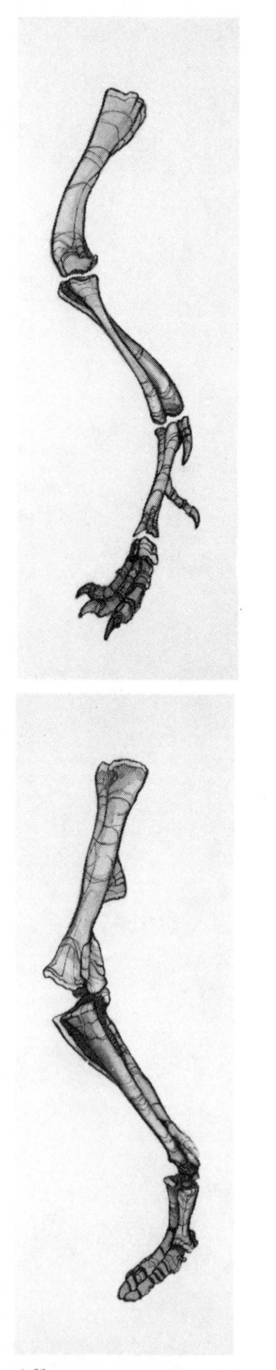

Albertosaurus *(top) has a relatively longer lower leg than* **Lambeosaurus** *(bottom) suggesting it was a faster runner.*

many modern predators, including cats and dogs, have a well-developed sense of smell and this is important to them for stalking prey.

Some dinosaurs, however, did have forward-facing orbits, and one of these, *Stenonychosaurus inequalis* from the Canadian Upper Cretaceous, was contemporaneous with *Albertosaurus*[18] This ostrich-sized dinosaur had particularly large orbits, suggesting relatively enormous eyes, and evidence from endocranial casts indicates that the brain was also large by dinosaur standards. It has been suggested that this was an intelligent, keen-sighted, and extremely active little dinosaur.

The fingers and toes of the tyrannosaurs terminate in sharp claws, in contrast to the hooves of their herbivorous contemporaries. There is little doubt that these claws were used for grappling and ripping, and the powerful hind legs probably inflicted the severest damage. One of the major differences between the tyrannosaurs and their Jurassic relatives (exemplified by *Allosaurus*) is the extreme reduction in the forelimbs. Not only is the length of the limb reduced, but the hand has only two fingers instead of three, each equipped with a long claw. The forelimbs are so small that they could not have reached the ground, and it has been suggested that their main function was to assist a resting tyrannosaur back onto its feet. By digging the front claws into the ground and applying a backward force, the forelimbs would have anchored the front of the body, preventing forward slip when the hind legs were raised beneath the body. Perhaps this was just one of their functions; they may have been used as grapples for steadying a leaping aggressor as it inflicted wounds with its hind claws. Cats, both large and small, often seize a victim with the front paws while kicking in unison with the back ones. Perhaps the forelimbs were also used for manipulating food in the mouth.

Until fairly recently it was believed that forelimb reduction was characteristic of all Cretaceous carnosaurs, but an exciting discovery made during the 1965 Polish–Mongolian expedition to the Gobi Desert changed this belief. As is so often the case in palaeontology, only a tantalizing glimpse of the new animal was obtained because most of the skeleton was missing, but the parts that remained stretched credibility to its limits. Visualize a dinosaur, a very large flesh-eating dinosaur, whose forelimbs are so long that they could reach inside a subway car and touch the doors on the opposite side and whose fingers are armed with three claws, each the length of a man's forearm. This dinosaur (which may be related to the ornithomimids) was named *Deinocheirus mirificus*.[19]

Albertosaurus has a relatively longer lower leg than *Lambeosaurus* and this is mainly because the metatarsus is relatively longer. This suggests that *Albertosaurus* could run faster than *Lambeosaurus*. The clawed toes might have provided greater traction than the hoofed foot of *Lambeosaurus*, as in the case of many present-day carnivores. *Albertosaurus* had no mechanism for retracting its claws like a cat, but an unusual dinosaur from the Lower Cretaceous of Montana, called *Deinonychus*, did have such a mechanism for one of its three toes. This toe has a very long and sharply curved claw that appears to have been kept well clear of the ground during walking. The claw would thus have been kept sharp, and was likely used for dispatching its unfortunate victims.[20]

We have seen some of the ways in which information can be extracted from the bony remains of extinct animals. We have also seen that skeletal data has its limitations, and that we can never be absolutely sure that we are drawing the correct conclusions from our observations. There are examples in present-day animals of skeletal features that seem to have little bearing on life styles. If the hippopotamus had been known only as a fossil we would probably never have deduced that it was primarily an aquatic animal. How would we know from the skeleton of an otter that this is not just another terrestrial carnivore like a weasel but an adept swimmer? Examples such as these are somewhat unusual, and most of our conclusions drawn from the study of a skeleton are likely to be close to the truth, provided they are circumscribed by information drawn from modern animals. Palaeontologists have to be especially circumspect in the interpretation of their data, and we will keep this principle in mind throughout the pages that follow.

5
On Being a Giant

Most—but not all—dinosaurs tended towards gigantism. Hadrosaurs, for example, were of only moderate size by dinosaur standards, but had an estimated weight of about three tonnes, comparable to that of an Indian elephant. The largest dinosaurs were the sauropods, the largest animals ever to walk the Earth, and *Brachiosaurus*, the heaviest sauropod, had an estimated weight of 78 tonnes, which is about the weight of a Boeing 727 aircraft.[1] These enormous body sizes have some interesting biological implications, but before considering them we should be clear about the physical effects of increasing the size of an object.

If we take an object and double its size, what changes have we caused? Many of us have built scale models of boats, and the choice of shapes and sizes is considerable. What is the difference between, say, two *Mayflowers* with hulls 10 cm and 20 cm long, respectively? All length measurements, such as the length of the main mast, are twice as great in the large model, but the sail area is four times as big and the weight is eight times that of the smaller model. The two ships look alike, but the relationships between mast height, sail area, and tonnage are entirely different for the two models and if we sailed them these differences would immediately be apparent in their different sailing performances. This is so because, as an object increases in size, its volume and hence its weight increases in proportion to the cube of the length, whereas areas increase only as the square of the length.

Terrestrial animals have to support the weight of their bodies on their legs, and the total area of bone available to do this is the combined areas of cross sections of the leg bones. When an animal walks one or more of its legs are lifted, consequently the area of bone available for support is reduced, but this does not affect the following argument. If the diameter of the leg bones of a growing animal increased in proportion to the length of the body, the area available for support would increase in proportion to the square of the length, whereas the body weight would increase in proportion to the cube of the length. A point would soon be reached when the bone area was no longer sufficient to support the weight, and the bones of the leg would collapse.

As the compressive strength of bone has fairly fixed limits, we would expect the problem to be resolved by increasing the diameter of the long bones by more than the increase in body length. It has been predicted that the diameter of a leg bone would need to increase in proportion to its length raised to the power 1.5 (see explanation on page 81). This relationship is

Why do area and volume relationships change with increasing size?

The simplest way to show the relationship between length, area, and volume is to compare several cubes of different sizes. We will assume that the cubes are made of a substance with a density of one; so that each cubic centimetre weighs one gram.

	A	B	C	D
Length	1	2	3	4
Area	6	24	54	96
Volume (weight)	1	8	27	64
Area ÷ Volume	6	3	2	1.5
Area of base	1	4	9	16
Magnification	1	2	3	4

The cubes have edges of 1 cm, 2 cm, 3 cm, and 4 cm, respectively, so that the largest is four times the length of the smallest. We can see that the area of each cube increases with the square of the increase in length. Cube B, for example, is twice as long as cube A, and the ratio of their areas is $\frac{24}{6} = 4 = 2^2 =$ *(increase in length)*^{2}. *Similarly, the ratio of the areas of cube C and cube A is* $\frac{54}{6} = 9 = 3^2 =$ *(increase in length)*^{2}. *Areas therefore increase with the square of the increase in length. It can also be seen that the volume of each cube increases with the cube of the increase in length. Cube D, for example, is twice the length of cube B, and the ratio of their volumes is* $\frac{64}{8} = 8 = 2^3 =$ *(increase in length)*^{3}.

Since the volume of an object increases much more rapidly than its area, it follows that the area-to-volume ratio (biologically an important variable) decreases with increasing length. Cube B, for example, is twice as long as cube A, but its area-to-volume ratio is only half that of cube A. Similarly cube C, which is three times as long as cube A, has an area-to-volume ratio which is only one-third that of cube A.

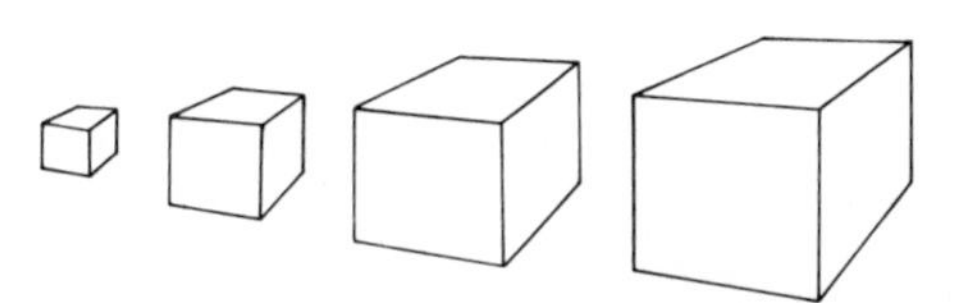

Why is the diameter of a bone expected to increase in proportion to its length raised to the power of 1.5?

The pressure acting on the base of each cube is the weight of the cube divided by the area of its base. The pressures acting on each of the four cubes are therefore: $\frac{1}{1}, \frac{8}{4}, \frac{27}{9}$ *and* $\frac{64}{16}$ *g/cm*^{2}. *The pressure therefore increases with the increase in length, the pressure on the base of the largest cube being four times that on the smallest. Suppose that one gram per square centimetre is the maximum pressure the material of the cubes can withstand. What area will the bases of the objects have to become in order to maintain this pressure? The weights of the four objects remain the same, namely 1, 8, 27 and 64 g, respectively. Only their shapes can change. To maintain a pressure of 1 g/cm*^{2} *the area of the bases of the four objects would have to become 1, 8, 27, 64 cm*^{2}, *respectively. The area of a square is the length of its edge multiplied by itself. Therefore the edges of the bases of the four objects would need to become* $\sqrt{1}$, $\sqrt{8}$, $\sqrt{27}$, *and* $\sqrt{64}$. *In other words, the edge of the base of each object would need to become equal to the square root of its volume. But volume = length*^{3}, *therefore the edges of the bases of the four objects would need to become* $\sqrt{(\text{length})^3} = \text{length}^{3/2}$ *or length*$^{1.5}$.

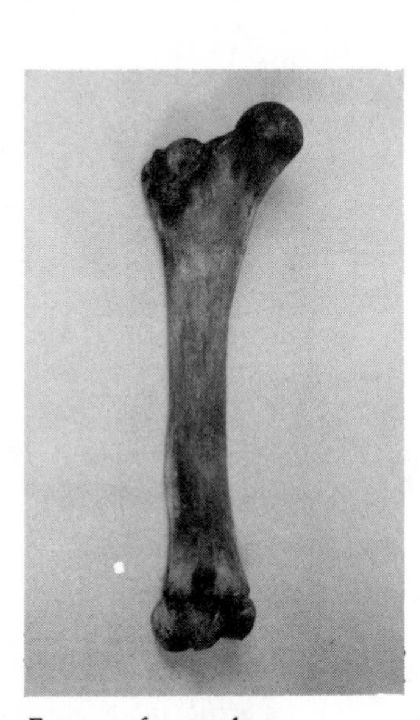

Femur of a modern elephant, **Loxodonta africana**. *Notice that the bone is not especially wide relative to its length.*

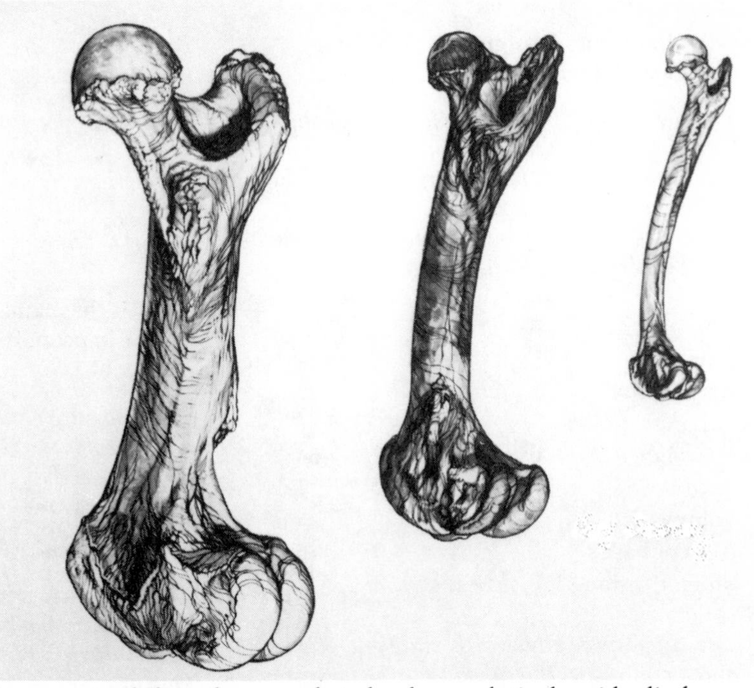

Large animals have been predicted to have relatively wider limb bones. From left to right: Hippopotamus, wapiti and dog. This prediction does not hold true across a wide range of body sizes—see text for details.

called a power function because it involves a term raised to a power. We would therefore expect larger animals to have relatively wider bones than smaller ones, and this is just what we find when comparisons are made within certain groupings of mammals. Generalizations, however, are notoriously dangerous, especially when based upon small sample sizes. When comparisons are made over a wide range of mammals it is found that the increase in diameter of the leg bones is approximately in step with their increase in length.[2] In the elephant, for example, the heaviest of living land animals, the femur and humerus are not very much wider, relative to their length, than they are in the smaller mammals.

These findings are initially rather surprising, but if we examine the situation more closely we can see why it should be so. Support of the body weight is only one of the functions of the limb bones, and, in terms of the stress (force per unit area) placed upon them, this is their least demanding role. This is because when animals are moving the stresses on their bones are several times higher than when they are standing still. As running speed increases the fraction of time during which a particular limb is in contact with the ground, called the duty factor, decreases. As the duty factor decreases the stresses in the limb bones increase, consequently the stresses in the bones increase with speed. When comparisons are made in the running patterns of different sized mammals it is found that the duty factor tends to increase with increasing body weight. The duty factor for each of the legs of a running elephant, for example, is more than 1/2, compared with only about 1/5 for an antelope. As large animals have larger duty factors the relative stresses in their bones are reduced, and this tends to compensate for their large body weights. From this it follows that the maximum stresses acting on the limb bones of large animals are comparable to those of smaller ones, hence their bones do not need to be more robust. Large animals, then, compensate for their heavy bodies mainly through their locomotory patterns, and this, as we shall see later, has important implications for the biggest dinosaurs.

Weight estimates for dinosaurs have been obtained by comparing them with other reptiles. The first step is to construct a scale model of the dinosaur in question, as it might have appeared in life. The model is based upon drawings of the original skeleton, to which muscles have been added, thus fleshing out the body form. We are able to "add muscles" to a dinosaur skeleton because the number and arrangement of muscles is conservative within the reptiles. Through comparisons with other reptiles, we are able to make a rough estimate of the muscular arrangement in a dinosaur. The volume of the scale model is measured by immersing it in water and measuring the volume displaced. The volume of the life-sized model is calculated by multiplying the volume of the scale model by the cube of the increase in length (the length of the actual dinosaur divided by the length of the model). To obtain an estimate of the weight of the living dinosaur, the estimated volume is multiplied by an estimate of its density. We do not have any evidence for the density of dinosaurs, but can obtain values for living reptiles. Crocodiles are the closest living reptilian relatives of dinosaurs and, like the dinosaurs, they are relatively large. So if we use the density of crocodiles, which can be obtained fairly readily, we are probably not introducing an excessively large error into the calculation. Weight estimates have been obtained for several dinosaurs using this method[3], and these are given in a table.

The legs of an animal must not only support the body weight, but also provide for movements. Most modern reptiles hold out the upper part of the leg (femur and humerus) horizontally from the body, and keep the lower part of the leg vertical. During

Estimated Body Weight of Dinosaurs (From Colbert 1962)

Genera	*Tonnes*
Theropods	
Allosaurus	2.09
Tyrannosaurus	6.89
Sauropods	
Apatosaurus	27.87
Diplodocus	10.56
Brachiosaurus	78.26
Ornithopods	
Camptosaurus	383 kg
Iguanodon	4.51
Corythosaurus	3.82
Anatosaurus	3.07
Stegosaurs	
Stegosaurus	1.78
Ankylosaurs	
Palaeoscincus	3.47
Ceratopsians	
Protoceratops	177 kg
Styracosaurus	3.69
Triceratops	8.48

Most reptiles, including all living ones, hold their legs out horizontally from the body, push-up fashion. The sinuous movements of their bodies help them to walk. Mammals and birds have their legs placed vertically beneath the body and they move with an essentially fore and aft movement.

locomotion the body sways from side to side, and this movement assists in the backward and forward excursions of the legs. While this arrangement is adequate for animals of moderate size, it is inconceivable that a large dinosaur could have had this type of limb posture. Not only would the stress on the horizontal bones have been enormous, but a considerable amount of muscular energy would have had to be expended just to maintain the posture (unless the animal rested its belly on the ground when not moving). Locomotion would have been laborious and wasteful of energy, though experiments with living reptiles have shown that we may be exaggerating the energy consumption of the sprawling gait.[4] Mammals and birds have resolved this problem by having the upper leg bones directly beneath the body, and we know that dinosaurs had a similar limb posture because of the position of the articular surfaces of their bones.

While the humerus and the femur are directly beneath the body in most four-footed mammals, they are also inclined in such a way that, when viewed from the side, they are seen to slope backwards and forwards, respectively. The chief result of this strategy is to increase the speed of the leg movements.[5] This is because inclination of the upper leg bones changes the angles of insertion and the relative lengths of the muscles attaching to the bones, effecting a more rapid excursion of the leg. The stress in the inclined bones is obviously increased, but this is compensated for by the fact that they are hollow. It is a well-known engineering principle that a horizontal or inclined pipe of a given weight can withstand more stress than a horizontal rod of similar weight. This principle is often used when large skeletons are being assembled, steel pipe being used in preference to steel rod for the internal supporting structure of the vertebral column. With increasing body size, a point is reached at which an inclined bone becomes a serious disadvantage. At this point, which in living mammals is reached in the elephant, the upper-limb bones are placed vertically, and the leg functions as a vertical supporting column. Such animals are described as being graviportal. The bones no longer have large marrow cavities because the strategy is now to maximize the area of cross section. The shafts of both the humerus and the femur are virtually solid in elephants, and sauropods, and the position of the articular surfaces shows that these bones were kept in an essentially vertical position in both groups. This evidence clearly shows that sauropods were graviportal, which is hardly surprising. *Camptosaurus*, on the other hand, appears to have been cursorial (adapted for running) because the position of the articular surfaces of the femur suggests that the bone was inclined from the vertical, and the shaft is hollow. The possession of inclined

Most mammals, like the reindeer (top), have their upper limb bones inclined to the vertical; the femur sloping forwards, the humerus inclined backwards. This is a strategy for increased speed. The bending stress in the bones is very high and heavy animals, like the elephant, have to keep their bones straight in line.

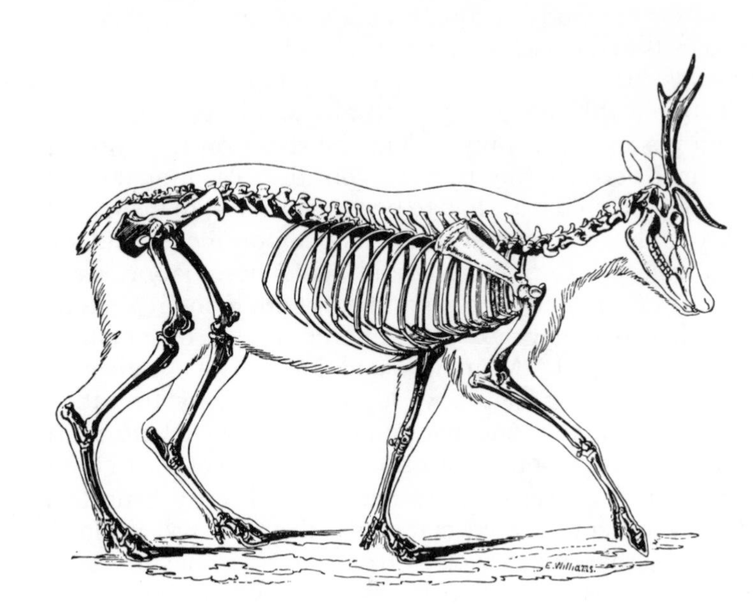

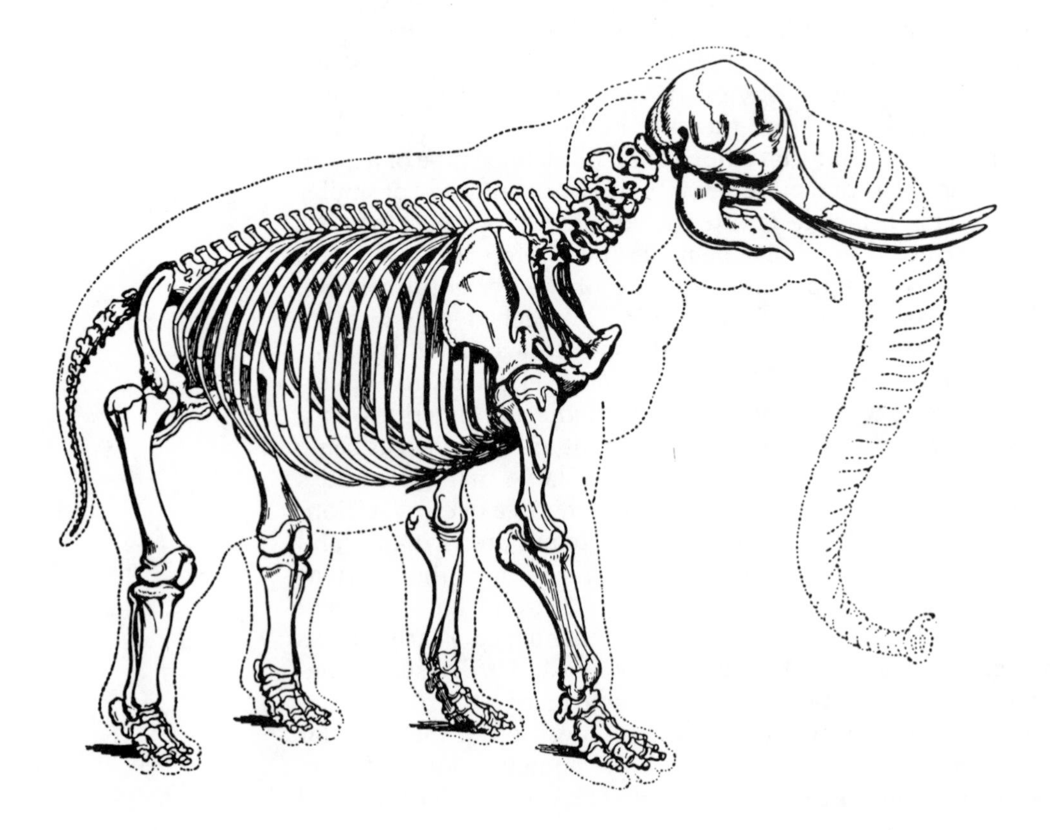

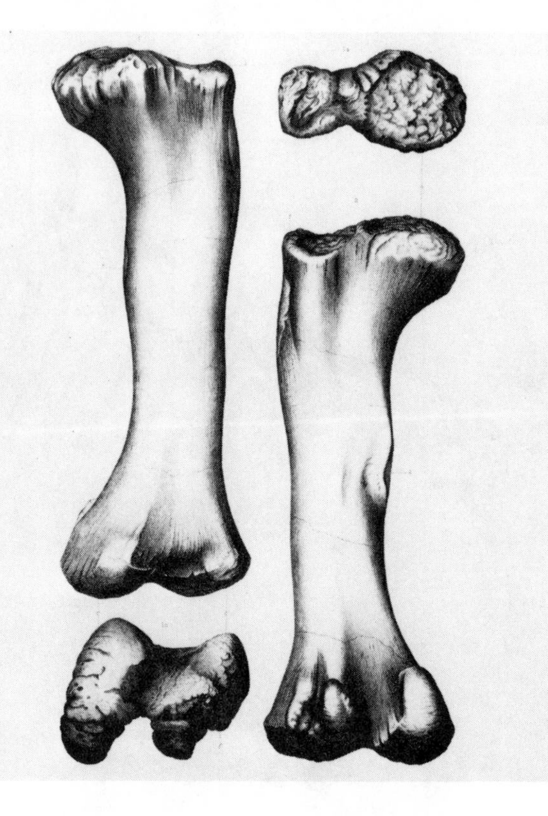

The (left) femur of the sauropod dinosaur **Camarasaurus grandis**. *The shaft is solid and the terminal placement of the articular surfaces shows that it was held vertically.*

(and hollow) upper-limb bones, however, is not an infallible indication that an animal is cursorial, because there are exceptions.

The weight of the body, which is transferred to the legs by the pectoral and pelvic girdles, is supported by the vertebral column, and this column is considerably modified in the large sauropods. The vertebral column of tetrapods is often compared with the structure of a bowstring girder bridge. The fore and hind limbs are the vertical supports, and the dorsal vertebrae, which curve in a gentle arc between the pectoral and pelvic girdles, form the bowstring girder. The weight of the body tends to reduce the curvature, but this is resisted by tension in the axial and abdominal muscles and ligaments, and by the rigidity of the individual vertebrae.

The weight supported by the vertebral column reached enormous proportions in the sauropods, and it is here that modifications for gigantism are most striking. *Apatosaurus*, which has a length of 17 m (57 feet) and an estimated weight of 28 tonnes, is not the heaviest sauropod, but its dorsal vertebrae are enormous, with centra that are about one third of a metre in diameter. If sauropod vertebrae were of solid bone they would

Marsh's reconstruction of the sauropod dinosaur **Apatosaurus excelsus**, *Upper Jurassic, Western U.S.A. Scale measures one metre. Marsh used the wrong skull in this reconstruction, namely the skull of* **Camarasaurus**.

add considerably to the weight of the skeleton without adding significantly to its strength. Examination reveals that the bone is concentrated in regions that experience the greatest forces, thus giving maximum strength for minimum weight. A deep excavation on either side of the centrum reduces the latter to a short I-beam, which can been seen clearly when a transverse section is cut across a centrum. An I-beam is exactly the structure an engineer would use to resist bending forces, but the vertebral column is more than this. The anterior and posterior surfaces of the centra of most or many of the dorsal vertebrae (there is some variation among the various species) are produced into a ball-and-socket joint, which provides a large area of contact between

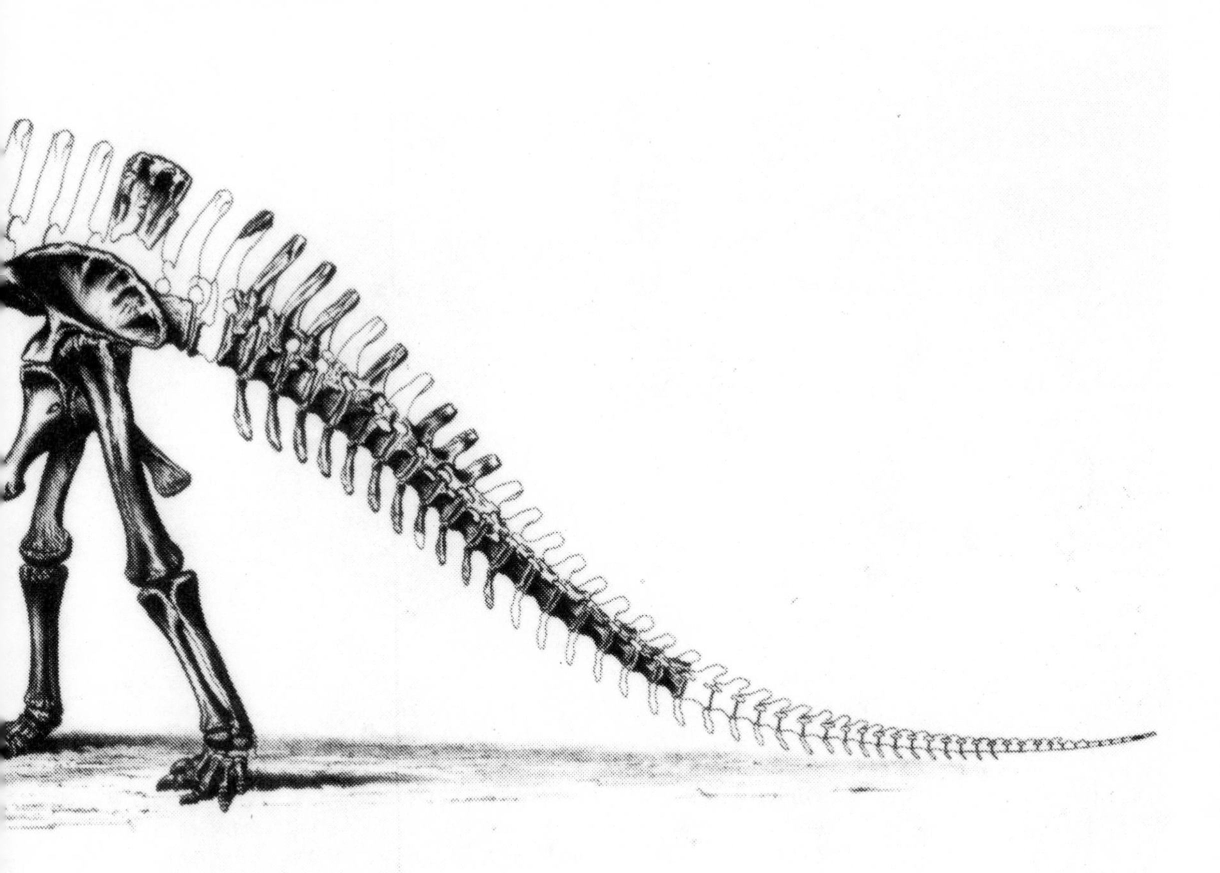

adjacent vertebrae. A degree of flexibility is therefore given to the column without sacrificing much strength. The economical use of bone is also seen in the neural arch and spine, and in the transverse processes, bony struts, and flanges being used instead of solid bone. An additional modification is a second set of articulating surfaces below the zygapophyses, reinforcing their action. These occur in the posterior dorsal, and sometimes in the caudal vertebrae.

Sauropods had long necks and tails and the effort of keeping these clear of the ground would have been substantial because of the great leverages involved, though dragging the tail on the ground would have reduced the problem somewhat. The head would have been held well clear of the ground, and sauropods probably used their long necks to reach high up into the trees, like giraffes, or down to lake bottoms to crop aquatic plants. Support of the head in terrestrial vertebrates is assisted by the

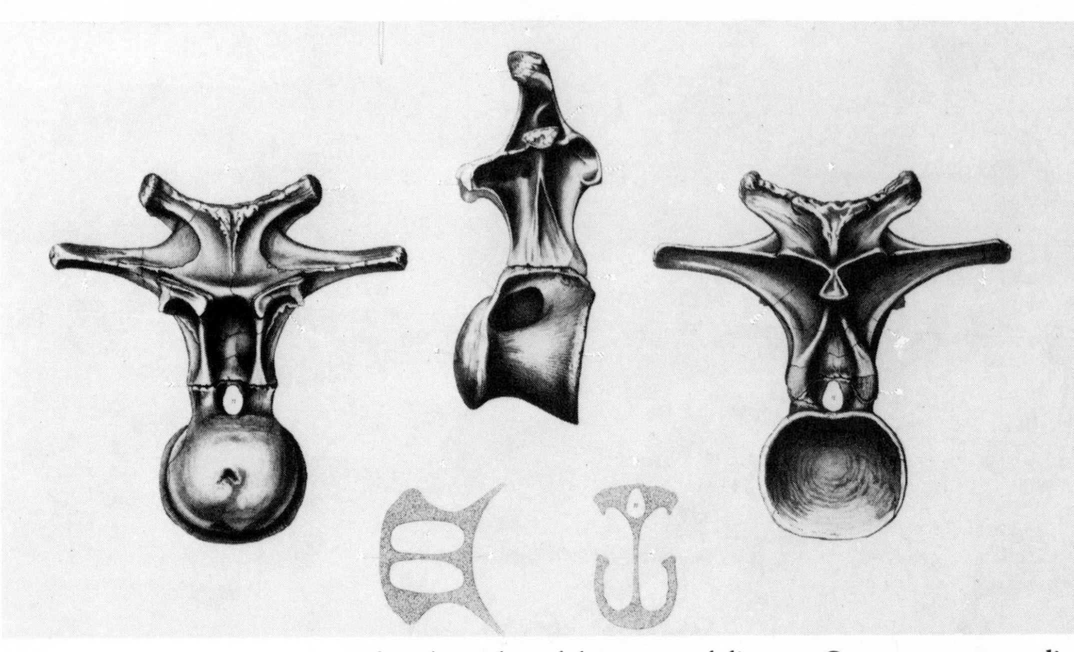

A dorsal vertebra of the sauropod dinosaur **Camarasaurus grandis**. *Upper figures, from left to right: Anterior, left side, and posterior views. Bottom figures, from left to right: Longitudinal section, and transverse section through centrum. The lateral surfaces of the centrum are deeply excavated and a transverse section through the centrum reveals that it is essentially a short I-beam. This strategy reduces the weight of the bone without sacrificing strength.*

nuchal ligament, which runs from the anterior dorsal vertebrae to an attachment at the back of the skull. When the ventral neck muscles contract, depressing the head, the ligament is stretched, and when the muscles relax again the ligament shortens, elevating the head. In many sauropods the neural spines of the cervical and anterior dorsal vertebrae have a prominent fork, which probably acted as a guide for a massive nuchal ligament. The extreme leverage generated by the long neck would have placed a strong selection pressure on the evolution of a lighter head and we find that sauropods have relatively small skulls. Furthermore the skull is lightly constructed, with large perforations in the bones. This strategy of bone reduction is especially obvious in the skull of *Camarasaurus* which has the form of an open framework. A similar strategy is seen in the massive skulls of the giant carnivores.

The weight supported by the vertebral column is transmitted to the legs by the pectoral and pelvic girdles. In most sauropods (*Brachiosaurus* and its allies being exceptions) the hind legs are longer and stouter than the front ones, and the pelvic girdle is more robust than the pectoral girdle, suggesting that most of the weight was carried by the hind legs. The sauropod pelvis is a

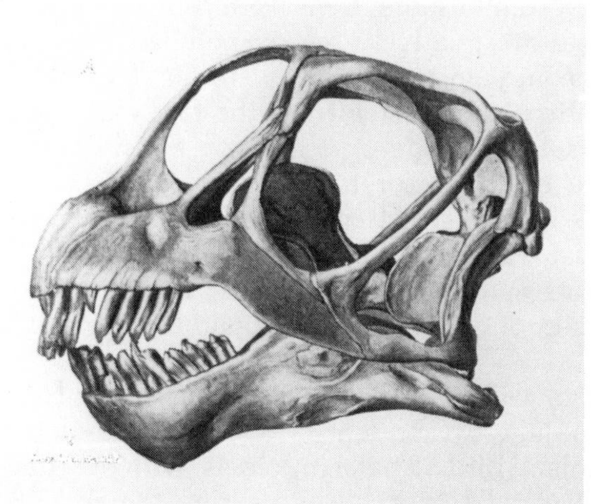

Many large dinosaurs reduced the weight of the head by having large openings in the skull. Skulls of the sauropod **Camarasaurus** *(left), and the carnosaur* **Tyrannosaurus**.

massive structure, which was firmly attached to a series of five or six fused vertebrae, the sacrum. The pectoral girdle comprises a pair of long shoulder blades, the scapulae, which were attached on either side of the rib cage by muscles and ligaments. Ventrally, each scapula was attached to a rounded bone, the coracoid, and the two bones formed a socket between them for the articulation of the humerus. In many mammals, especially the fast runners, the scapula moves freely on the rib cage and functions as an extra segment of the limb, increasing both the length and the speed of the stride. It seems very unlikely that the sauropod scapula was movable, and equally unlikely that sauropods could run fast, if they could run at all.

The sauropods were so large that there has been considerable doubt in some minds that they could have supported their weight on land and from the time of their discovery it was suggested that they were completely or partially aquatic. The controversy over whether they were aquatic or terrestrial is more than a century old, and the same evidence has often been used in support of both arguments. The strongest evidence for an aquatic mode of life is probably the position of the nostrils. In *Camarasaurus* and *Brachiosaurus*, the nostrils are fairly high on the head, while in *Diplodocus* they are right on the top. Edward Drinker Cope and Othniel Charles Marsh, pioneers of American palaeontology, and early students of sauropods, were both impressed by this feature and drew obvious parallels with living aquatic animals such as the crocodiles and the whales, which also have their nostrils high on the head. However, there are some essentially terrestrial animals such as the elephants and the tapirs, that have nostrils high on the head, and some aquatic animals, including most marine turtles, otters, seals, ichthyosaurs, and plesiosaurs, that have nostrils low on the skull.

Evidence from the dentition of sauropods has often been used to support the contention that they were aquatic. In contrast to most other herbivorous dinosaurs, their teeth lack an extensive grinding surface and are relatively few in number. This suggested to some palaeontologists that they were suitable only for cropping soft aquatic plants. Aside from the fact that not all aquatic plants are soft, the type of vegetation eaten does not necessarily indicate the mode of life of the consumer.[7] The hippopotamus, for example, which spends most of its time in the water, eats considerable quantities of terrestrial plants, while the moose, which spends much of its time out of the water, consumes large quantities of aquatic plants. Again the evidence is equivocal.

The most significant clue in the puzzle of the sauropod's habits was stumbled upon quite by accident in Texas, one day late in November 1938. Roland Bird,[8] a palaeontologist with the American Museum of Natural History, was nearing the end of a disappointing field season when he heard about some unusual dinosaur footprints in the bed of the Paluxy River, near the town of Glen Rose, Texas. Being especially interested in trackways, he decided to make the necessary detour and spend a short time talking with the locals and prospecting in the river bed. He did not find anything particularly unusual at first, and decided to collect two rather fine sets of tracks that had been made by a pair of large carnivorous dinosaurs walking close together. That these tracks had been made by carnivores was clear from their distinctive three-toed print with impressions of sharp claws.

When the job of collecting was completed he made absolutely sure that there were no other tracks there by clearing an area of about a metre wide all around the specimen. As he shovelled away he came upon a round pot hole, about 1 m in diameter and partly filled with silt. "When I dug into it and threw back a few shovelfuls for a look-see, my heart nearly jumped out of my mouth. There, right at my very feet, was a depression totally unlike any I had ever seen before, but one I instantly surmised must be a sauropod footprint."

Bird had indeed discovered a sauropod footprint, and he correctly identified it as having been made by a right hind foot. By following the direction in which the toes were pointing he tried to estimate the position of the next footfall of the same foot. With mounting excitement he cleared away the river debris, but he found nothing. He ran his shovel along the river bed farther and farther from his estimated position for the next print. Eventually his shovel hit the rim of the next depression and he was amazed to find it was 4 m in front of the first. Imagine an animal whose stride was the length of an automobile!

Bird returned with a field crew the following season, and some remarkable trackways were excavated and taken back to the museum. A second locality was subsequently discovered in Bandera County, Texas, and the information gained at these two localities has added considerably to our knowledge of these

Sauropod dinosaur tracks uncovered in the bed of the Paluxy River, Texas.

incredible dinosaurs. With one exception, the trackways were four-footed, and fairly deep, which strongly suggests that the animals were walking on land, through fairly soft mud, rather than moving in water. The prints made by the fore feet are smaller and shallower than those of the hind feet, supporting the conclusion drawn from skeletal anatomy that most of the weight was carried by the hind legs. In many instances there were rolls of mud that had been squeezed out at the sides of the feet as the great weight bore down on soft ground.

One short section of trackway, some little distance from the rest, was unusual because it was made up almost entirely of prints made by the fore feet. The stride was just under 2 m, and the prints were about 60 cm across.[9] The explanation for this trackway is that the animal was floating in water, using its front legs to push itself along. At one point the animal turned to its right, and the partial impression of a hind foot at this point suggests that it used a back leg to change course. The footprints were so numerous in one area that they overlapped one another and were obviously made on the same occasion. Twenty-three individual sets of prints, all pointing the same way, bear testimony to the passage of a great herd of sauropods millions of years ago. From the large numbers of tracks, it seems likely that the area was once an access route, probably running beside a lake or river. Among the sauropod trackways were others, that had been made by large carnivores. Some of these had been stepped upon by the sauropods, and it is obvious that these carnivores had preceded the great herd. Other carnivore tracks crossed over the sauropod prints, so they had clearly been made by feet that had passed that way after the herd had gone by. In one case the track of a carnivore was alongside that of a sauropod, and close inspection revealed that the carnivore's track was made shortly after the sauropod's. When the sauropod trackway swung to the left, that of the carnivore followed, and this has suggested to many people that the carnivore was actually stalking the sauropod. The carnivore may have been merely travelling the same route, though; the fact that some carnivores had preceded the herd makes this seem likely. Furthermore, as will be discussed later, it seems unlikely that a carnivorous dinosaur would attack an animal many times its own size. In one or two of the sauropod trackways a groove was seen between the footprints, and this has been interpreted as the mark of the tail dragging along the ground.

The evidence from the trackways is fairly convincing: sauropods appear to have been capable of supporting their own weight on land. This conclusion is corroborated by the skeletal evidence, where strategies for the support of a large body mass can be seen. This does not prove that they were terrestrial, but it does mean that they possessed the faculty to be terrestrial.

The problems presented by gigantism are numerous, and we have only touched upon some of the skeletal implications. There are just as many physiological problems (pertaining to the working processes occurring within living things), but palaeontological data are unsuitable for investigating these, and we can only make some general comments. Some of the physiological problems arise from the changing relationship between surface areas and volumes as animals become larger. We have seen that larger animals have relatively smaller surface areas, and, since most of the heat lost from a body escapes through the skin, this is germane to the question of whether dinosaurs were warm-blooded. This is the subject of the next chapter, but we will spend a little time here considering one of the implications of warm-bloodedness in sauropods, namely, whether they are likely to have been very active.

In his book *The Hot-Blooded Dinosaurs,* Adrian Desmond

published Dr. Robert Bakker's reconstruction of the Jurassic sauropod *Barosaurus*.[10] Two of these massive dinosaurs are depicted trotting briskly along with only two feet on the ground at any one time. What is the likelihood that they could have trotted? Direct evidence is unavailable, and all we can do is to make comparisons with large living animals. The only living land animal of any size is the elephant, which is considerably smaller than most sauropods. Elephants can walk and amble at considerable speed, both forwards and backwards, but are incapable of trotting, cantering, galloping, or jumping.[11] In spite of their large size, elephants are remarkably agile, and they are capable of some extraordinary feats of poise and balance. Wild elephants have occasionally been seen to rear up on their hind legs to reach into trees, and captive ones can be trained to perform impressive balancing tricks. These movements, however, are always performed very deliberately in order to avoid sudden stresses. As *Barosaurus* was many times heavier than an elephant, it is very unlikely that it could have trotted. Warm-blooded or not, sauropods would have been obliged to move with care, and they are envisaged as moving about their business quite ponderously.

One of the many problems facing giant terrestrial animals is that of maintaining an adequate flow of blood to all parts of the body. We know from the human condition of varicose veins that the problem of pumping blood back to the heart from the lower legs can become serious. By the time the blood has been forced through the arteries, arterioles, extensive capillary networks, venules, and finally into the veins, the pressure has been considerably reduced. Blood returning to the heart from the legs is therefore at low pressure, but it still has to overcome the force of gravity. The return is greatly assisted by the pumping action of the leg muscles, and the extreme discomfort we experience in our legs when forced to stand still for any length of time is largely due to the absence of this pumping action.

The problem of pumping blood up the towering legs of a sauropod, to a heart that might be twice the height of a man above the feet, must have been considerable. A similar problem existed in pumping blood up the long neck to the head, and it is interesting to see how this is resolved in the giraffe. When a giraffe is in a standing position the head is about 3 m above the heart, but the pressure of the blood entering its head is similar to that of blood entering our head. In order to achieve the necessary pressure at the level of the head, the giraffe's heart has to discharge blood at about twice that pressure, which is probably one of the highest blood pressures of any living animal.[12] It is so high that it would burst the blood vessels in any other animal, but two mechanisms appear to resolve this problem in the giraffe. First, the arterial walls are much thicker than in other mammals, and, second, the pressure of the fluid that bathes the cells of the body and the capillaries is maintained at a high pressure. This appears to be achieved by the thick and tightly stretched skin, which functions in a way similar to the G-suit worn by fighter pilots.

Those of us who are a little out of condition know the unpleasant sensation in the head that is associated with rising from a sitting to a standing position. This is caused by a temporary drop in pressure in the blood reaching the head. Giraffes sometimes lie down to rest, and when they stand up again they tend to do so in stages, squatting first and waiting for a brief interval before raising themselves to the fully erect posture. This is presumably to give the vascular system a chance to stabilize the pressure of the blood to the head. When a giraffe is drinking, the head is lower than the heart, and this tends to increase the pressure of the blood to the head. The extent of this increase is reduced by a splaying of the front legs while drinking, which reduces the difference in height between the head and the heart. We may reasonably conclude from this account of the giraffe that sauropods probably raised and lowered their heads fairly slowly.

Another problem posed by the possession of a long neck is the large volume of the air in the trachea, the tube that connects the lungs with the pharynx. This air is unavailable for respiration, and the volume it occupies is referred to as the dead space. In the giraffe the dead space has a volume of about 2.5 litres, and as this air has to be moved each time the animal breathes in or out, the rate of ventilation has to be increased to compensate for the reduced air flow. A resting giraffe takes about 20 breaths per minute, compared with our 12. The dead space must have been considerably larger in a sauropod, but we do not necessarily have to envisage a respiratory rate higher than that of a giraffe. Sauropods were reptiles, not mammals, and they probably had modest respiratory requirements, as we shall see in the next chapter.

Having considered some of the problems of being a giant, and some of the solutions, the logical question is, what are the selective advantages of large size? Large size is not the prerogative of the dinosaurs alone, for many other animal groups have evolved towards gigantism. The trend is so common in the fossil record that the phenomenon has been described as a rule, and is named Cope's Rule, in honour of Edward Drinker Cope, who first discussed the phenomenon. Like most generalizations there are many exceptions; some of the earliest ichthyosaurs, for example, are also the largest ones known. However, if the emphasis is placed on the fact that groups of animals have tended to evolve from smaller ancestors, rather than implying that groups of animals have evolved towards larger size, the numbers of exceptions is negligible.[13] The distinction is rather pedantic for this discussion, and it can be stated that a large number of groups of animals did evolve towards large size, and that this trend must have had a selective advantage. The most obvious advantage of being large is that it discourages predators. Carnivorous dinosaurs were an ever-present threat to the herbivores, many of which possessed horns, tail spikes, armour plating, and various other structures to ward off attackers.

As part of our evaluation of the defensive role of large body sizes in sauropods we should look at the situation in present-day animals. As few large reptiles are alive today, we will look at some mammals. The hunting behaviour of the African lion has been extensively studied in recent years and provides some useful comparative data.[14] Adult lions weigh between 110 and 180 kg and hunt alone, in pairs, or in small groups. A solitary adult can kill animals that are as much as twice its own weight, but larger prey, such as buffalo, which average 420 kg and reach 850 kg, are usually attacked by several individuals working together. Lions prey largely upon the wildebeest (130 kg), the zebra (165 kg), Thompson's gazelle (12 kg), and the buffalo (420 kg), and most of their other prey are smaller than themselves. Lions usually make no attempts to attack the elephant (3,500 kg), the hippopotamus (1,800 kg), or the rhinoceros and giraffe (usually over 1,000 kg). Thus, animals weighing over 1,000 kg are relatively safe from lions, and indeed from other predators.

Lions can run very fast, but only for short distances, whereas their prey can usually run just as fast, or even faster, and can sustain their top speed over longer distances. The advantage that the lion has is its greater acceleration, and it is therefore essential for it to approach its prey as closely as possible (usually 30–50 m) before making its charge. Most charges end in failure. The average hunting success for solitary lions is about 20%, and this is approximately doubled when two or more hunt together. Of prime importance to the success of an attack is the ability to stop the prey as soon as contact has been made. The fleeing prey is usually seized by the hindquarters, and this usually knocks it to the ground. If the victim is not seized and taken to the ground, the attack may fail, and success is largely determined by the difference in weight between hunter and hunted. A lion has far greater difficulty attacking an animal many times its own size, such as an adult buffalo, than with an animal nearer its own weight. It is important that a victim be killed fairly rapidly once it has been seized, because a prolonged struggle may lead to serious injury to the lion, especially if there is a large weight difference. The lion is very efficient at killing, and usually accomplishes this within minutes by biting deeply into the neck or throat.

African wild dogs, which weigh between 17 and 20 kg, usually select victims that do not exceed 65 kg. Sometimes larger prey are taken, but usually only with difficulty, because although they hunt in a pack their relatively weak jaws make it difficult for them to subdue their victims. One pack seen attacking a large wildebeest calf took eight minutes to drag it down, while another pack took five minutes just to chew through the abdominal wall of a female wildebeest. Wild dogs have been known to kill adult zebra, which are 10 times their own weight, but this is unusual.

Adult cheetahs weigh between 35 and 55 kg and prey largely upon Thompson's gazelles, which seldom exceed 20 kg. Larger prey are taken, but the preference is for animals that do not exceed 60 kg and this is because of the difficulties cheetahs have in subduing large prey. Leopards weigh about the same as cheetahs, but they do not experience such difficulties with larger animals. Their preferred size of prey is in the range 20–70 kg, but they will take animals of up to 150 kg. which is three times their own body weight.

Some generalizations may be made from the survey among living predators. Solitary hunters tend to select prey that are about their own weight, but will attack animals up to three times as large as themselves. When hunting is done in groups, larger prey are taken, but it is unusual for carnivores to attack prey that exceed about five times their own weight. The large herbivores, which exceed 1,000 kg appear to be immune from predators, although their offspring frequently fall victim to them.

Before we return to the Mesozoic, it is important to note that the data for living mammalian predators can only serve as a very approximate indication of possible predator-prey relationships among dinosaurs. Dinosaurs were not mammals, and while they may have been warm-blooded and some of them may have been as active as mammals, we cannot assume this. Furthermore, the environment of the Mesozoic was not the same as that of present-day Africa.

Allosaurus weighed about two tonnes, compared with 11 tonnes for *Diplodocus*, a rather light sauropod (certainly not the lightest, but the lightest for which we have an adequate weight estimate), 28 tonnes for *Apatosaurus*, and 78 tonnes for *Brachiosaurus*. These Jurassic dinosaurs were contemporaneous with a number of smaller herbivores, including *Camptosaurus*, which had an estimated weight of less than one tonne, *Stegosaurus*, weighing about two tonnes, and *Iguanodon*, which probably weighed about 4 tonnes. There were also a number of very small dinosaurs weighing about 50 kg and less. I suspect that *Allosaurus* may have selected the smaller herbivores in preference to the sauropods, though juvenile sauropods may have been fair game for it. Perhaps *Allosaurus* hunted in packs, and may then have attacked even *Diplodocus*, but it seems unlikely that the larger sauropods would have attracted their attention. A sauropod skeleton in the American Museum of Natural History in New

York has score marks on some of its bones that correspond in their spacing to the spacing of the teeth of *Allosaurus*, and this is often interpreted as evidence that *Allosaurus* preyed upon sauropods. But of course we do not know that this particular sauropod had been killed by *Allosaurus*, and it may well have been merely scavenged.

Animals spend much of their time searching for and consuming food, and the quantity required varies considerably from species to species. It has been found for a wide variety of animals, both vertebrate and invertebrate, that smaller animals require relatively more food per unit of body weight than larger animals. A ten tonne dinosaur would obviously eat more than a one tonne dinosaur but its consumption would be far less than ten times higher. Therefore the advantages of being a giant in terms of reducing the risk of predation may not be at a greatly increased food cost. It has often been argued that the sauropods must have spent all their time eating in order to obtain sufficient energy to maintain their enormous bodies, but this argument is without a sound foundation. It is true that elephants consume large quantities of food, but it must be emphasized that mammals have high metabolic rates and the same cannot be assumed for sauropods.

Unlike birds and mammals, most reptiles continue to grow throughout their lives, but their rate of growth falls as they get older. When I was four years old I was given a tortoise, and he was obviously more mature than his new owner. At the time of writing, more than 30 years later, he was still growing, whereas my growth had stopped more than half that time earlier. Tortoises are known to live to great ages, and longevity is suspected for many other reptiles. The long life spans that reptiles enjoy may be attributed to the slower pace of their lives compared with the lives of mammals and birds, but their continuous growth may be a more significant factor. One of the reasons why we grow old is that several of the cell types in our body cannot be replaced as they wear out, but if we continued growing, new cells would be added. If there is a correlation between continuous growth and longevity in reptiles, the enormous sizes reached by the sauropod dinosaurs may be partly a result of a selection pressure for prolonged life. The selective advantage of longevity is self evident—animals that live longer tend to produce more offspring. This does not mean that an elephant which lives for 40 years produces more offspring than a mouse that lives for two years (the reverse happens to be true), but it does mean that an elephant that has a particularly long reproductive life has potential to produce more offspring than an elephant whose reproductive life is shorter. Perhaps the largest dinosaurs lived for more than a century,[15] and it is even conceivable that their unhurried lives may have spanned several centuries. All of this, however, is entirely speculative.

6
The Hot-Blooded Debate

In 1975 Adrian Desmond, a student of the history of science, published a book entitled *The Hot-Blooded Dinosaurs* in which he popularized the concept that dinosaurs were warm-blooded.[1] No claim was made to originality, the idea having been proposed by several earlier investigators[2], and Desmond's thesis was largely influenced by the studies of Dr. Robert Bakker of Johns Hopkins University[3]. Bakker's evidence and conclusions, vigorously challenged by some[4] but generally accepted by others[5], have stimulated tremendous interest in dinosaurs and their relationships to other animals. Desmond's book was subtitled *A Revolution in Palaeontology,* and while this may overstate the importance of the debate there is no question that it has raised some interesting points, causing us to re-evaluate our traditional picture that most dinosaurs were slow and lumbering animals. Before we can assess the fossil evidence and take sides in the battle, we need to be familiar with the thermal strategies of living animals.

Like other mammals, and like birds, we are warm-blooded. By this we mean that our body temperature is maintained at a fairly constant level, independent of the ambient (external) temperature. Our own body temperature of 98.4°F, or 37.1°C, is maintained within such narrow limits that fluctuations are interpreted as signs of illness. Constant body temperatures in the order of 37°C are maintained by many mammals, while others have a less precise regulatory mechanism, with temperatures fluctuating by two or three degrees. Birds generally have higher body temperatures than mammals, averaging about 40°C, but their temperature usually drops a few degrees at night when they are not active. These high body temperatures are maintained whether the animal lives in the tropics or the frozen tundra. The body temperatures of polar bears and penguins are no lower than those of lions and parrots.

The heat required to maintain these high temperatures is generated within the body. All living cells generate small amounts of heat as a by-product of the chemical processes occurring within them. This chemical activity is called metabolism. Muscle cells generate more heat than any other cells, and about 80 per cent of the energy output of a contracting muscle cell appears as heat. Mammalian and avian cells have higher rates of metabolism than the cells of reptiles, which are generally higher than those of amphibians and fishes. A resting frog, for example, can generate between 64 and 95 calories per 100 g per hour, compared with more than 600 calories per 100 g per hour

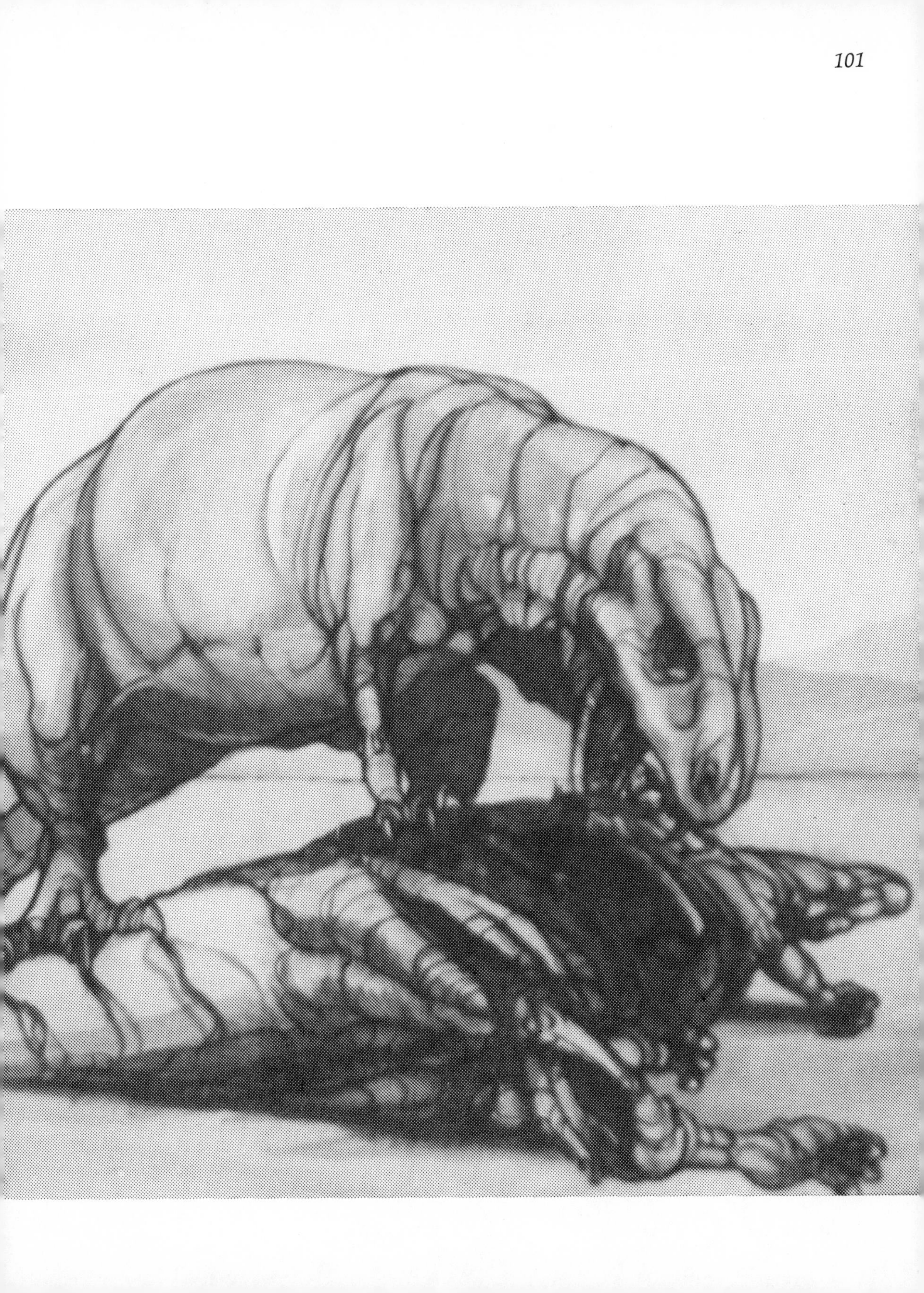

for a bird of similar size.[6] (A calorie is the amount of heat required to raise the temperature of one gram of water by 1C°.) Mammals and birds are therefore able to maintain high and constant body temperatures by virtue of their high metabolic rates, and this strategy is called endothermy. The metabolic rates of other animals are too low to enable them to be endothermic. The term homeothermy may also be used, emphasis being placed on the constancy of the body temperature rather than on the source of heat, but we will use the term endotherm.

In contrast to the endotherms are the modern reptiles—the snakes, turtles, crocodiles, lizards, and their kin—who generally derive most of their heat externally, from the sun. Most reptiles are inactive in the cold light of dawn, and have to bask in the sun to raise their body temperature before they can become very active. Once they have reached their working temperature they can keep it at a fairly constant level: when they are too hot they seek the shade, when too cold they bask in the sun. Active reptiles have an average body temperature of about 35°C, which is only a little lower than that of most mammals, but there is probably much variation from species to species. As their major source of heat is external to the body, the term ectothermy is used to describe the strategy. Sometimes an older term, "poikilothermy," is used, indicating a variable temperature, but ectothermy is a more precise term for most modern reptiles, and it will be used here. The term poikilotherm will be used for animals such as fish that typically do not regulate their body temperature, which consequently fluctuates with the ambient temperature. The reasons for belabouring the terminology is that homeothermy and endothermy, on the one hand, and poikilothermy and ectothermy, on the other, do not have the same meanings but are often used interchangeably, sometimes with confusing consequences. Because there has been so much confusion, an international committee was set up, and the recommendations it made regarding the definitions of the terms are adopted in this chapter.[7]

The obvious advantage an endotherm has over an ectotherm is that it is always in a state of readiness to flee, fight, or go about its business, regardless of the ambient temperature—but this is at a high cost. A resting mammal uses about three times as much energy as a resting reptile of the same size, and therefore requires relatively more food.[8] Birds and mammals, particularly the smaller ones, spend most of their waking hours foraging for food, but the frog sits idly on his lily-pad watching the world go by.

The relationship between metabolic rate and food consumption became very apparent to me during the temporary illness of a close friend. I have a fairly large appetite and invariably eat

Galapagos land iguana. Reptiles spend much of their day sunning themselves. By alternately basking and seeking shade they are able to maintain fairly constant body temperatures.

much larger meals than he, but the situation was reversed when he succumbed to an overactive thyroid gland. The main function of this gland, which is located in the neck, is to control the metabolic rate, and when it becomes overactive the metabolic rate is elevated. Being a doctor, he was able to extract much information from his condition, and he estimated that his metabolic rate was elevated by about one-third. This elevated rate of heat production gave him an appetite that had to be seen to be believed. He would devour a meal considerably larger than mine, then fill his plate and repeat the performance. He was only able to last to the next meal by making frequent visits to the kitchen, and his wife's twice-monthly shopping trips became weekly!

A compromise strategy to endothermy is to elevate one's temperature just before periods of activity. This minimizes costs during periods of inactivity and permits activities to be conducted over a wide range of ambient temperatures. Many flying insects have evolved this strategy, which is described as behavioural temperature regulation. The temperature of a grounded moth or a bee varies with the ambient temperature, but in flight the wing muscles generate enough heat to keep the thorax at a fairly constant high temperature. Prior to take-off, these insects undergo a pre-flight warming up procedure that lasts for five or 10 minutes. By simultaneously contracting both the muscles that depress the wings and those that elevate them, they generate heat without wing movements, apart from a slight shivering[9]. As the temperature of a muscle rises, its force of contraction increases. Maximum power is attained when the working temperature is reached, at which point flight can be sustained and the insect is able to take off.

Behavioural temperature regulation was graphically illustrated for me during a field trip. While prospecting for fossils in a cave, I came upon the carcass of a sheep that had fallen to its death some months before. The flesh was in an advanced state of decay, and well-fed flies scurried about their unsavory business. The flies made no attempt to fly away, and I soon realized that they were unable to, even when rudely harassed with the end of my trowel. Although it was a hot day, the inside of the cave was quite cold, and their flight muscles were presumably below their working temperature and unable to generate sufficient power for take-off. Had the flies been endotherms rather than behavioural temperature regulators they would have been able to fly instantly.

Although many animals are endotherms (mammals and birds), behavioural temperature regulators (many flying insects), or ectotherms (most reptiles), the majority of animals are poikilotherms and have no control over their body temperature, which therefore varies passively with the ambient temperature. Being poikilothermic does not necessarily mean having a widely fluctuating body temperature. Fishes living in Antarctic waters, for example, experience an almost constant temperature (-1.9°C) that varies by only one-tenth of a degree throughout the year[10]. Tropical fishes, similarly, live in a stable temperature regime, but most animals are exposed to widely fluctuating temperatures.

When non-endothermic animals are exposed to a temperature gradient they usually select a preferred temperature range, which is called the normal activity range. This range is often quite narrow, while in other cases it is quite broad. It is a universal property of matter that chemical reactions are speeded up by raising the temperature, and it has been found that speeds are approximately doubled with each 10C° rise. Within the normal activity range of an animal, an increase in temperature brings about an increase in its activity. If a particular lizard, say, has a normal activity range of 20–40°C, raising its temperature from 25°C to 35°C will cause an approximate doubling in the rate of all its body functions. Thus, the lizard would take only half as long to digest a meal[11], and it would walk approximately twice as fast.

To understand the rationale for an animal selecting a specific activity range, it is necessary to look into the internal workings, or physiology, of animals. Thousands of chemical reactions occur within the body, and these are facilitated by organic catalysts called enzymes, which are proteins manufactured by the body. Each enzyme works best within a particular, and usually a narrow, temperature range. If an enzyme is exposed to temperatures outside of this range, its catalytic powers are reduced or eliminated. Each animal species has its own system of enzymes, adapted to its own normal range of temperatures. Thus, the Antarctic fishes are adapted to life at -1.9°C, while tropical fishes are adapted to life at about 25°C. The Antarctic fishes are operating at their maximum efficiency at -1.9°C just as the tropical fish are at their maximum efficiency at 25°C.

Because endotherms maintain their body temperature at a fairly constant level, their enzymes are always operating at their maximum efficiency. Now that we are familiar with the thermal strategies of living animals we can return to the dinosaurs.

According to Bakker, all dinosaurs were endothermic, with high metabolic rates and high body temperatures, like birds and mammals. This conclusion was reached on several lines of evidence including the microscopic structure of bone, limb postures, and predator-prey ratios, and these will now be assessed.

The bones of mammals and birds are richly supplied with blood, and the bone mineral is usually arranged in regular concentric layers around the fine penetrating vessels, giving the characteristic pattern of Haversian bone, mentioned in Chapter 3. This type of bone is capable of rapid growth and also permits bone mineral (essentially calcium phosphate) to be absorbed rapidly into the bloodstream. Rapid growth and the rapid mobilization of calcium are both considered to be characteristic of endotherms, and the fact that dinosaurs have Haversian bone has therefore been interpreted as independent evidence for endothermy.[12] However, not all mammals have highly vascular bone, and some living reptiles that are known to be ectothermic have bone with a mammalian appearance.[13] The fine structure of bone cannot, therefore, be interpreted as conclusive evidence for endothermy.

We saw in Chapter 4 that the hip joint in dinosaurs was so constructed that the legs were held vertically beneath the body, as they are in birds and mammals. Since birds and mammals are the only modern vertebrates having an erect leg posture, and since they are the only endothermic vertebrates, Bakker concluded that there must be some correlation between upright posture and endothermy. He therefore argued that the erect posture in dinosaurs was evidence for endothermy. This argument of "guilt by association" is unsound, and, while there may be a correlation between limb postures and thermal strategies, this might be spurious.

Endothermy is expensive, as we have seen. Lions need to consume their own body weight in prey every eight or nine days and wild dogs every seven days,[14] whereas the carnivorous Komodo Dragon, a large lizard, eats its own weight only about every 60 days.[15] Endothermic carnivores therefore require relatively larger numbers of prey animals than ectothermic carnivores. Bakker found that the ratio of the biomass (total weight of all animals) of predators to the biomass of prey animals was about 2–3% for several modern African mammalian communities.[16] Similarly low ratios were obtained for some Tertiary fossil mammalian communities, but the ratio for a community of Permian fossil reptiles—which because of their primitive nature were almost certainly not endothermic—was about 25%. These results suggested that predator–prey ratios could be used to indicate the presence of endothermic carnivores in fossil communities. Bakker calculated the ratio for three different Cretaceous dinosaur assemblages. The ratios were between 2 and 3%, suggesting that the predatory dinosaurs were endothermic. Care must be taken when inferring relative abundances of fossil animals, because we do not know whether our fossil samples are truly representative of the original community ratios. An estimate of the ratio of lions to ungulates in the Serengeti Park, for example, would probably not be very accurately reflected in the ratio of their bony remains picked up in the park; the ratio could only be established by conducting a careful census of living animals over a period of many years. Furthermore, we do not know whether the herbivores in a given fossil community were all preyed upon by the carnivores, so we cannot be sure that we are measuring the actual predator–prey ratio. There are also other criticisms of this method,[17] but in spite of the problems the fact remains that herbivorous dinosaurs are far more abundant than carnivorous ones, and this suggests that these carnivores may have been endothermic.

A major flaw in Bakker's thesis is the contention that *all* dinosaurs had the same thermal strategy, and that they were high-metabolic-rate, high-body-temperature endotherms. While some dinosaurs may have been endothermic, I believe that most of them were probably not, but that they nevertheless maintained fairly constant body temperatures. We shall see that this was a consequence of their large size. We shall also see that some dinosaurs probably maintained relatively high body temperatures, but not through having high metabolic rates. To make my case, we have to consider modern animals once more. In particular, we have to consider the possible advantages of maintaining high body temperatures.

The advantage that insects derive from warming up their flight muscles prior to take-off is increased muscle power, and it seems that birds may elevate their body temperatures for similar reasons. Observations on starlings have shown that their body temperatures are elevated by between 2 and 4C° directly they start flying.[18] It is usually argued that birds cannot avoid this elevation because of the enormous quantities of heat liberated by their flight muscles, but this does not seem to be the case here. The starlings maintained an elevated body temperature over a wide range of ambient temperatures (0°C–28°C), but they only began shedding excess heat (by opening their bills and extending their legs into the air stream) at temperatures above 10°C. The fact that they did not gape at lower temperatures shows that they were easily coping with their heat load, and that their elevated body temperature was not an unavoidable consequence of their muscular activity. The evidence suggests that elevated body temperature is a strategy for increasing the power output of the flight muscles. Our own body temperature is raised during strenuous activity, and it has been suggested that this increases the power of our muscles.[19] Another aspect of high body temperatures is that they may enable muscles to maintain their rapid contractions for long periods. Active muscles generate waste products that have to be removed, and they also require a continuous supply of nutrients. It seems that both processes may occur more readily if the temperature of the muscle is high.[20]

Fishes that live in polar waters are fairly sluggish, and can only make the shortest bursts of speed. Tropical fishes, in contrast, are swift and can swim at high speeds for long periods.[21] It would be advantageous to fishes living in cold waters if they could conserve the heat generated by their active body muscles, but this heat is rapidly lost to the surrounding water. Some fishes, however, are able to maintain their swimming muscles at a relatively high and fairly constant temperature, and this is achieved by modifications in their blood vascular system. The tuna is one such fish, and its ability to regulate its body temperature by muscular activity was observed in 1835 by John Davy, a British physician. Davy, who was voyaging in the tropics, was amazed to find that the blood of the tuna fish was relatively warm, about 10C° higher than the water. Tunas are very active fishes that swim continuously and are capable of reaching high speeds. The larger ones have higher body temperatures than the smaller ones and can achieve a temperature of about 35°C. The warmest parts of the body are two strips of muscle that run along on either side. These strips are brown due to their rich blood supply. Those of us who enjoy our fish served on the bone will have noticed this strip of muscle in many other fishes besides the tuna, but relatively few species are capable of keeping this muscle warm. The tuna frequently travels between the warm upper layers of the sea and the deeper cold layers, and by maintaining its body at an elevated and fairly constant temperature it is able to maintain the same powerful swimming movements regardless of the ambient temperature.

The evidence suggests that increased muscle power may have been a significant factor in the evolution of high body temperatures, but this does not exclude the possibility that other factors may have been significant. Some animals may have evolved high body temperatures as an inescapable consequence of their high levels of muscular activity.[22] The cheetah, for example, can only sprint for periods of about 30 seconds, apparently because it is unable to shed heat rapidly enough (though the shortage of oxygen may be an important factor).

Professor A.W. Crompton and his Harvard University colleagues have challenged the argument that high body temperatures have evolved to maximize the power output of muscles.[23] They did not question the fact that muscles contract more rapidly with increased temperature, but believed that there is an optimum temperature, perhaps as low as 20°C, above which there is no increase in power. If this were the case, why would flying insects and birds elevate their body temperatures to the low 40s during flight? Their argument was supported by an observation that the top running speed of a particular insectivore whose body temperature was 28°C was higher than that of a white rat whose body temperature was 38°C. While this appears to be a valid criticism, it is not a sound one because these two animals differ from each other in many more ways than just their body temperature.[24] Even if it could be shown that increased muscle power was not a significant factor in the evolution of high body temperatures, it cannot be denied that high rates of muscular activity release large quantities of heat. Consequently, high activity levels and high body temperatures are inseparably linked.

Modern reptiles, as we have seen, are ectothermic, and gain heat by basking in the sun. As they can only absorb heat through their skin, the smaller ones, because of their relatively large area to volume ratio (see Chapter 5), heat up (and cool down) more rapidly than the larger ones. Observations made on spiny lizards weighing between 12 and 85 g, showed that they can raise their body temperature from 27°C to 43°C in 15 minutes of basking in the Arizona sun.[25] In another study, small alligators weighing about 50 g were found to take a little over a minute to warm up by 1C°, whereas larger ones, weighing about 13 kg, took more than seven minutes.[26] From these results it was calculated that a 9,000 kg dinosaur (a moderate-sized sauropod) would take more than three days to warm up by 1C°! Conversely, at night, the

Very large reptiles, like this Galapagos tortoise, maintain fairly constant body temperatures by virtue of their thermal inertia.

rate of cooling would have been so low that body temperature would have remained at a fairly constant level and this can be seen in large living reptiles. The Galapagos tortoise weighs about 200 kg, which is very small by dinosaur standards but large enough to give them a considerable thermal inertia. Thus, although ground temperatures fall by about 20C° during the night, their body temperature only falls by about 3C°.[27] I had an opportunity of seeing the effectiveness of their thermal inertia during a trip to the Galapagos islands. Our party had climbed to the top of a volcano, some thousand metres above sea level, and were camped overnight at its rim. Although it had been quite hot during the day, the temperatures plummeted at night and we all felt cold, even in our sleeping bags. As I emerged from my tent the following day, cold and stiff, I encountered a tortoise who had spent the night around our camp. He was wide awake and active, and when I touched his body with my cold fingertips he felt quite warm. Dinosaurs, by virtue of their large size, must have had fairly constant body temperatures.

In a mathematical study of the thermal strategies of large dinosaurs, the conclusion was reached that constant body temperatures could have been maintained only if the climate re-

The bony plates of **Stegosaurus** *may have been used to dissipate excess heat from the body.*

mained mild.[28] In this study, the dinosaurs were considered to have had a typically reptilian level of metabolism, which we have seen is far lower than that of birds and mammals, and solar radiation was assumed to have been a significant source of heat. No account was taken of the heat generated by muscles, which is considerable; living reptiles can produce up to six times more heat when they are active than they do when they are resting.[29] The heat generated in the leather back turtle by swimming enables this reptile to maintain a body temperature about 18C° higher than the surrounding sea water, which is remarkable when one considers how readily water, especially cold water, conducts heat away from a body.[30] It is therefore likely that even modest activity in a large dinosaur would have made a major contribution to its thermal budget, and vigorous activity might have posed serious problems of shedding excess heat. A convincing case has been made that the bony plates of *Stegosaurus*, a stockily built dinosaur, may have been used for dissipating excess heat.[31]

We may therefore conclude that large dinosaurs maintained

fairly constant body temperatures, an inescapable consequence of their large size, and that, although the end result was similar to that achieved by most birds and mammals, the mechanism was not the same. Birds and mammals are referred to as endotherms because they maintain their constant temperature by virtue of their high metabolic rate, and to distinguish the mechanism of the large dinosaurs the term "inertial homeotherm" is used. Inertial homeothermy does not necessarily imply having a high body temperature, or being particularly active, and we may envisage a wide range of thermal strategies among the dinosaurs. Bakker, however, dismissed the idea that dinosaurs were inertial homeotherms, arguing that they were all high-metabolic-rate, high-body-temperature endotherms. But modern mammals do not all have similar metabolic rates and body temperatures, so why should the dinosaurs? The three-toed sloth, for example, has a body temperature of between 32 and 34°C, and is noted for its lethargy. These mammals tend to have relatively high critical temperatures (the temperature at which a resting animal increases its metabolic rate to cope with any lowering of temperature) and are vulnerable to sudden drops in temperature. The shrew, in contrast, has a body temperature that approaches 39°C and a high metabolic rate.[32] Being small it has a relatively large area-to-volume ratio, and, because it is not large enough to carry a thick coat, its heat losses are relatively enormous. As a consequence, its appetite is also huge and it spends most of its short life in a frenzy of feeding activities.

Bakker's most persuasive argument that dinosaurs may have been endothermic is the evidence for fast running, but this only applies to certain kinds of dinosaurs. Furthermore, whereas fast running implies high body temperatures, it does not necessarily imply high metabolic rates. Many tropical fishes, for example, have high swimming speeds, but they may not have high (mammalian/avian) levels of metabolism. We will now survey the dinosaurs for evidence of their activity levels and see what the implications are regarding their possible thermal strategies.

Few would dispute the point that lightly built dinosaurs such as *Ornithomimus*, with its elongated hind legs and feet, were cursorial (modified for running). It is inconceivable that these features could have evolved in a slow-moving animal. The carnosaurs, though generally larger and less slenderly built than the ornithomimids, also possess cursorial features that suggest high running speeds.[33] The same is also true for the hadrosaurs,[34] as we saw in Chapter 4, though to a lesser extent. There are, therefore, several kinds of dinosaurs that possess features suggesting that they were capable of running fast. According to the argument developed earlier, high running speeds require fast muscle contractions, and these require high body temperatures.

The long hind legs and light build of the ostrich-sized dinosaur **Ornithomimus** *suggests fleetness of foot, which in turn suggest high body temperatures.*

Even if this argument is unsound, it cannot be denied that rapidly contracting muscles release large quantities of heat. Fast-running dinosaurs could therefore not have avoided having relatively high body temperatures, and, because of their large size, these temperatures would have been fairly constant. *Ornithomimus* was about the size of an ostrich, probably weighing about 100 kg, and may therefore have been too small to have been an inertial homeotherm. However, a study of the Komodo Dragon, which has about the same body weight as *Ornithomimus,* has shown that fairly stable body temperatures can be maintained at this size range.[35] Far less body heat is lost through the skin than was previously believed, and the study showed that the conductivity of the skin of reptiles that weigh between 10 and 100 kg is about the same as that of mammals of similar size, even though reptiles lack external insulation. *Ornithomi-*

mus and its allies may therefore have been able to maintain a fairly constant, and probably high, body temperature, even in the absence of any external insulation.

Although high and fairly constant body temperatures could have been achieved in cursorial dinosaurs possessing a reptilian (low) level of metabolism, we cannot dismiss the possibility that some may have had a mammalian/avian level of metabolism. Bakker's evidence from predator–prey ratios suggests that certain carnivorous dinosaurs may have had high food requirements, which supports an endothermic interpretation. Remember also that hadrosaurs, which were their potential prey, had a complex grinding dentition which suggests large food requirements. Perhaps they were endothermic.

The smallest dinosaurs, such as *Compsognathus*, also possess cursorial features that suggest high running speeds. Weighing only a few kilograms, however, they were probably too small to have been capable of maintaining a constant body temperature in the absence of an external layer of insulation. Is there any evidence that they were insulated? Skin impressions are rare—they are known for several hadrosaurs, and for at least one ceratopsian dinosaur. In each case the skin had a pebbled texture of rounded tubercles with no evidence of feathers, fur, or any other external insulation. Unfortunately, no skin impressions have been found in association with small dinosaurs.

Feather impressions, however, are known for *Archaeopteryx*, the earliest bird, and we will see in Chapter 11 that this animal is anatomically so similar to small theropod dinosaurs that it would have been described as a small dinosaur, but for the presence of feather impressions.[36] We naturally associate feathers with birds and with flight, but several authorities believe that feathers probably evolved to serve an insulative role and became modified for flight only secondarily.[37] Admittedly, only evidence of wing and tail feathers has been found, and these feathers probably had little insulating value, but it seems likely that insulatory contour feathers were present, as in modern birds, but these have not been preserved in the fossil. The presence of an external insulating layer tends to rule out the possibility that *Archaeopteryx* was an ectotherm, because an animal probably cannot absorb heat efficiently when insulated from the sun's rays.[38] Poikilotherms do not possess external insulation, so we have to conclude that *Archaeopteryx* was either an endotherm or perhaps a behavioural temperature regulator.

Small dinosaurs may also have been feathered, and perhaps the absence of feather impressions should be viewed as absence of data rather than as evidence for the absence of feathers. Feathers are rarely preserved as fossils and easily overlooked even when they are, as in the case of two of the specimens of *Archaeopteryx* which had formerly been misidentified as reptiles simply because their feather impressions were so faint. It must be pointed out, though, that a careful examination of *Compsognathus* has failed to reveal any evidence of feathers[39] and it was found in the same lithographic limestones as *Archaeopteryx*. While it is tempting to suggest that *Archaeopteryx* and the small dinosaurs had similar thermal strategies because of their similar anatomies this would be entirely speculative. All we can conclude is that there is some circumstantial evidence that the smallest dinosaurs *may* have been endothermic.

What about the largest dinosaurs? When we were considering gigantism (Chapter 5) we saw that the largest dinosaurs, the sauropods, were probably slow moving. Slow body movements do not require rapid muscle contractions, and consequently do not require high body temperatures. Conversely, low levels of muscular activity do not release heat rapidly, and it seems reasonable to conclude that their body temperatures were relatively low. Because of their enormous size, their surface area would have been relatively small compared with their volume. As most of their excess body heat would have been shed through the skin, it would seem that severe limitations would have been placed on the rate at which heat could have been lost. This in turn would seem to rule out any vigorous activity. The African elephant, which is much smaller than a sauropod (the largest sauropod had an estimated body weight more than 10 times greater than that of an elephant), has a relatively small area to volume ratio. This causes major problems of heat dissipation. They are prone to heat stroke, and seek shade and avoid vigorous exercise during the hottest part of the day. Much of their excess heat is shed through their ears, which are large and richly supplied by blood vessels, and these are flapped to and fro to assist the cooling process. Perhaps the long necks and tails of the sauropods were important sites for shedding excess heat. On the grounds of heat dissipation alone it seems unlikely that sauropods could have been very active animals, or that they had a high level of metabolism. Bakker, however, believes that sauropods did have a high (mammalian/avian) level of metabolism and a correspondingly high body temperature. If this were true, their food requirements would presumably have been high. Sauropods have remarkably small heads for the size of their bodies, with relatively few teeth, and it is difficult to visualize how they could have obtained sufficient food to have been endothermic. The head of *Diplodocus* for example, was somewhat less than that of an African elephant, but its body was almost twice as large.[40] *Brachiosaurus* was even larger—about 10 times heavier than an elephant, but its head was only about half as big again. Could such a small head have gathered enough food for such a huge body? The daily food consumption of a wild African elephant is about 160 kg and feeding takes up at least 16 hours of every day—it is therefore difficult to imagine how a great sauropod could have gathered much more food than this. The evidence strongly suggests that sauropods could not have obtained enough food to support a mammalian level of metabolism.

To summarize our conclusions so far:

1. Most dinosaurs, because of their large size, had a fairly constant body temperature, and they are described as being inertial homeotherms. This does not necessarily imply high body temperatures or high metabolic rates.
2. Many dinosaurs, including the ornithomimids, carnosaurs, and hadrosaurs, have skeletal features that suggest an ability to run fast. These cursorial features suggest high body temperatures. Although this does not imply a high (mammalian/avian) level of metabolism, we cannot rule out the possibility that some dinosaurs may have been endothermic.
3. The smallest dinosaurs, such as *Compsognathus*, have cursorial features that suggest high body temperatures, but they were too small to have been inertial homeotherms. It is possible that they had feathers, like the anatomically similar *Archaeopteryx*. Possession of feathers in *Archaeopteryx* is compelling evidence for endothermy, or behavioural temperature regulation.
4. The largest dinosaurs, the sauropods, do not possess cursorial features; quite the reverse. This suggests that relatively low body temperatures were maintained. Their low area-to-volume ratios suggest that heat dissipation may have been a major problem. Vigorous activity and high metabolic levels can be dismissed on these grounds alone. Furthermore, it is difficult to conceive how sauropods could have obtained enough food to maintain high metabolic levels.

If most dinosaurs achieved constant warm bodies by virtue of their large size, how could their offspring have survived? The available evidence, which is scanty, indicates that hatchling dinosaurs were moderately large compared with, say, most modern lizards and birds. Eggs have been found in association with the horned dinosaur *Protoceratops*, and eggs tentatively ascribed to the sauropod *Hypselosaurus* are also known. In both instances the eggs are relatively large (compared with those of most birds), suggesting that the hatchlings were also fairly large, and it has been suggested that *Protoceratops* hatchlings may have been about 25 cm long, while those of *Hypselosaurus* were about 40 cm long.[41] The 1978 discovery of a hadrosaur nesting site in Montana has given us a good deal of information about young dinosaurs, and the smallest individual found there had an estimated length of 45 cm.[42] An almost complete skeleton of a young prosauropod(?) dinosaur, discovered in Argentina in

1977, has an estimated length of about 24 cm[43], while the smallest of all babies (based on skull length), a juvenile of the horned dinosaur *Psittacosaurus*, has an estimated length of 23 cm.[44] Many birds are without feathers when they hatch, and are considerably smaller than these estimates for hatchling dinosaurs. At first, chicks are unable to regulate their body temperature when the ambient temperature is below 35°C. Within a few days they can regulate their temperature moderately well, even at low temperatures, and sometimes even before their feathers have appeared.[45] Young mammals have a good capacity for heat production, even those that are born naked. Piglets, for example, are able to maintain their normal body temperature even when the ambient temperature is down to 5°C.[46] Much of the ability of young endotherms to survive at low temperatures is attributed to their huddling together in nests. We know that *Protoceratops* laid its eggs in nests because examples of these were found during an expedition to Mongolia in 1923. So too with the hadrosaurs found in Montana in 1978, and wear-facets on the teeth of these juveniles show they were already feeding while in the nest. This has been taken as evidence of parental care[47], but this is not necessarily the case.[48] Some dinosaurs might have borne their young alive at a relatively advanced stage of development (many modern reptiles are live-bearers). The survival problem of young dinosaurs due to heat loss is therefore surmountable.

Having discussed the possible thermal strategies of dinosaurs, we will assess the evidence for their reptilian contemporaries. The pterosaurs have long been considered as likely candidates for endothermy. Flying is very demanding in terms of energy, requiring considerable muscular activity and generating large quantities of heat. As more power can be obtained from muscles at higher temperatures, it is a logical consequence that pterosaurs should have maintained a high constant body temperature, at least during flight. Direct evidence for endothermy came as early as 1927 when a German palaeontologist, F. Broili, described impressions of hair-like material in a well-preserved specimen of the small pterosaur *Rhamphorhynchus*.[49] His findings were not widely accepted, but in 1971 a Russian palaeontologist removed all doubts when he described impressions of a furry body covering in a new Jurassic pterosaur that he named *Sordes pilosus*.[50] Whether pterosaurs were endotherms or behavioural temperature regulators cannot be determined. Perhaps they were like most present-day birds, maintaining a constant body temperature during the daytime, but dropping it by a few degrees at night, or they may have been like humming-birds, and allowed their body temperature to fall to ambient temperatures at night.

Evidence for endothermy in other Mesozoic reptiles is entirely circumstantial, and the ichthyosaurs, which lived in the sea, are the most likely candidates. Some exceptionally well-preserved specimens have been found, with the body outline preserved as a carbonaceous film. From the shape of the body (discussed in detail in Chapter 8), it is deduced that they were probably capable of high swimming speeds, comparable to present-day sharks and dolphins. Rapid swimming requires a high level of muscular activity, which in turn generates much heat. Was this heat lost to the water, or did ichthyosaurs have a layer of fat beneath their skin to insulate their bodies—like the blubber of dolphins and whales? We have no direct evidence for blubber, but as we will see in Chapter 8, the carbonaceous body outlines that are sometimes preserved are rich in fat.

We have now taken sides in the hot-blooded debate. Most dinosaurs, by virtue of their large size, maintained fairly constant body temperatures, but these were not necessarily high. While some dinosaurs may have been endothermic, many of them probably had relatively low metabolic levels, typical of reptiles, and this offers a possible explanation for their extinction.

It is generally believed that the close of the Mesozoic Era was marked by a general cooling trend in world climates.[51] If dinosaurs did have a relatively low metabolic rate they may have been vulnerable to this climatic deterioration. Certain modern mammals that have low metabolic rates, such as the sloth, appear to be vulnerable to sudden drops in temperature and are restricted to the tropics. The fact that sloths have a relatively thin fur is probably also a contributing factor. Elephants, which are essentially naked, acclimatize to cold climates quite readily, responding by increasing the thickness of their coat. The Ice Age relatives of the elephant, the mammoths and mastodons, had thick coats to withstand the cold. As far as we know, most dinosaurs were naked, but, unlike the elephant, they were probably unable to respond to climatic deterioration by growing a thick coat. Furthermore, their generally large size would have made it difficult for them to find shelter from the elements. The possibility that the dinosaurs were the victims of a climatic change has always been a popular explanation for their extinction, and the question will be discussed further in Chapter 10.

7 Brains and Intellect

A popular insult a few years ago was the epithet "bird brain", an obviously uncomplimentary expression because birds are not noted for the large size of their brains. The reptilian brain is even more impoverished, and it has often been suggested that dinosaurs had absurdly small brains for the size of their bodies. The large size of our own brain has probably been the hallmark of our success, and it is hardly surprising that *Homo sapiens*, the wise man, should be so condescending when discussing the intellectual abilities of other species.

The average weight of the adult human brain is about 1.4 kg (though there is a wide variation, from about 1 kg to 2 kg), which is about three times greater than that of our closest living relatives, the great apes. But some animals have even larger brains. An adult African elephant, with a brain almost four times the size of ours, has the largest brain of any living land animal. The whales, however, have the biggest brains of all, and that of the sperm whale, which is six times the size of man's, is probably the biggest that has ever existed. Does this mean that elephants and whales are intellectually superior to man? There is certainly no question that whales are extraordinary intelligent animals, but they are probably no brighter than we are.[1] Absolute brain size is obviously not a reliable guide to intellect—what we need is a method of assessing relative brain size. Before considering how this can be done, however, we will direct our attention to the anatomy of the brain. We will see that the relative development of different parts of the brain are of considerable importance in interpreting an animal's behavioural potential. Our starting point, as usual, will be with living animals, and specifically with the structure and function of the vertebrate brain.

There is considerable variation in the structure of the brain throughout the vertebrates, but a basic pattern can be recognized, so it is possible to describe a generalized vertebrate brain. While we have an approximate idea of the functions of the brain's different parts, our knowledge is based largely upon studies of our own brain, and the brains of certain other mammals, and is accordingly circumscribed. Our account of the form and function of the various regions of the vertebrate brain is therefore overgeneralized and serves only as a broad guide.

The brain is essentially a thick-walled tube and it has three main parts, the forebrain, midbrain, and hindbrain. Arising from the front of the forebrain are two swellings, the olfactory bulbs, which are associated with the sense of smell. Most birds

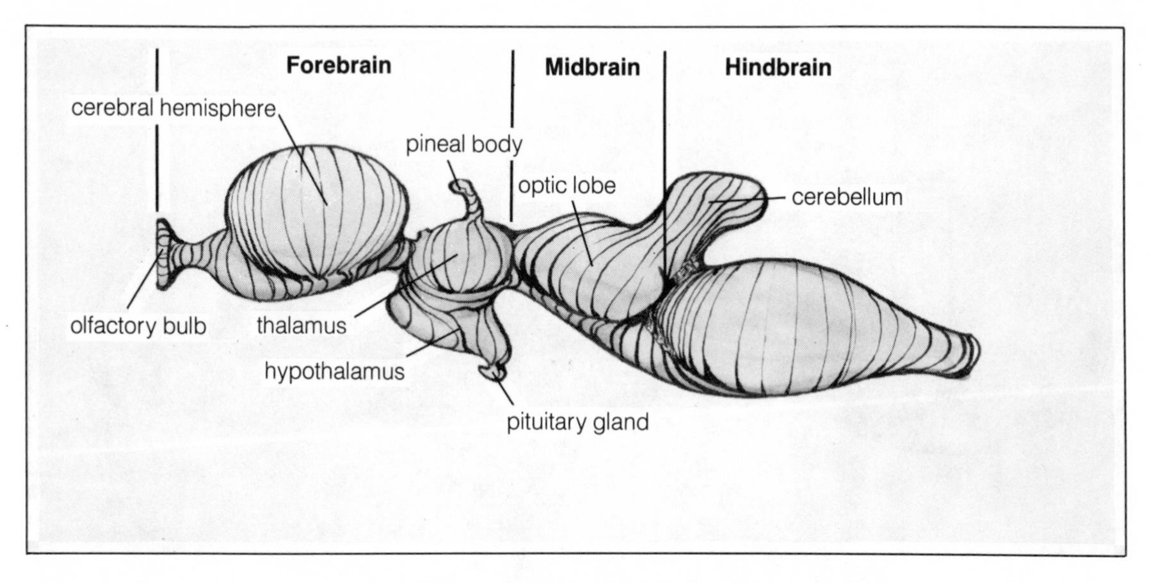

Diagrammatic representation of the main features of the vertebrate brain.

have a very poor sense of smell, and correspondingly small olfactory bulbs, while reptiles and mammals (higher primates, including man, being notable exceptions) generally have a well-developed olfactory sense and correspondingly large bulbs. A swelling of the roof and sides of the forebrain constitutes the cerebrum, which is usually a paired structure, each half being called a cerebral hemisphere. This region is so large in some mammals that it overlies most of the rest of the brain. The cerebrum is associated with the integration of the senses, and with what is commonly referred to as intelligence. The word intelligence comes from the Latin, *intelligere*, to understand, but there is little agreement among specialists as to how intelligence should be defined. Definitions include the ability to adapt to new circumstances, the ability to learn[2], and the capacity to construct a perceptual world[3].

Many different tests have been devised to assess intelligence in humans and other animals. Some of these test the ability to solve problems, and others test the readiness with which an individual learns, but it is important to realize the limitations of these procedures. In the first place, tests are usually conducted in a laboratory, far from the real world of the animal. An animal may fail a test, not because of shortcomings in its mental capacities, but because the task it is expected to perform is far removed from its normal behavioural patterns. As a hypothetical example, a test which required an animal to push open a door using its nose would probably be more successfully completed by a dog than a cat merely because dogs frequently use their noses for pushing, whereas cats do not. Another point is that we cannot always equate intelligence with learning abilities. A chimpanzee is considered to be far more intelligent than a dog

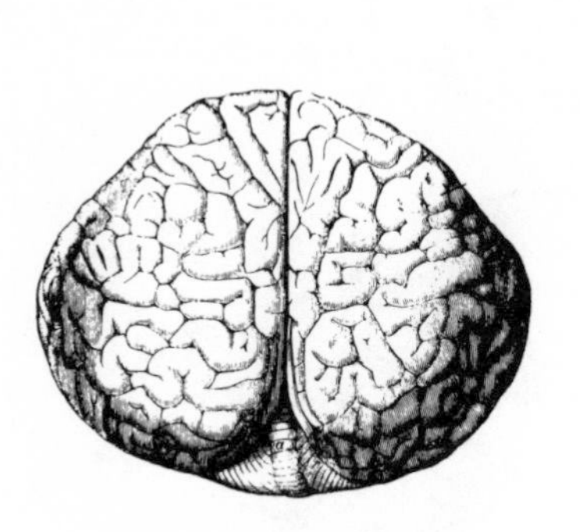

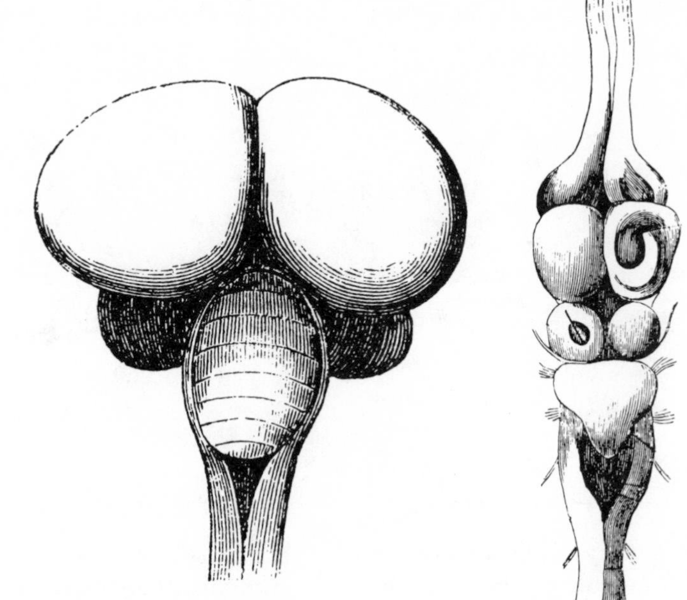

Brains of selected vertebrates. Left: A dolphin; the convoluted cerebral hemispheres are so large that they obscure the rest of the brain. Center: A bird (**Larus**)*; the cerebral hemispheres are large, but unconvoluted. Right: A turtle* (**Chelone**)*; the cerebral hemispheres are small and unconvoluted.*

but is apparently far more difficult to house-train.[4] Lastly, we should realize that, although hundreds of tests have been performed on animals, these have been confined to few species, notably the laboratory rat, the chimpanzee, and the pigeon. Few reptiles have been tested and the study of reptilian behaviour is in its infancy. Sweeping generalizations that certain types of animals are less or more intelligent than others are therefore unfounded, but they continue to be made. There is also a great tendency to underestimate the capabilities of animals, but as more and more investigations are conducted upon animals in their natural environments it becomes apparent that they are capable of far more than we ever believed. When we refer to the intellectual abilities of animals, then, we must remember that we are on uncertain ground.

The walls of the cerebral hemispheres are referred to as the cerebral cortex. In the most intelligent mammals, which include man, the great apes, and whales and dolphins (the Cetacea), the cerebral cortex is very thick and highly convoluted, in the less intelligent mammals it is smooth. The cerebral cortex is thin and unconvoluted in fishes, amphibians, reptiles, and birds, and appears to be largely associated with olfaction. The floor of the cerebrum is thickened, forming a pair of swellings, the corpora striata. These are especially prominent in birds, which correspondingly have relatively large cerebral hemispheres. The classical interpretation of birds has been that, because their brain lacks a thick cerebral cortex, they are incapable of intelligent behaviour, and their behavioural patterns which are often complex (as in nest building, courtship displays, and navigation) are largely instinctive. Instinctive behaviour is inherited, and is characteristically stereotyped and inflexible, unlike learned behavioural patterns, which can be modified according to changing circumstances. The corpora striata have been interpreted as the seat of instinctive behaviour, and birds were viewed almost as automatons, largely incapable of modifying their behaviour by experience. This view is now being modified, however, because it has been found that birds can perform some remarkable feats of learning. In some learning experiments birds have even outperformed some mammals.[5] The centre for this level of behaviour in birds is now understood to be the corpora striata and not the cerebral cortex as it is in mammals.

The hind portion of the forebrain is called the diencephalon. The walls are referred to collectively as the thalamus, the roof is called the epithalamus, and the floor is called the hypothalamus. The thalamus is concerned with the integration of sensory activities, the hypothalamus with controlling the internal functions of the body. A small outpushing from the floor of the hypothalamus, the pituitary gland, produces a large number of hormones that co-ordinate certain physiological processes, including growth. Throughout our history there have been tales of giants, and some of these are founded in fact, as witnessed at fairgrounds and circuses. Gigantism is often the result of an enlarged and over-active pituitary gland, and it is interesting to find that large dinosaurs also appear to have had particularly large pituitaries.[6] Arising from the epithalamus is a small stalked outpushing, the pineal body. In some of the lower vertebrates, including the reptile *Sphenodon*, this is light-sensitive and is often referred to as the third eye. Many reptiles, including *Sphenodon*, have a hole in the roof of the skull that transmits light to the pineal body.

The midbrain is the smallest of the three divisions of the brain, and gives rise to a pair of swellings, the optic lobes, which are associated with vision. Birds usually have a very well developed sense of sight, and the optic lobes are correspondingly large. These lobes are also fairly well developed in reptiles, and even more so in the bony fishes. Most mammals have keen vision, but the visual impulses are interpreted in the cerebrum rather than in the optic lobes, which therefore tend to be fairly small. In tetrapods there is another pair of swellings from the midbrain, the auditory colliculi, which are associated with hearing.

The third division of the brain, the hindbrain, is largely associated with balance and muscular co-ordination and is therefore something of a control centre for locomotion. The specific centre of balance is the cerebellum, a convoluted swelling from the roof of the hindbrain. As might be expected, the cerebellum is particularly well developed in animals that move in the three planes of space—the birds, the bats, and most aquatic animals, especially the cetaceans.

Because the brain holds so many clues to the sensory and behavioural potentials of living animals, it is of considerable interest to the palaeontologist to see whether its structure can be determined from the skull. The brain is encased in a bony capsule, the cranium, and in mammals and birds this conforms so closely to its contours that even impressions of blood vessels can be seen imprinted on the surface of the bone. The reptilian brain, however, usually does not fill the cranium, and is not always completely encased in bone. Consequently, there is a less precise correspondence between the shape of the brain and that of the cranial cavity.

For mammals, birds, and, to a lesser extent, reptiles, the structure of the brain can be reconstructed simply by making an internal cast of the cranial cavity, and this has been a most useful tool to palaeontologists. The procedure is quite simple and the first step is to close all the holes that lead into the cranial cavity. In life these holes transmitted blood vessels and nerves to and from the brain, and they can easily be plugged with plasticene. With the skull held vertically, liquid rubber latex is poured into the foramen magnum (the hole through which the spinal cord passes on its way to the brain). Enough latex is used to form a skin on the endocranial surfaces, and the latex is swirled around to ensure an even coating. When the latex has dried and cured, which takes a few days, it is carefully peeled away and pulled out through the foramen magnum. The outside surface of the latex cast faithfully reproduces the contours of the endocranial surfaces, and the whole structure, which has the shape of the brain, is called an endocast. The endocast can be filled with plaster to make it rigid, and a mould can be formed around it so that it can finally be cast in plaster.

Sometimes, a skull becomes filled with sediments during preservation, and the consolidation of the material in the cranial cavity produces a natural endocast. One such rare event appears to have occurred during the preservation of the British Museum specimen of *Archaeopteryx*, the oldest known bird. Some time after the consolidation of the endocast, the cranium became exposed to the environment and was completely weathered away, leaving exposed a natural endocast.

Endocasts have been made for a large number of extinct animals, including many dinosaurs,[7] but as the reptilian brain does not completely fill the cranium, allowances have to be made for this when deducing brain sizes for them. An estimate of the discrepancy has been made by comparing endocasts with

Natural brain casts are sometimes formed by the consolidation of earthy particles within the endocranial cavity. This rare event occurred during the preservation of the British Museum (Natural History) specimen of **Archaeopteryx**.

actual brains for some present-day reptiles.[8] The endocasts were found to be about twice the size of the actual brain. Consequently, reptilian brain volumes are taken as being half the volume of their endocasts. This is only a rough estimate, however, because in some cases the reptilian brain completely fills the cranium, while in others it may occupy less than half of the cranial volume. Dinosaur endocasts are not only larger than the actual brain was but lack much of the original detail. Consequently they do not always look very brain-like, and we cannot get any precise picture of the shape, or draw many conclusions about their potential. The most obvious feature of the brain of a dinosaur is that it was typically reptilian, lacking any regional enlargements. The most prominent region was the cerebrum, but this was not particularly large, except in the small theropod dinosaur, *Stenonychosaurus*. The pituitary gland was usually well developed, and we have seen that this is associated with growth. The cerebellum, which is largely concerned with the coordination of body movements, was moderately well developed. Some dinosaurs had reasonably well developed olfactory bulbs, suggesting that they may have had a good sense of smell, but the optic lobes, which are associated with sight, can barely be identified. The size of the brain was often quite large. An endocast obtained for the hadrosaur *Endmontosaurus*, for example, is nearly 27 cm long, but we have already seen that absolute brain size is a poor guide to an animal's "intellectual"

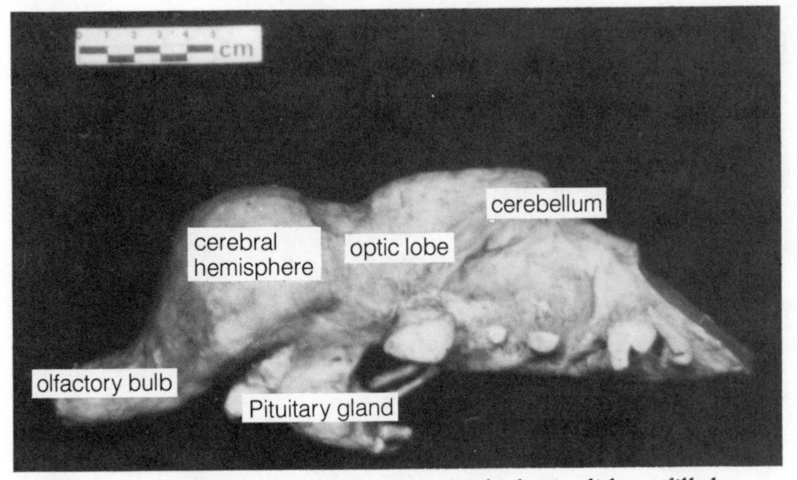

A plaster endocast of **Edmontosaurus***. As the brain did not fill the cranial cavity the endocast is larger than the actual brain, and lacks detail.*

abilities, and we have yet to find a meaningful indicator of relative brain size.

Some of the early investigators of the relationship between brain size and body size merely divided the weight of the brain by the weight of the body, but the results were not very helpful. The brain of the domestic cat, for example, represents 0.94% of its body weight, whereas that of the lion is only 0.18%. This would suggest that domestic cats have far greater intellectual potentials than lions, but this is obviously erroneous. Even before the turn of the century it was realized that the relationship between the brain and body weight was exponential, that is, one set of variables (in this case, body weights) increases more rapidly than the other (brain weights), but relatively few data were available for verification.

If exponential data are graphed, a curve is obtained, but if logarithms of the original data are used a straight line is obtained.[9] The gradient, or slope, of the line is easily measured, and gives the rate of change of one variable relative to the other (for a fuller explanation see pages 126-27). When H.J. Jerison, pioneer in the field of assessing relative brain sizes, plotted logarithmic data for brain and body weights for a wide variety of recent vertebrates, he obtained two straight lines.[10] The upper line is derived from data that have been obtained for birds and mammals; the lower one is for bony fishes, amphibians and reptiles. At any given body size the brain of a bony fish or reptile is smaller than that of a bird or mammal, and this dichotomy of the vertebrates is of much evolutionary significance, as will be seen. (If cartilaginous fishes—the sharks and skates—are included, they cluster along the upper line with birds and mammals. This suggests high intellectual potentials, but it may be partly attributed to their large olfactory bulbs. More research is obviously needed before inferences can be drawn.)

The slope of each line is 2/3, which suggests that the relationship between brain weight and body weight is a surface-related phenomenon. Such a relationship could have been predicted. The brain processes information received from sensory structures such as those in the skin, and transmits impulses to such structures as the body muscles. Since most impulses originate and terminate at surfaces, it follows that as animals increase in size, the work of the brain, hence its size, has to increase in step with increases in surface areas. We would therefore expect the brain weight to increase in proportion to the body weight, raised to the power 2/3. Since the slope of these two lines (2/3), and the point where each cuts the vertical axis can be directly measured, the equations of the two graphs can be stated. Jerison found that the bird/mammal equation was given by:

$$\text{brain weight} = 0.07 \times (\text{body weight})^{2/3} \text{ (equation 1)}$$

while the bony fish/reptile equation was given by:

$$\text{brain weight} = 0.007 \times (\text{body weight})^{2/3} \text{ (equation 2)}$$

At any given body weight, the brain weight of a bony fish or reptile is therefore about 1/10 that of a bird or mammal.

Using these equations, it is possible to calculate the size of the brain of an animal of known body size, provided that it has an average-sized brain for its kind. For example, suppose that we want to calculate the brain weight of a lizard whose body weight is 540 g. Substituting this value in equation 2:

$$\begin{aligned} \text{brain weight} &= 0.007 \times (540)^{2/3} \text{ g} \\ &= 0.007 \times (66.04) \text{ g} \\ &= 0.46 \text{ g} \end{aligned}$$

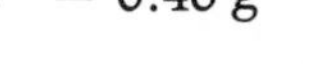

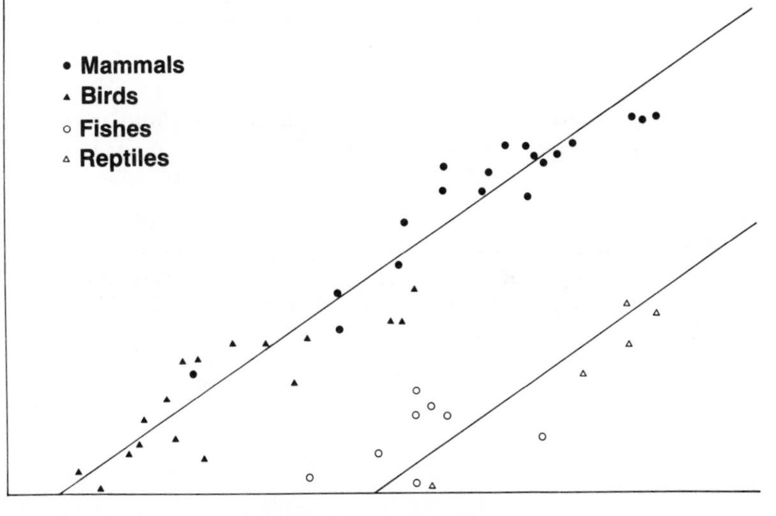

Logarithmic graph of brain weight plotted against body weight for a wide range of vertebrates.

Graphs, gradients and exponentials

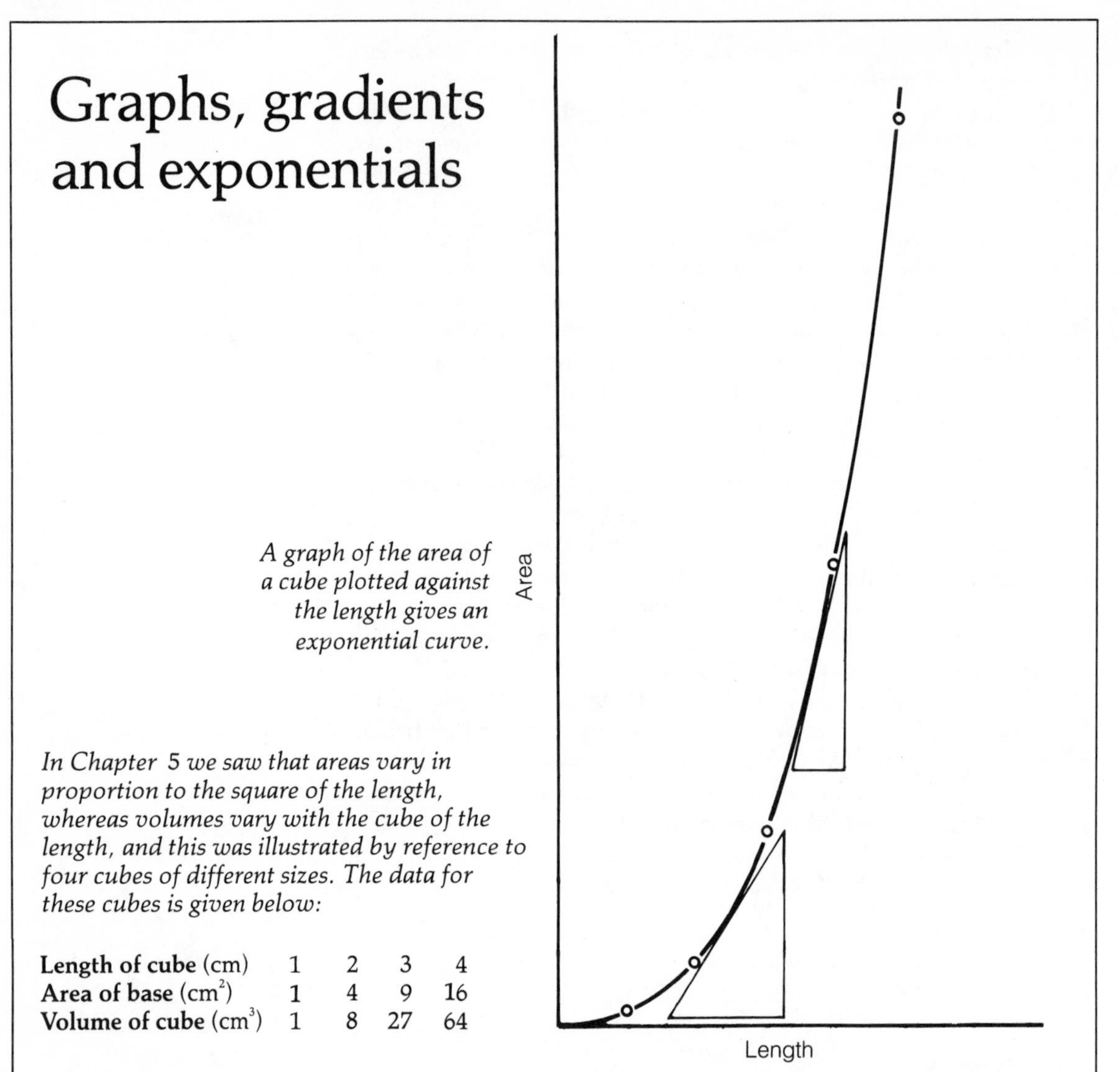

A graph of the area of a cube plotted against the length gives an exponential curve.

In Chapter 5 we saw that areas vary in proportion to the square of the length, whereas volumes vary with the cube of the length, and this was illustrated by reference to four cubes of different sizes. The data for these cubes is given below:

Length of cube (cm)	1	2	3	4
Area of base (cm^2)	1	4	9	16
Volume of cube (cm^3)	1	8	27	64

If a graph is plotted of the area of the base against the length of the cube, a curve is obtained. If we then plotted a graph of the volume of the cube against its length we would obtain a similar but steeper curve.

The slope of a graph, like the gradient of a road, gives the rate of change. Curves do not have a constant slope, and if the slope is measured at a particular point as shown in the diagram, it will be different from the slope measured at some other point. Curves lack constant gradients because the variables do not change at the same rate, and such relationships are called exponential.

If instead of plotting the raw data we plot the logarithms of the data, we obtain a straight-line graph, and the slope of the line is the rate of change. Thus we can read directly from the logarithmic graph that the area of the cube varies with the square of the length (gradient = 2) while the volume varies with the cube of the length (gradient = 3).

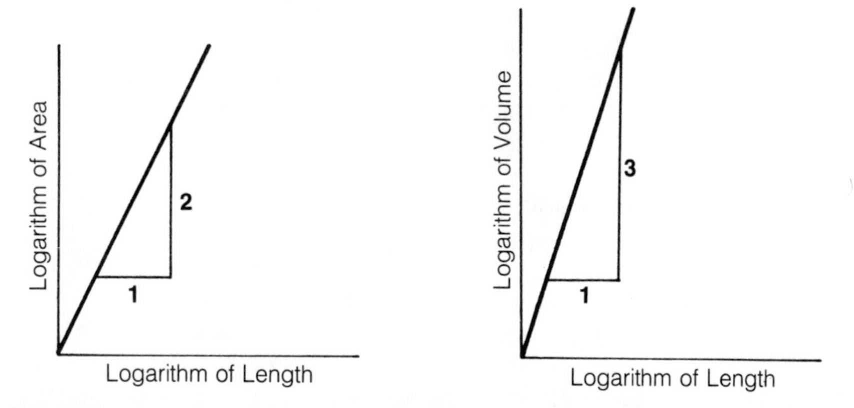

When logarithmic data are plotted for exponential relationships straight line graphs are obtained. Logarithm of the area of a cube plotted against the logarithm of the length (left), and of the logarithm of the volume plotted against the logarithm of the length.

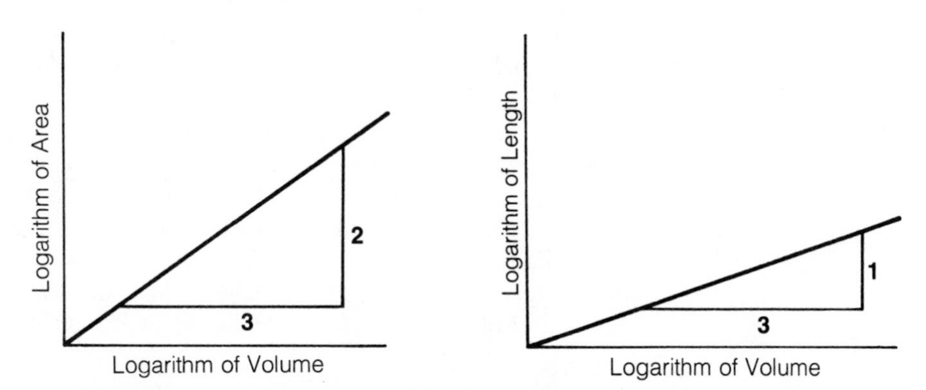

Logarithmic graphs of area against volume (left) and length against volume (right) give gradients of 2/3 and 1/3 respectively.

If a graph of the logarithm of the area is plotted against the logarithm of the volume, a straight line is obtained, the gradient of which is 2/3. Similarly, a logarithmic graph of the length of the cube plotted against its volume gives a straight line with a gradient of 1/3.

Logarithmic graphs of various organ measurements are often plotted against body weights during investigations of size-related phenomena, and this is equivalent to plotting them against body volumes.

The weight of a body = volume × density. As density remains constant, weight is directly proportional to volume. Most animals have a density close to unity, therefore the volume of the body, in cubic centimetres, and body weight, in grams, may be used interchangeably. The straight lines obtained frequently have slopes of about 2/3, suggesting that they are area-related phenomena.

If we look at Jerison's graphs we see that some animals, for example, man, the great apes, and the whales, lie well above the relevant line, which means that their brains are larger than would be predicted from the equation. Others lie below the line and have smaller brains than would be predicted for their kind. For example, from equation 1, the brain weight of a squirrel monkey of 1,000 g body weight is given by:

$$\begin{aligned} \text{brain weight} &= 0.07 \times (1{,}000)^{2/3}\ \text{g} \\ &= 0.07 \times (99.54)\ \text{g} \\ &= 6.97\ \text{g} \end{aligned}$$ [11]

But the actual brain weight is 24 g, and therefore the monkey has a brain which exceeds the predicted weight by the ratio 24/6.97 = 3.44. Jerison used the ratio of the actual brain weight to the predicted weight as an index to the relative development of the brain, calling the ratio the encephalization quotient. For our own species the encephalization quotient is about seven. It is about three for porpoise and dolphin , two for chimpanzee, just over one for the African elephant, and just under one for the lion. The encephalization quotient appears to be a useful index of relative brain size, and this in turn appears to give an indication of intellectual potential. Equipped with the endocast technique, and the encephalization quotient, we are now able to assess the behavioural potentials of dinosaurs and their contemporaries.

Is there any truth in the widely held belief that dinosaurs had such small brains that they were intellectually deficient? Jerison[12] estimated endocast volumes for a number of different dinosaurs, comparing these with the values predicted using equation 2. Encephalization quotients derived from these, and additional data, are given in a table. (Since the density of living animals is close to that of water, volume and mass can be used interchangeably.)

Before we discuss the implications of these results, it must be pointed out that the estimates of body and endocast volumes are only approximate. Furthermore, halving the endocast volume to obtain an estimate for the brain volume is a gross approximation that is probably the source of much error. The values obtained for the encephalization quotient can therefore serve only as a rough guide to the real situation.

Even by reptilian standards the giant sauropods *Brachiosaurus* and *Diplodocus*, the armoured dinosaur *Stegosaurus*, and the horned dinosaur *Triceratops* had very small brains. On the other hand *Stenonychosaurus*, a lightly built coelurosaur that was only about 2 m long, had a remarkably large brain. The remainder had brains that were typically reptilian in size. Dinosaurs, therefore, had a wide range of relative brain sizes.

What sort of behaviour might be expected of a dinosaur with a typically reptilian-sized brain? How limiting might this have

Brain and Body Relationships for Dinosaurs (Modified from Jerison, 1973)

Genus	*Estimated body volume (10^6ml)*	*Estimated endocast volume (ml)*	*Estimated brain volume (ml)*	*Predicted brain volume (ml)*	*Encephalization quotient*
*Diplodocus**	11.7	100	50	363	0.1
*Brachiosaurus**	87.0	309	154.5	1383	0.1
Triceratops	9.4	140	70	329	0.2
Stegosaurus	2.0	56	28	112	0.2
Protoceratops	0.2	30	15	24	0.6
Iguanodon	5.0	250	125	206	0.6
Camptosaurus	0.4	46	23	38	0.6
Anatosaurus	3.4	300	150	160	0.9
Tyrannosaurus†	7.7	530	265	288	0.9
Allosaurus	2.3	335	167.5	122	1.4
Stenonychosaurus††	0.045	49	49	9.2	5.3

* Hopson did not halve the endocast volume to obtain an estimate of the brain volume for the sauropods, on the grounds that the brain probably filled the cranial cavity. If he is correct, the values for their encephalization quotients should be doubled. Reference: Hopson, J.A., 1977. "Relative brain size and behavior in archosaurian reptiles," *Annual Review of Ecology and Systematics*, volume 8, pages 429–48.

† Osborn, H.F., 1912. "Crania of *Tyrannosaurus* and *Allosaurus*," *Memoirs of the American Museum of Natural History*, volume 1, pages 1–30.

†† It appears that the brain of *Stenonychosaurus* filled the cranium, as it does in birds and mammals. Therefore, the estimated brain volume is taken as the volume of the endocast. Data derived from: Russell, D.A., 1969. "A new species of *Stenonychosaurus* from the Oldman Formation (Cretaceous) of Alberta," *Canadian Journal of Earth Sciences*, volume 6, pages 595–612.

been to the complexity of its life style? Was such a dinosaur doomed to the life of a simpleton? We will never have answers to these questions but can make an educated guess based upon knowledge of living reptiles. The closest reptilian relatives of the dinosaurs are the crocodiles, and these are a logical group upon which to model our ideas of dinosaurian behaviour. A digression into the world of crocodiles will therefore provide a useful insight into the lives of large reptiles.

Crocodiles have traditionally been pictured as relatively inactive animals, which spend most of their lives basking on sun-baked river banks or floating like logs in the water. However, observations on the Nile crocodile[13] made over a period of several years have shown that this interpretation is erroneous and that crocodiles have a varied repetoire of complex and often social behavioural patterns. Crocodiles frequently capture large prey, which they dismember by seizing and jerking movements, sometimes twisting their whole body over and over in the water until a suitable piece is torn off. Sometimes the carcass is too awkward for one crocodile, and the assistance of a second is obtained. The second crocodile holds the carcass still while the first rotates, or they may both rotate in opposite directions. Each individual swallows the parts it rips off, without any indication of aggression towards the other. In early spring, when river levels are rising, subadults (individuals that are not yet fully mature) often co-operate in catching fish by forming a semicircle around the mouth of channels that are being flooded. Each individual keeps its own station, even though it might mean losing a fish to its neighbour, and there is no fighting over the fish.

Male crocodiles reach sexual maturity after 12 to 15 years, and the competition for females results in the establishment of a hierarchial system similar to that of many species of birds and mammals. Males participate in ritualized displays of aggression, and, if a defeated male is too slow in his retreat, he is able to appease the victor by a submissive gesture in which the vulnerable throat region is exposed. A similar submissive gesture is seen in a number of mammals, including wolves. Once pairing has taken place, it appears, partners remain together for a long time. Copulation only occurs after an elaborate courtship ritual, and the female deposits the eggs into a burrow excavated in the river bank. When all the eggs have been laid (up to 80) the burrow is covered up, and she then begins a vigil of guard duty that lasts for about three months. She apparently does not feed during this period and, although the male remains in the vicinity, making occasional visits, he does not approach the nest. A most remarkable event now occurs. The young crocodiles, which are still inside their eggs and buried beneath almost half a metre of soil, begin to call. The sounds are apparently loud enough to be heard from a distance of 20 m, and the female responds by uncovering the nest. Using the same great jaws that can dismember a carcass, she gently picks up the hatchlings, carrying them to the water where they are washed and allowed to swim to shore. At this time the male returns to the nest, and he may help to carry the hatchlings to the water. Sometimes a youngster has difficulty in breaking through the egg, in which case it will be taken into an adult's mouth and rolled back and forth until the shell breaks. The hatchlings are looked after for about two months, after which time they leave the parents and, joining up with other youngsters, dig communal burrows in the river bank where they can retreat from danger. They live in this secluded environment for about five years. If the crocodile, with its typically reptilian brain, is capable of such complex behavioural patterns, there is no reason to suppose that dinosaurs with similarly developed brains should have led less complex lives. But what about those dinosaurs, such as the sauropods, that had such small brains?

As we saw in Chapters 5 and 6, there is evidence that the sauropods were slow-moving, and this interpretation fits well with the small size of their brain. *Stegosaurus* and *Triceratops* also had very small brains, were heavily built, and had skeletal features that suggest a fairly ponderous gait. We may visualize these two plant-eaters as leading fairly unhurried and perhaps relatively uncomplicated lives.

Stegosaurus, and several other dinosaurs have been credited, facetiously, with having two brains:

Behold the mighty dinosaur,
Famous in prehistoric lore,
Not only for his power and strength
But for his intellectual length.
You will observe by these remains
The creature had two sets of brains-
One in his head (the usual place),
The other at his spinal base.
No problem bothered him a bit
He made both head and tail of it.
If something slipped his forward mind
'Twas rescued by the one behind.
And if in error he was caught
He had a saving afterthought.
Thus he could think without congestion
Upon both sides of every question.

(excerpt from a poem by B.L. Taylor)

Bizarre as these lines may sound, there is an element of truth in them. Dinosaurs, like all vertebrates, had only one brain, but the spinal cord, the large nerve trunk running from the base of the brain to the tail, was considerably dilated in the sacral region. We know this because the neural canal (the bony arch that surmounts each vertebra and provides a passageway for the spinal cord) is considerably expanded in the sacral vertebrae. Adjacent vertebrae are partially fused together, forming a bony cavity that has a volume about 20 times that of the endocast. All tetrapods have a spinal enlargement in the sacral region[14] (and another in the shoulder region), but it is unusual for it to be as big as it is in some dinosaurs.

The significance of this enlargement becomes apparent when the role of the spinal cord is considered. When an animal moves its limbs or its tail, the actions are not solely controlled by the brain—the spinal cord serves as a local centre of co-ordination. We have all experienced touching something hot or treading on a pin, and seeing the affected limb withdraw automatically, even before we are aware of what has happened.

Such automatic responses, termed reflex actions, involve three sets of nerves: sensory nerves, which transmit impulses from the limb to the spinal cord, motor nerves, which transmit impulses from the spinal cord to the muscles of the limb, and

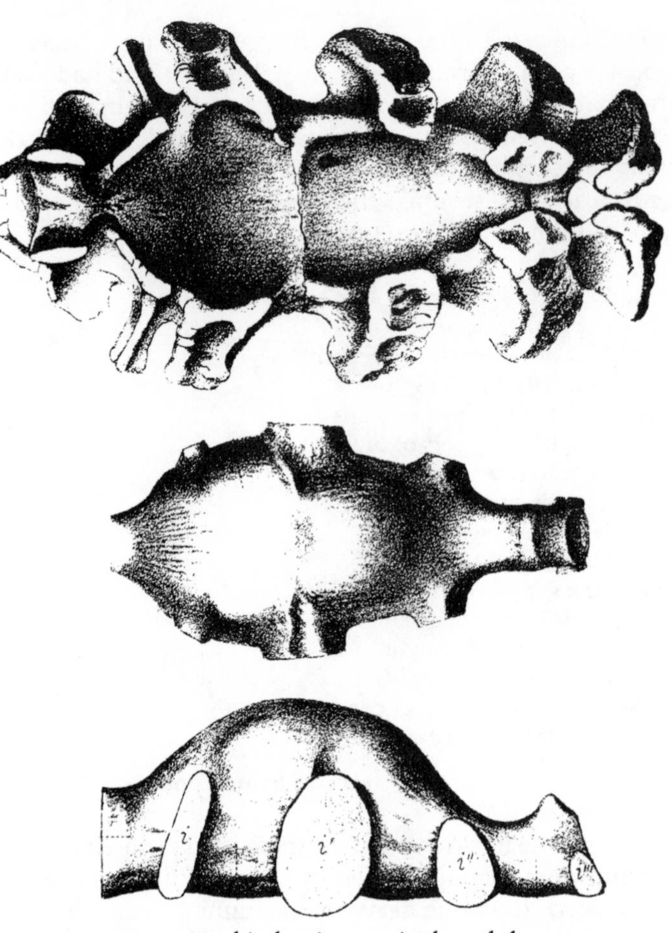

Stegosaurus *was unusual in having a spinal cord that was considerably enlarged in the sacral region. This is revealed by the expanded neural arches in the sacral vertebrae, which form a large chamber (top). An internal cast gives an approximate idea of the shape of the spinal enlargement (middle—dorsal view; bottom—lateral view).*

relay nerves, which link these two sets of nerves together. Dinosaurs are characterized by their enormous hind limbs and long tails. *Stegosaurus* had the additional complication of having a spiked tail, probably used as a weapon of defence, and sauropods such as *Diplodocus*, had a tail that was half the length of its entire body. There was, therefore, a need for considerable neuro-muscular control, which in turn required large numbers of sensory, motor, and relay nerves, and the spinal cord was accordingly enlarged to accommodate them.

At the other end of the scale from these lumbering giants, both in stature and brain development, were the coelurosaurs. This group of small, lightly-built dinosaurs, which includes *Ornithomimus* and *Stenonychosaurus*, were the intellectually élite among the dinosaurs. *Stenonychosaurus* had an encephalization quotient of 5.3, which is probably higher than that of any other dinosaur and even exceeds that of the earliest known bird, *Archaeopteryx*. This interesting little dinosaur, from the Late Cretaceous of western North America, is unusual for its enormous orbits, which are directed forwards, suggesting that it possessed very large eyes with well-developed binocular vision. Remains of its skeleton are fairly fragmentary, but it was obviously fairly small, perhaps about 2 m long, and lightly built. The hind limbs appear to have been fairly long and slender, and its well-developed grasping hands suggest a predatory mode of life. Perhaps it preyed on large insects, small reptiles, and mammals.[15]

The intellectual potentials of the dinosaurs, therefore, may well have covered a broad spectrum, but how did they compare with other Mesozoic vertebrates? Unfortunately our knowledge of the brain structure of the contemporaries of the dinosaurs is scanty. We have some information for the pterosaurs, for *Archaeopteryx* and for the ichthyosaurs, and also for the early mammals. The pterosaurs (flying reptiles), like all flying animals, were subject to a high selection pressure for reduction in weight, and the bones were thin and light. As a consequence, the bones of the cranium were thin and conformed closely to the contours of the brain. Endocasts taken from pterosaurs look brain-like, as they do for birds and mammals, and the volume of the cast probably corresponds closely to the volume of the actual brain. The pterosaurian brain, perhaps not surprisingly, had a distinctly avian appearance, with well-developed cerebral hemispheres, a prominent cerebellum, and fairly large optic lobes. These features suggest high levels of body co-ordination and balance, essential prerequisites for flight. The large optic lobe correlates with the large orbit and sclerotic ring, both of which indicate the possession of a large eye. Estimates of the encephalization quotient are difficult to make, not because of problems of estimating the volume of the brain but because of the difficulty of obtaining a reliable estimate of the weight of the body. The evidence suggests that the brain was of the reptilian order of size, contrasting with the brain of birds, which is relatively much larger.

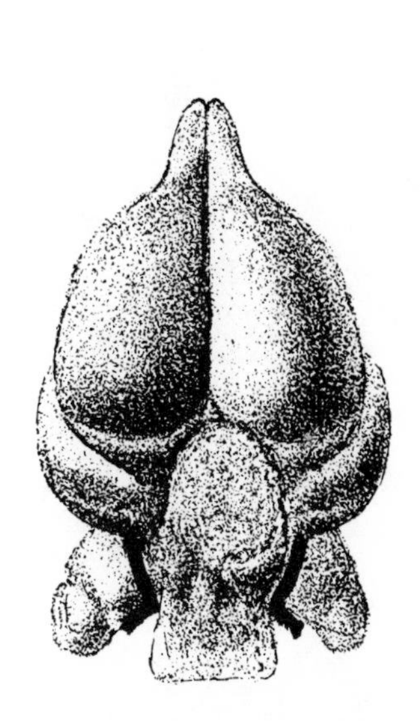

A natural endocast of the pterosaur **Scaphognathus**. *The appearance is remarkably avian, with large, smooth, cerebral hemispheres, large optic lobes, and a prominent cerebellum.*

Archaeopteryx, the earliest known bird, lived during the late Jurassic Period, and is the only Mesozoic bird with reliable endocast data.[16] The natural endocast of the British Museum specimen, mentioned earlier, reveals a typically avian organization, with fairly large but unconvoluted cerebral hemispheres, a well-developed cerebellum, and moderately well-developed optic lobes. Estimates for the volume of the brain[17] are not so problematic as those for the weight of the body, and there is considerable disagreement among specialists regarding the latter. By reptilian standards, *Archaeopteryx* clearly had a large brain, and its relative size was probably intermediate between those of reptiles and those of modern birds and mammals. There is some evidence that brain enlargement was not completed during the evolutionary history of the birds until after the close of the Mesozoic era.[18]

We have but a single endocast for the ichthyosaurs but this is only partial so that our data is incomplete.[19] The evidence suggests a well-developed cerebellum, very large optic lobes, moderate cerebral hemispheres, and fairly well-developed olfactory bulbs. These features suggest that sight was an important sense, and this is supported by the evidence for enormously large eyes. Olfaction was probably also important, which contrasts with the condition in the members of the order Cetacea (whales and dolphins), which have lost their olfactory bulbs and, presumably, their sense of smell.

While the primary concern of this book is not the reptiles of the Mesozoic, to look at what was happening with the Mesozoic mammals, the group that inherited the Earth after the demise of the reptiles, is of great interest. Compared with the quantities of reptilian material that have been recovered from Mesozoic deposits, the remains of Mesozoic mammals are relatively scarce and largely fragmentary. The mammals at that time were fairly small animals. Most were the size of rats and mice, and the largest were no bigger than a domestic cat. They may well have been numerous, but, because of their small size and because many of them (apparently) lived in forested areas, which are notoriously poor for the preservation of fossils, our knowlege of them is far from complete. The ancestors of these early mammals, were a group of reptiles, the mammal-like reptiles, which themselves possessed some mammalian characteristics. In terms of their relative brain size, however, most members of this ancestral group were typically reptilian, and one of the major events in the evolutionary history of the mammals was a marked increase in relative brain size. By present-day mammalian standards Mesozoic mammals were not particularly well endowed with grey matter, their encephalization quotients being in the vicinity of one-half, but compared with reptilian contemporaries of similar size they had very large brains. We might infer from this that they were intellectually superior to the dinosaurs and other reptiles, but this is nothing more than a suggestion for which we have no supporting evidence.

This raises the question of why mammals remained in relative obscurity throughout the Mesozoic Era. In attempting to answer this question, we have to consider the possible circumstances under which natural selection might have favoured the evolution of large brains. The earliest mammals did not appear in the fossil record until the late Triassic, at which time reptiles already had firm footholds in a wide diversity of niches, on the land, in the air, and in the water. It is believed that most of the Mesozoic reptiles were diurnal, that is, active during the daytime and relatively inactive at night, just like most modern reptiles and birds.[20] The nocturnal habitat was therefore virtually unoccupied by reptiles, and it has been suggested that the mammals evolved from their reptilian ancestors as creatures of the night.[21] According to this view, natural selection would favour those primitive mammals that possessed features giving them improved survival chances in the nocturnal world, and many mammalian features can be recognized as nocturnal adaptations.

One of the requirements of nocturnal life is the ability to find one's way around in darkness, and under these conditions acute hearing and a keen sense of smell may be more useful than good eyesight. The mammalian ear is usually more sensitive than that of the reptile, and this is reflected in its increased complexity. An outer ear flap (the pinna) directs sound waves towards the ear-drum, and three small bones transmit these impulses, with amplification, to a receptor organ deep in the skull. Reptiles lack a pinna and have only a single bone to transmit vibrations from the ear-drum. Furthermore the receptor organ is usually less specialized and perhaps less sensitive.

It is perhaps difficult for us to appreciate the importance of a good sense of smell in direction-finding, because our own olfactory sense is so poor, but we have only to recall the way a dog will follow a scent, or the way lions purposefully stalk their prey from down wind, to realize that olfaction is important.

Eyes, of course, are not necessarily ineffective at night. Indeed, many nocturnal animals, including cats and owls, have very good night vision. Two types of light-receptor cells occur in the retina of the eye—rods and cones, adapted, respectively, for black-and-white and colour vision. Rods are about a thousand times more sensitive to light than cones. Animals with good night vision usually have only rod cells, and are therefore colour blind. The fact that most mammals are colour blind supports the argument that they had a nocturnal ancestry.[22]

The ability to locate objects using the ears and the nose requires a high level of integration of nervous impulses from these organs, and this apparently requires an enlarged brain.[23] It has therefore been suggested that the increase in brain size during the evolutionary history of the mammals was correlated with an increased sensitivity to sound and smell, and that these changes occurred under nocturnal conditions. The ability to maintain a warm and fairly constant body temperature in the absence of the sun would also appear to be of considerable importance to nocturnal animals, although there are some nocturnal ectotherms (rattlesnakes, for example). A case has therefore been made that endothermy evolved in mammals as an adaptation to nocturnal life.[24]

The concept that early mammals were nocturnal has considerable merit, because it would explain why they existed in relative obscurity throughout the Mesozoic Era. If most mammals were nocturnal and most reptiles diurnal, the two would not have been in direct competition. With the demise of the reptilian empire at the end of the Mesozoic, the mammals were free to invade the diurnal niches vacated by the reptiles, and they then underwent an explosive diversification. The new age was an age of mammals.

8 The Fish-Lizards

A Jurassic lagoon, from Hawkin's book of Sea Dragons. Notice that ichthyosaurs have been given a straight tail and a predilection for sunbathing.

English summers are invariably wet, and 1833 was no exception. "Deluges of rain—deluge upon deluge—floods by land, tempest at sea . . ." wrote Thomas Hawkins, an avid collector of fossils whose regular visits to fossil-rich localities of Dorset and Somerset brought him into contact with other worthies, including Mary Anning, the Reverend William Conybeare, Henry De la Beche, and the great Richard Owen.[1] By his unsparing efforts he built up a major collection of ichthyosaurs that can still be seen in the British Museum (Natural History) in London. His enthusiasm for collecting might be better described as an obsession, and the actions of this eccentric Englishman, who dined on peacock eggs each morning, must have been a constant source of wonder to those around him.[2] His exploits are vividly brought back to life in the folio-sized pages of his book, *Memoirs of Ichthyosauri and Plesiosauri*, and the companion volume, *The Book of the Great Sea Dragons*.

Let us join Thomas Hawkins in that wet summer of 1833.[3] He has just called at the home of a collector in Dorset.

"Have ye sid my animal sir," said the fossilist Jonas Wishcombe of Charmouth as I called at his house in August to enquire if he had anything worth buying;—

"I should like vor yer honor sir to see 'un." My heart leaped to my lips—"animal! animal! where!"

"Can't be sid to day sir—the tide's in."

"What—nonsense! I *must* instantly—come, come along."

"Can't see 'un now yer honor—the tide's rolling atop o' 'un fifty feet high."

"In marl or stone?"

"Why in beautiful ma-arl—and—

"Washed to death"—and I threw myself in despair upon a chair. . . .

Wishcombe could not persuade me that it was at all possible for a fragile delicate saurian remain to continue unharmed beneath the tremendous breakers which I but too well knew were at that moment wildly careering over the spot where he said it was situated. My vexation had no limits until I half persuaded myself that the fellow was making jest of me, but he assured me that all he said was identical fact. . . .

We determine therefore to be on the beach next day at the hour of low-water, if by hap we might then snatch a glance at the buried saurus. All we could expect was but a glance as it lay upon the very verge of the lowest low-water mark and was left dry only when a stiff off-land breeze assisted the equinoctial tide.

The weather-cock looked the right way as we descended the execrable path by which the good people of Lyme are content to wade to the sea-shore between their delightful town and the pleasant village of Charmouth. . . .

"Do ye see that tuff o' sea-weed just tipping up there yer honor; he's there about."

"There, there, don't ye see the weed sir in the hollow o' them there waves."

Jonas, who thus addressed me, in his anxiety to point me out the spot had advanced shoe deep—in a moment the returning brine drenches him to the knees. . . .

The surges fail from the sloping shore—they are fainter—fainter—Wishcombe rushes amongst the shallows, laves them with a furze-bush [gorse] provided for the occasion—"Here, here yer honor"—the object of my Egyptian-like idolatry, the adored lizard is at my feet. . . .

Jonas gladly sells me the right to the skeleton, of which I have heard he had known many months, while no opportunity presented him for its extrication. He chuckled when I gave him a guinea earnest-money, convinced that he had made brave of a discovery that no one could render useful—that his ill-fortune must be mine too.

"Yer honor, sir, 'ill be here to-morrow at low-tide."

"Aye, and Jonas—bring as many men and tools to help as you think proper."

"You will never get that animal," said Miss Anning, as we made our devious way towards Lyme through the mist and flashing spray, "or if you do, *per-chance*, it cannot be saved."

My eyes glare upon the intellectual countenance before me,—the words of those lips were I knew oracular as those of a Pythoness and my heart fainted within me.

She saw my change of blood and stopped—"because the marl, full of pyrites, falls to pieces as soon as dry."

I revive—"that I can prevent."

"Can you."

I lay upon a thorny pillow listening the livelong night to the rumbling gale . . . but the day breaks and—the wind's the wrong way, south-west.

Hawkins probably dispensed with his customary breakfast of peacock eggs, dressed hurriedly, and made his way through the streets of the waking town. A glance at the weathercock confirmed his worst suspicion; strong onshore winds were blowing, piling the heavy seas high upon his precious ichthyosaur. There was absolutely no chance of recovering the specimen. The wind continued to blow from the southwest for the next three weeks. Disappointment and frustration gave way to a mood of black despair. Then one morning he awoke to find that the wind had changed direction.

The weather had veered to the right quarter at last and if it continued a few hours I might accomplish my long deferred hope;—all my friends congratulate me.

"Make haste; the tides going out fast" said Miss Anning as I passed her on the way to the Chiropolyostinus [Hawkins' name for this particular ichthyosaur]. I seize this opportunity of thanking her for the brief exhortation; it secured me the saurus that same day. Really the tide seemed to gallop away!

Half a dozen of us—all lusty and eager for the occasion—meet; we arrange the mode of exhumation, dispose our instruments and wait the crisis when the retreating waves shall desert the remain.

It arrives. "Let no one invade this"—a square marked around the skeleton in the marl, six feet and a half by three feet and a half.

"What d'ye think zir to dig 'un out whool," exclaimed the Atlaean Blue—the best tempered but unhappily Bacchanal fellow that ever lived.

"Yes."

The tide goes back—back—back—our square is cut ten inches thick: I lessen its length and breadth a foot: "the crow-bars and pick-axes to loosen it from its bed:—now my boys—now—now; does it come in one piece?"

"Eas."

The spectators say the tide flows—it does: we attempt to raise the heavy mass upon its side but—our strength fail us, 'tis more than we can accomplish . . . . other gentlemen . . . came to our help . . . we at length effected it . . . .

The tide flows fast.— We try to lift it into the vehicle prepared for its transport from the reach of danger—we cannot. "You must break 'un in half sir."

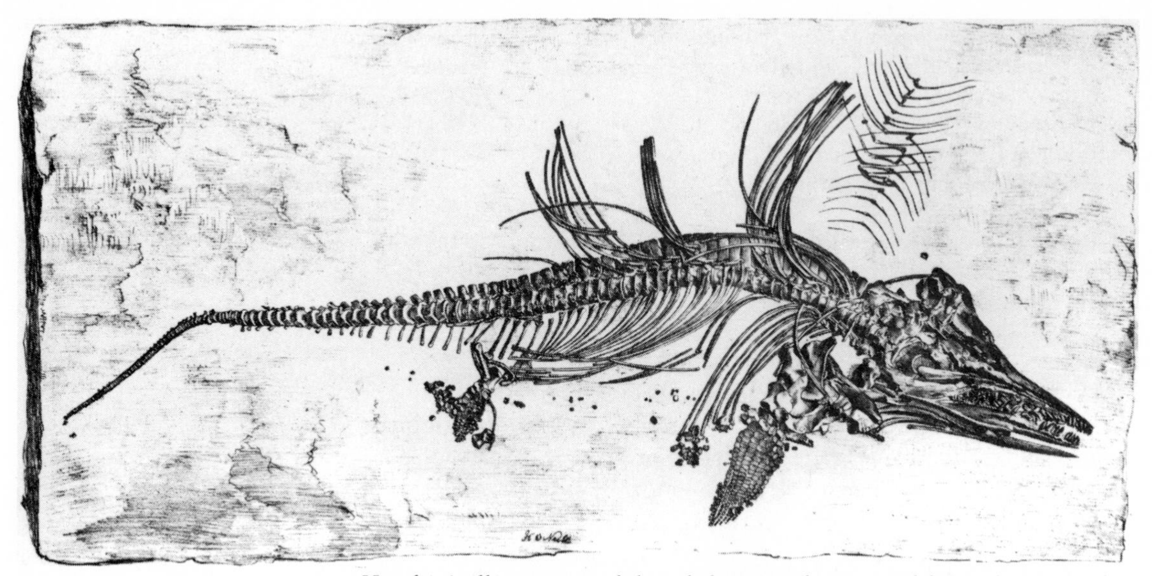

Hawkin's illustration of the ichthyosaur he rescued from the sea in the summer of 1833. The skeleton, which is almost 2 metres long, is now in the British Museum (Natural History), London.

> "No." The waters approach us—they make a breach in the rude bank cast up by us against them—another, and another—another, they are at our heels: "one more trial my boys, your own reward if successful—ye-o; "—the saurus is safe.

Hawkins worked on the specimen well into the fall. Using a hammer and chisel, he laboriously removed all the matrix that covered the skeleton, but it was a labour of love. As Mary Anning had predicted, the marl cracked and crumbled as it dried, but liberal use of plaster of Paris kept the specimen intact. Hawkins was hardly surprised that Mary Anning should have been right, because this remarkable woman knew more about fossils than most other collectors. Her outstanding accomplishments as a collector of fossils had earned her the highest respect of the palaeontological fraternity, and all serious visitors to this geological haven paid their respects at her curiosity shop in the town of Lyme Regis.

Born in Lyme Regis in 1799, Mary Anning was only six years old when Nelson defeated the French at the Battle of Trafalgar. Her father, Richard, was a cabinet maker and had a small workshop in the town. At that time Lyme Regis was a major sea port as well as a thriving holiday resort for the well-to-do. The summer months brought many visitors through its narrow, winding streets, and Richard Anning supplemented his income by selling them fossils he had collected from the cliffs along the seashore between Lyme Regis and Charmouth. He was often accompanied on his collecting forays by Mary and her older brother, Joseph. He taught them how and where to look for fossils, and his daughter proved to be a particularly talented pupil. Richard Anning did not enjoy good health, and perhaps some premonition of the future spurred him to teach his children how to earn a living as fossil collectors. He died in 1810, leaving a widow and two children who were entirely dependent upon the meagre earnings of Joseph, who worked in a local furniture shop. Economic necessity forced Mary into becoming a professional fossilist at the tender age of 11, and the money she earned made a significant contribution to the family budget.

The first major discovery that involved her was made towards the end of the year of her father's death, although the date is in some doubt.[4] The specimen in question was an enormous skull with parts of a pectoral girdle and a number of vertebrae, now located in the British Museum (Natural History) in London. The specimen was apparently found and partly collected by her brother late in 1810, and she collected the remainder the following year. The skull was sold for £23 to Henry Host Henley, owner of the land upon which it had been found. This was an impressive sum of money at that time, and a small fortune to the Annings. Henley, in turn, donated or sold the specimen to William Bullock, entrepreneur and owner of the Egyptian Temple, a private museum in London's fashionable Piccadilly. Although the skull was mentioned in the 1814 edition of the museum's catalogue, it was not listed in the sale catalogue that was published in 1819 when Bullock auctioned his entire collection. Several lots were purchased by the British Museum (Natural History), but there is no record of the skull having been among these. It is therefore not known when, or how, the British Museum (Natural History) obtained the specimen.

This was not the first ichthyosaur to be found (an imperfect skeleton had been discovered in 1803, and examined by Sir Everard Home in 1818, but disappeared soon afterwards[5]) but it was the first to be adequately described and recognized as being new to science. Mary Anning's place in history was assured, but this was only the beginning of an outstanding career. In 1821 she discovered the remains of another new animal, for which the name plesiosaur was coined, and in 1828 she collected Britain's first pterosaur. Mary Anning never married, and she was tragically struck down in her middle years by a fatal illness. A stained glass window in the church of Lyme Regis is dedicated to her memory.

The scientific community was no doubt anxious to examine Mary Anning's first discovery, and Sir Everard Home of the Royal College of Surgeons was privileged to study this impressive skull. Home, who published his first account of the specimen in 1814,[6] was initially impressed by its resemblance to a crocodile, and this led him to the premature conclusion that it was a new species of that reptilian group. However, when he

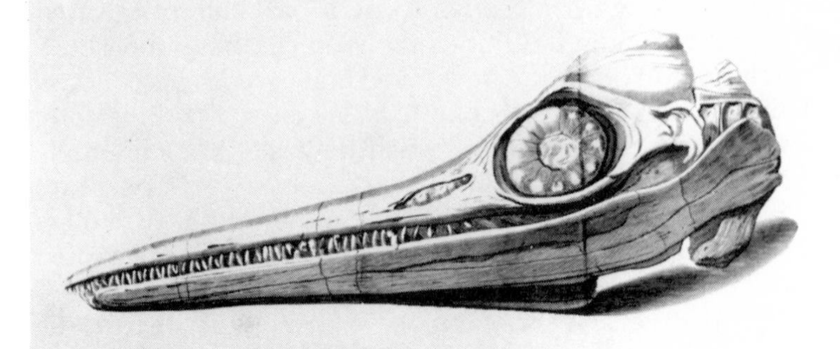

This ichthyosaur skull, which is well over one metre long, was collected by Mary Anning in 1811, and subsequently described as a new animal by Sir Everard Home in 1814. Specimen in the British Museum (Natural History), London.

examined the vertebrae he found that the centra had hollows on both the anterior and the posterior surfaces, a condition hitherto found only in fishes. He therefore concluded that the new discovery belonged in the same class as the fishes. But he said, "I by no means consider it as wholly a fish," and he believed that it formed a connecting link with the crocodiles.

Home wrestled with the problem for the next five years. He wavered between considering it to be allied to the fishes, and believing it to be an air-breathing animal. He finally concluded that it was intermediate between the lizards and the amphibians of the salamander type.[7] The amphibian that seemed to be most closely related to the new fossil was the genus *Proteus*, and he therefore coined the name *Proteosaurus*. He noted, however, that other specialists had proposed the name *Ichthyosaurus*, to reflect its resemblance to fishes and reptiles, and it is this name that came to be accepted.[8]

Although it was Home who first brought this group of animals to the attention of the scientific community, his contribution to our knowledge was not as significant as those of several other authorities. Sir Richard Owen, one of the greatest anatomists of all times, made the most disparaging remarks about Home's contribution. Writing in 1881, during the autumn years of his life and long after Home's death, Owen commented that the beautiful drawings by William Clift (Owen's father-in-law) that appeared in Home's papers "enabled contemporary investigators, more capable than Home in determining the true nature and affinities of the fossils, to contribute a durable and rich accession to their science."[9] The contemporary investigators referred to were primarily Sir Henry De la Beche and the Reverend William Conybeare, both of whom made important contributions in the 1820s to our knowledge of ichthyosaurs. But they had far more material at their disposal than Home did, and Owen's remarks therefore appear to be unwarranted.

When we look into the lives of Owen and Home, however, we discover the reasons for Owen's scathing criticism. We also find evidence of fraud and gross professional misconduct.

Owen studied medicine at the University of Edinburgh and graduated in anatomy and medicine in 1824, at the age of 20. He spent the next two years at the Royal College of Surgeons, in London, where his outstanding abilities in dissection were soon recognized by its president, Professor John Abernethy. He obtained his membership of the Royal College of Surgeons on August 18, 1826, and his diploma was signed by a number of his teachers, including Sir Everard Home.

Owen set himself up as a medical practitioner in London and Professor Abernethy offered him a part-time post at the college to "fill in his leisure time." His duties were to assist William Clift, the conservator of a collection of natural history specimens that had been purchased by the government and placed in the care of the college. The collection had been made by John Hunter, a pioneer surgeon and naturalist, who had died in 1793. Clift, a former student of Hunter's, was well liked and respected by Owen, and the two got on together famously. Clift had a daughter, Caroline, with whom Owen fell in love. They were married in 1835 after a long engagement during which Owen worked hard to improve his financial prospects. He was appalled by the failings of the previous curator, who had not even produced a catalogue of the specimens during his 25 years in office. This curator was Sir Everard Home.

When Hunter died he left a large number of unpublished manuscripts in the safekeeping of his executor, but these mysteriously disappeared soon afterwards. It was later discovered that the executor had committed these valuable papers to the flames. The executor was Hunter's brother-in-law, Sir Everard Home. Now Sir Everard, who is said to have had only a modest scientific ability, was the author of a number of scientific publications, and the suspicion naturally grew that he had plagiarized Hunter, then destroyed the evidence.[10] Unbeknown to Home, Clift, who was Hunter's assistant as well as his favourite pupil, had copied out the manuscripts and kept the copies tucked away. Towards the end of his life he handed these over to Owen, now his son-in-law, who published them in 1861.[11] Little wonder that Owen was so harsh in his criticisms of Home's writings on the ichthyosaurs.

During the 1820's, the studies of Conybeare and De la Beche established that ichthyosaurs were marine reptiles, and several different species were recognized and described.[12] Most of the specimens studied were from the Lower Jurassic deposits of Dorset and Somerset, and many had been collected by Mary

Anning and Thomas Hawkins. Ichthyosaurs were also being collected on the Continent, notably in southern Germany, and by 1840, when Owen began taking an interest in them, a reasonable number of specimens had accumulated. Owen, the revered and well-travelled ambassador of British science, had the additional advantage of having studied the German material, and he published two accounts of ichthyosaurs in 1840.[13] One of the features that interested him was the apparent dislocation of the tail, as shown in many skeletons by an abrupt downturn of the vertebral column, about two-thirds of the way along its length. He correctly surmised that this indicated some sort of tail fin, but erroneously supposed that the abrupt bend was a post-mortem effect, possibly brought about by a contraction of a tail ligament. Owen therefore believed that the vertebral column was essentially straight in life.

Although ichthyosaurs had always been recognized as being marine animals, it was believed that they used to haul themselves up on land, like seals. Nineteenth-century restorations of ichthyosaurs frequently depict them basking on rocks, and this is the pose Owen selected for the life-sized models that were built in the grounds of the Crystal Palace, in the London suburb of Sydenham.

The Crystal Palace, an impressive edifice in iron and glass, was originally erected in 1851 in Hyde Park, London, to house the Great Exhibition. This Victorian extravaganza in celebration of science and technology was organized by the Prince Consort, and Owen was one of his many advisers. When the Crystal Palace was relocated in Sydenham, Owen supervised the reconstruction of a number of extinct animals to adorn the grounds. Completion of the models was celebrated, with typical Victorian eccentricity, at a banquet held inside the hollow body of the dinosaur *Iguanodon*. Twenty-one gentlemen were accommodated within the beast, with another seven seated at a side table.

The straight-tailed, rock-basking image of ichthyosaurs prevailed until about the time of Owen's death, when some unusual specimens were discovered in southern Germany. These specimens were exceptional in that the body outline was preserved as a thin film of carbon. Quite clearly, the tail bend was a natural feature and formed the lower lobe of a deep and crescentic tail fin. This new information was difficult to reconcile with the idea that these animals hauled themselves up on land. Not only was it difficult to visualize such a deep-bodied animal balancing itself on its belly, but the tail would have got in the way. But old ideas die hard, and this one lingered on for many more years.

The quarries of southern Germany have been worked for slate for several hundred years,[14] and ichthyosaur remains had almost certainly been found long before the time of Mary Anning, but their significance was not recognized. Once the importance of

The Crystal Palace. Three years after its erection in Hyde Park, to house the Great Exhibition of 1851, this wrought iron and glass edifice was relocated in the London suburb of Sydenham. It was destroyed by fire in 1936.

these discoveries was realized, however, the quarrymen became far more alert, because well-preserved specimens could be sold for relatively large sums of money. The number of ichthyosaurs recovered from the Holzmaden quarries far exceeds that from the quarries of southwestern England, and much of the material is more complete and better preserved. Large collections were built up, primarily in Germany, which became the new centre for research on ichthyosaurs.

The turn of the century and first half of this witnessed a proliferation of German publications, with major contributions by Professor Eberhard Fraas of the University of Munich, and, later, by Professor Friedrich von Huene of the University of Tübingen. Von Huene wrote extensively on many different fossil vertebrates, but ichthyosaurs were his first love, and he published more papers on them than any other palaeontologist. Von Huene was largely concerned with the interrelationships among the ichthyosaurs, especially the German species, and also with the relationships of ichthyosaurs with other reptiles. Other German palaeontologists interested themselves in interpreting the conditions under which the ichthyosaurs became preserved. As many of the German specimens were remarkably well preserved, a considerable amount of information was obtained from these studies.

While the ichthyosaurs were fairly popular during Victorian times, they never captured the popular imagination in the same way that dinosaurs did, and this may have been because most of them were of only moderate size. They are, however, among the best-known fossil vertebrates and provided us with a wealth of palaeontological information. They also give us an insight into life in the Mesozoic seas, as we shall soon discover. Before getting our feet wet, however, it would be useful to look at their distribution in space and time, and this will also give us an overview of their diversity.

Ichthyosaurs first appear in the fossil record in the Lower Triassic, and they extend all the way to the end of the Cretaceous, a period of some 150 million years.[15] Our knowledge of the group, however, is rather patchy, both because of the vagaries of preservation and because good exposures of sedimentary rocks are uncommon. We therefore catch only glimpses of their evolutionary history, as if viewed through a series of rents in a curtain. Each glimpse, represented by a single fossil locality, spans but an instant of geological time and covers the smallest speck on the globe. Some glimpses are more revealing than others, and we get our first good view in the Middle Triassic exposures of southern Switzerland, and another glimpse shortly afterwards in the Upper Triassic of neighbouring northern Italy. Numerous well-preserved skeletons have been found in both localities, and almost all of them belong to a single species, *Mixosaurus cornalianus*, which barely exceeded 1 m in length. The skeletons are beautifully preserved, some with traces of skin, and we can see that the tail is not downturned as it is in later ichthyosaurs. The fore and hind limbs were already modified as fins, but still retained the primitive five-fingered (pentadactyl) condition that is found in so many vertebrates, including ourselves. The fore fin is about twice the length of the hind fin, and both are broad. The slender rostrum is armed with numerous teeth, set in individual sockets as they are in several other reptilian groups. The anterior teeth are sharply pointed, but they become blunt and quite button-like towards the back of the jaws. In later ichthyosaurs the teeth lie in a continuous groove instead of being set in individual sockets, and there is no obvious distinction between sharp and blunt teeth.

Mixosaurus was one of the earliest and least specialized ichthyosaurs, and may be regarded as transitional between the fully terrestrial ancestor that gave rise to the group, and the highly specialized swimmers that appeared later in the fossil record. Ancestral (or primitive) features include the pentadactyl limb,

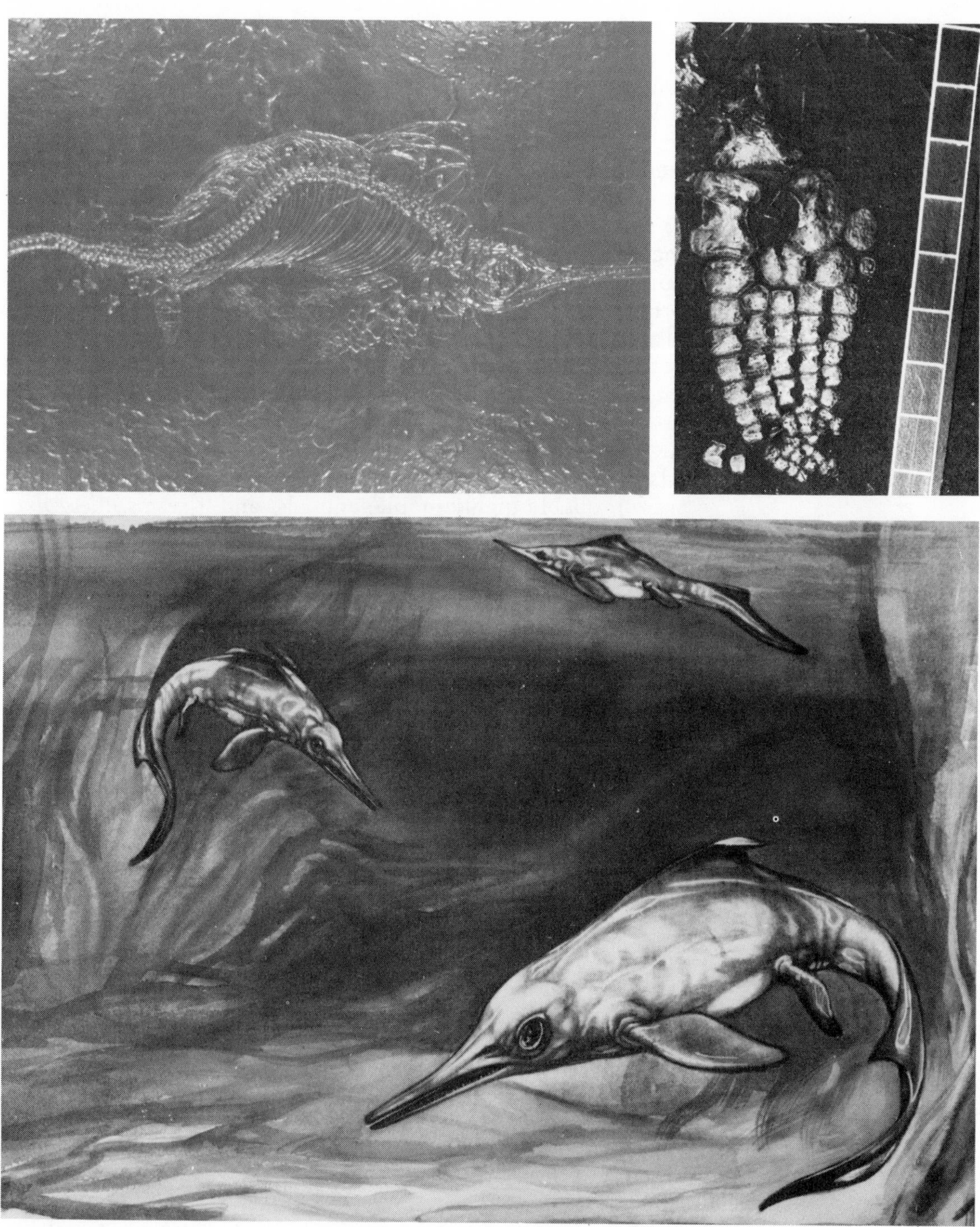

The small Triassic ichthyosaur **Mixosaurus** *retained the primitive straight tail (top) and pentadactyl limbs (right), but, as the restoration shows (bottom), the body was fish-like, and the eye large, as in later forms.*

straight tail, and socketed teeth; while the fins, enormous orbit, and streamlined body shape are advanced features associated with aquatic life.

We have so far been unable to identify the group from which the ichthyosaurs evolved, but this has not discouraged speculation, and most reptilian groups have been proposed at one time or another as the most likely ancestral stock. The Swiss palaeontologist Emil Kuhn-Schnyder, however, who believes that each major group of reptiles had an independent origin from the amphibians, proposed that the ichthyosaurs had an independent origin from primitive amphibians. This view has not been generally accepted.[16] Most of the specimens of *Mixosaurus* were collected from Switzerland and northern Italy, but the genus was much more widespread. It has been found in Spitzbergen, an arctic island group to the north of Norway, on Exmouth Island in the Canadian Arctic, in Alaska, China, and Nevada, and on the island of Timor in the Indonesian Archipelago. Ichthyosaurs were probably highly mobile animals, and it seems likely that they were widely distributed. (The reason why some species appear to be geographically restricted is probably because of the localized nature of good fossiliferous strata.[17]) *Mixosaurus* also had a wide geological range, spanning most of the Triassic, for a period of about 40 million years. The fact that it was such a small ichthyosaur (one of the smallest genera) could lead us to believe that the earliest ichthyosaurs were the smallest ones. This is not the case, however, because *Mixosaurus* shared its Triassic world with the largest of all the ichthyosaurs. These giants lived and died in the seas that once covered western North America, and to find out more about them we will visit their last resting place, Nevada.

Nevada is a vast and desolate state in the American southwest that gives the traveller a feeling of utter loneliness. Much of the land is dry and dusty and supports little vegetation besides cacti and other such desert plants. You can drive for hours and hours without seeing another car, and one of the few signs that man has ever ventured beyond the road are the barbed-wire fences which stretch for miles in places. These are marked by ominous warnings that the area is used for weapons testing. Travelling west on Highway 50 takes the traveller through the old silver-mining town of Austin, and a little farther west is a small sideroad that runs south. This road follows the course of the Reese River, which has carved a wide flat valley through the Shoshone Mountains. Fifty dusty miles down this road stands the tired little town of Ione, whose few wooden buildings have the aspect of a ghost town. A few miles beyond Ione and the road climbs into the foothills. Cactus and sagebrush give way to juniper and pinyon pine, and the tumbledown buildings of a real ghost town come into view. This was once the gold-mining town of Union, which sprang up during the gold rush of the 1860s and then was abandoned when the gold ran out. There are dozens of other ghost towns in this part of the West, but Union is unique because it stands within the boundaries of a singular park—Ichthyosaur State Park.

Ichthyosaurs were first found in Nevada during the latter half of the 19th century, but it was not until the beginning of the 20th century that an intensive collecting effort was made.[18] The central figure in these expeditions, from the University of California, was Annie Alexander, an enthusiastic and capable amateur. Her father, a pioneer of the Hawaiian sugar-cane industry, moved his family to California when Annie was 15. She completed her schooling at a public high school in Oakland. The Alexander family travelled extensively during this period, spending relatively little time in their Oakland home.

Nevada, in the American south-west, is a vast and desolate land comprising largely desert.

The winter of 1900 saw her parents enjoying the sunshine of India, but Annie preferred to stay in Oakland. To amuse herself she attended some lectures by Dr. John C. Merriam, assistant professor of palaeontology at the University of California at Berkeley. She soon became deeply interested in the subject, and her love for the outdoors led to her participation in a palaeontological field trip the next year. This was the first of many trips, and it was not long before she was organizing expeditions herself. Her sound financial position enabled her to sponsor these expeditions, to various parts of California and Nevada, and her continued generosity to the university led to the founding of the Museum of Paleontology at Berkeley, in 1921.

Since her early 20s she had suffered from eye problems, but this did not seem to affect her in the field. She collected hundreds of specimens, including ichthyosaurs that were new to science. One of these was named *Shastasaurus alexandrae* in her honour. Her contributions to palaeontology were considerable, and one is reminded of that other great woman, Mary Anning, who lived a century before her.

The most complete ichthyosaur material collected from Nevada during this period belongs to the species *Cymbospondylus petrinus*, which is represented by several specimens including an almost complete skeleton and a well-preserved skull.[19] This material, and much more, is in the Museum of Palaeontology at Berkeley. *Cymbospondylus petrinus* was a large and robustly-built animal which had an estimated length of 10 m, about the length of a killer whale *(Orcinus)*. The skull has a very long rostrum, armed with conical teeth that are all about the same size and shape, unlike those of *Mixosaurus*. Compared with the size of the skull, which is huge, the teeth are relatively small and do not extend farther back than the level of the external nares. The orbit is not set as far back as it is in *Mixosaurus*, and is relatively much smaller. An unusual feature of *Cymbospondy-*

View across the valley of the Reese River from Ichthyosaur State Park, Nevada.

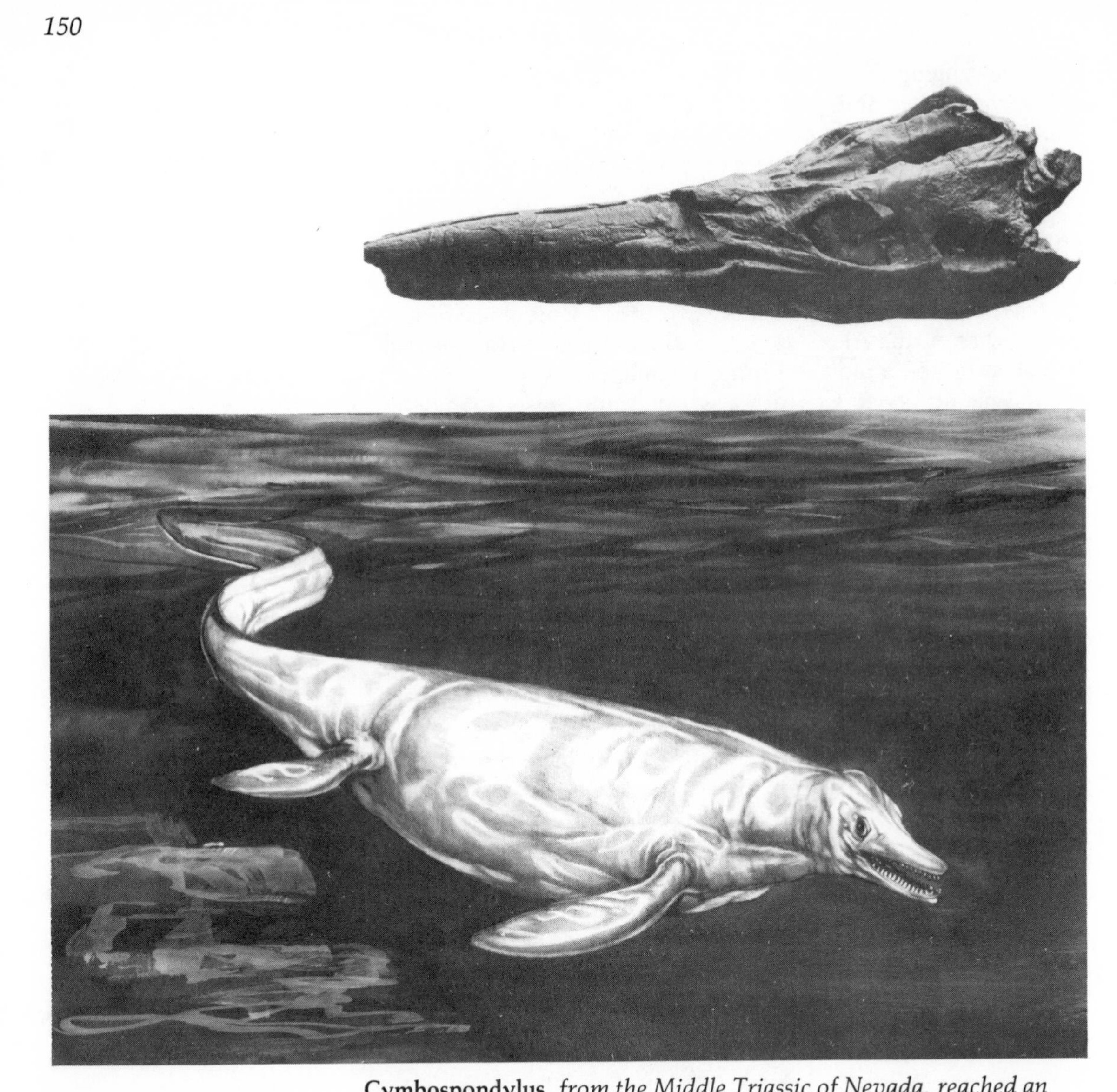

Cymbospondylus, *from the Middle Triassic of Nevada, reached an estimated length of 10m. The skull (top), which exceeds one metre in length, is armed with sharp teeth. The tail, which shows no evidence of a bend, may have been long and tapering as depicted in the restoration.*

lus is the crest on the top of the skull, at the level of the orbits. Another unusual feature, which is in fact unique, is that the occipital condyle, the knob at the back of the skull that articulates with the first neck vertebra, is concave rather than convex, as it is in all other ichthyosaurs and in most reptiles. It is unfortunate that the post-cranial skeleton is not as complete as the skull. The fore and hind fins are incomplete, but they appear to have been long and narrow, and of about equal size. The body was very long, with far more presacral vertebrae (the vertebrae between the skull and the pelvic girdle) than in any other ichthyosaur. It is not clear whether there was a definite tailbend, and we therefore do not know whether the animal had a well-developed caudal fin, but the evidence suggests that it probably did not. Until fairly recently *Cymbospondylus* was the best known of American Triassic ichthyosaurs, but excavations at Ichthyosaur State Park have unearthed a number of skeletons that belong to a new genus, one which was even larger than *Cymbospondylus*.

Ichthyosaur State Park came into being largely through the efforts of Professor Charles L. Camp, who was the director of the Museum of Paleontology at Berkeley. Fossils were first discovered in the area in 1928, and when Camp paid his first visit, in 1953, he was impressed by the richness of the site and staggered by the immense size of the ichthyosaur skeletons he found. This was unquestionably an important palaeontological area, but it also had the potential to be of considerable interest to the public. Some years previously, a rich dinosaur quarry in Utah had been developed as a visitor centre, and named the Dinosaur National Monument. Camp no doubt had this successful venture in mind when he discussed his ideas for an ichthyosaur park with authorities of the State of Nevada. He volunteered his services to develop the site and spent several summers there with his family and with students from the University of California. The remains of more than 30 ichthyosaurs were located, and a number of these were excavated for exhibition. A large building was erected over one of the quarries, to protect the skeletons from weathering and to provide visitors with a convenient facility for viewing the material.

The skeletons are Upper Triassic in age and therefore geologically younger than *Cymbospondylus*. While sharing some features with *Cymbospondylus*, these ichthyosaurs are obviously quite distinct, and Camp recognized them as being new to science. He accordingly erected a new genus group name, *Shonisaurus*, for these new ichthyosaurs, and recognized three distinct species within the genus.[20] The commonest species, *Shonisaurus popularis*, is represented by 37 individuals, but the other two species are based upon very little material. *Shonisaurus* is the largest of all ichthyosaurs, and reaches a length of 15 m, which is about half as large again as *Cymbospondylus*. The skeleton is robust, like that of *Cymbospondylus*, the individual bones being thick and heavily built. The fore fin and hind fin, which are of similar size, compare in length with the height of a man. Both are slender and have undergone reduction from the primitive five-fingered condition that typifies *Mixosaurus* and most other vertebrates. These fins were probably used to produce a propulsive thrust for swimming, and the pectoral and pelvic girdles to

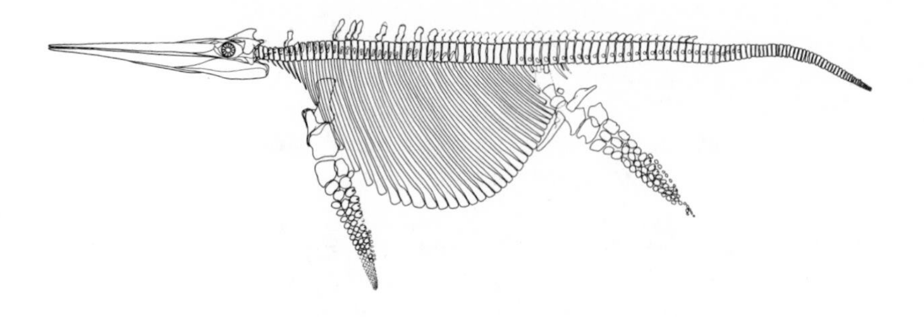

Camp's reconstruction of **Shonisaurus** *(Upper Triassic, Nevada). Reaching an estimated length of 15 m, this is the largest of all ichthyosaurs.*

which they were attached are substantial. *Shonisaurus* has fewer vertebrae than *Cymbospondylus*, and is in this respect more typical of the later ichthyosaurs. There are, for example, only 42 presacral vertebrae, compared with more than 60 in *Cymbospondylus*. There appears to have been a tailbend, but this is not very pronounced, suggesting that *Shonisaurus* probably had only a modest caudal fin. Although there are many skeletons, not one has a complete skull, and our knowledge of this region is based upon three incomplete specimens. As in *Cymbospondylus*, the rostrum is long and slender, the orbit is small and set not very far back along the length of the skull, and there is a median crest on the top of the skull. The teeth are set in sockets, which appears to be characteristic of almost all Triassic ichthyosaurs, and they are relatively small as in *Cymbospondylus*, but restricted to the front of the rostrum. The basioccipital condyle is convex, as it is in all other ichthyosaurs (except *Cymbospondylus*). An unusual feature of *Shonisaurus* is that the ends of the ribs are expanded, and this has not been seen in any other ichthyosaur.

During the excavations, Camp became aware of something most unusual: the majority of the skeletons were lying in the same direction. The skeletons that were close together were obviously lying parallel to one another, and compass bearings taken from the other skeletons showed that they, too, had the same north-south orientation. Camp concluded that the animals had probably been stranded on a sandbar, just as sometimes happens today with whales.

Strandings of whales are not rare, and every few years there are reports of a major stranding in some corner of the world, usually involving one of the smaller species. Strandings usually occur on remote beaches, but there have been a few eye-witness reports of schools of whales swimming towards shore, and many of them becoming beached. Attempts to save the stranded whales by towing them out to sea are usually unsuccessful because, when released, they tend to swim back to shore and beach themselves again.

Several explanations for whale strandings have been offered, and most of these involve the cetacean system of navigation. Cetaceans navigate by emitting short bursts of sound. The echoes, which bounce back from objects in the water, are received by the ears and analysed in the brain. It has been suggested that the gently shelving beaches that are so often associated with strandings in some way interfere with the echolocation mechanism, causing the animals to misjudge the depth of the water. Some stranded whales have been found to have diseased ears, which might explain their unusual behavior, but others have perfectly healthy ears. Whales are highly social animals, and it is possible that strandings are precipitated when a leader of a school accidentally runs aground. But this is purely speculative. We are a long way from understanding whale strandings, and even farther from understanding why those giant ichthyosaurs became stranded on a Nevadan sandbar all those millions of years ago.

The ichthyosaurs so far considered—*Mixosaurus, Cymbospondylus*, and *Shonisaurus*—are represented by relatively large amounts of material and are consequently well known, but the same is not true for the remaining Triassic genera: *Shastasaurus, Delphinosaurus, Merriamia*, and *Toretocnemus*. All four are from the Upper Triassic of California, and appear to have been dolphin-sized rather than whale-sized animals. *Shastasaurus*, the largest of the four, is robustly built, like *Cymbospondylus*, and reaches a length of between 4 and 5 m. The fore and hind fins are both incomplete, but appear to be narrow and had probably undergone reduction to three digits, as in *Cymbospondylus* and *Shonisaurus*. The next largest genus, *Delphinosaurus*, is between two and three metres long and is better known than *Shastasaurus*. The body proportions are similar to those of Jurassic ichthyosaurs, with about 45 presacral vertebrae and a distinct tailbend some distance behind the sacrum. The fore fin is not well preserved but is obviously narrow and appears to have only three digits; the hind fin is fragmentary. The remaining Triassic genera, *Merriamia* and *Toretocnemus*, are both small, only about the size of *Mixosaurus*, that is about 1 m long. *Merriamia*, the better-known genus, has narrow fore and hind fins, each with only three digits and remnants of a fourth. The hind fin is only about half the length of the fore fin, as it is in most Jurassic ichthyosaurs. From what remains of the skull, it seems that the teeth may have been set in an open groove rather than in individual sockets, and this again is typical of Jurassic forms. The teeth are sharply pointed and extend back to the level of the orbit, which contrasts with the condition in *Cymbospondylus* and *Shonisaurus*, and in this regard *Merriamia* is similar to *Mixosaurus*. There is little that can be said about *Toretocnemus* because the material is very incomplete. The fore and hind fins are both narrow and appear similar to those of *Merriamia*, but there is little difference in length between the two fins.

What conclusions can we draw from this wide, and perhaps confusing, array of Triassic ichthyosaurs? The first point is that early ichthyosaurs were not only highly specialized but were widely diversified. Consider the differences between the small and relatively short-bodied *Mixosaurus* with its wide fins and huge orbit, and the long-bodied giant *Cymbospondylus* with its narrow fins and relatively small orbit. A second point is that within each genus we can see some features that are primitive, that is, that are in a condition typical of many early reptiles, and some features that are advanced, that is, in a condition typical of some later ichthyosaurs. As we saw earlier the five-fingered fin of *Mixosaurus* is a primitive feature, because early reptiles have five fingers, whereas the enormous orbit is an advanced feature, few reptiles having such a large orbit relative to the length of the skull. This occurrence of primitive and advanced characters within the same animal is referred to as mosaic evolution. It shows us that some features change during the evolutionary history of a group, while others remain essentially unchanged. Mosaic evolution appears to be the rule rather than the exception.

Although Triassic ichthyosaurs are diverse, two basic types can be recognized: those with narrow fins and those with broad fins. A similar division can be seen during later geological periods, and this has led most investigators to recognize two separate groups, the longipinnates (narrow fins) and the latipinnates (wide fins). While this classification has been useful in the past, it is no longer satisfactory and will not be used here.[21] For our next glimpse of the evolutionary history of the ichthyosaurs we have to return to the place of their discovery, the Lower Jurassic sediments of southwestern England.

The sea cliffs at Lyme Regis, Dorset

It is many years now since the sea cliffs at Lyme Regis were quarried for their limestone. The handcarts that once clanked to and fro along the foreshore have long since disappeared, but rusting remnants of the old iron rails may still be seen. Mary Anning's regular visits to the quarries were often fruitful, and the quarrymen, whom she knew well, kept a weather eye open for anything of interest to her. Thomas Hawkins also walked this same stretch of coastline, but most of his ichthyosaurs were collected in the vicinity of Street, a small town in the adjoining

Ichthyosaurus communis, *the commonest English species, seldom exceeds 2 m in length. The skeleton (above) collected from Somerset by Thomas Hawkins, is in the British Museum (Natural History). Notice the large tail fin and shark-like dorsal fin in the restoration.*

county of Somersetshire, some 40 km from the coast. Both localities have been productive and many complete and near-complete skeletons have been collected over the years. We are presented with a wide array of species and we shall soon see that a similar situation exists in southern Germany, though for a slightly younger geological horizon. The Lower Jurassic pro-

Top: This complete skeleton of the rare species **Ichthyosaurus conybeari** *is less than one metre long, Lyme Regis, Dorset. Scale measures 20 cm. Middle: One of the best preserved skeletons of the long-snouted species* **Ichthyosaurus tenuirostris**, *Street, Somerset. Scale measures 25 cm. Bottom: The skull of the short-snouted species,* **Ichthyosaurus breviceps**. *Lyme Regis, Dorset. Scale measures 6 cm.*

vides us with our best view of the history of the group, and the majority of ichthyosaurs that have been found are of this age. We therefore have good reason to spend a little longer in this time zone than we did in the Triassic.

Most of the ichthyosaurs from the English Lower Jurassic, usually referred to as the Liassic, can be referred to two genera: *Ichthyosaurus* and *Temnodontosaurus*. (The genera *Stenopterygius* and *Leptopterygius* are also found in the English Lower Jurassic, but are uncommon.) *Ichthyosaurus* is a moderate-sized genus that is very common, while *Temnodontosaurus*, a veritable giant, is far less common and complete skeletons are seldom found. In contrast to their Triassic predecessors, these ichthyosaurs all have a distinct tailbend, and their teeth, which are sharply pointed and numerous, are set in a continuous groove instead of in individual sockets. *Temnodontosaurus* has a relatively long and slender body compared with *Ichthyosaurus*, and the fore and hind fins, which are approximately of equal length, are relatively narrow, having undergone reduction to three or four digits. *Ichthyosaurus*, in contrast, has a fore fin that is usually at least twice the length of the hind fin, and is relatively wide, having at least five digits and usually six or seven. There are four species of *Ichthyosaurus*, and the commonest, appropriately named *I. communis*, is known from dozens of skeletons that have been collected from Lyme Regis and Street.[22] Examples of this dolphin-sized ichthyosaur, which seldom exceeds 2 m in length, may be seen in many museums. The smallest species, named *I. conybeari* in honour of the Reverend William Conybeare, was similar in size to the Triassic *Mixosaurus*, barely exceeding 1 m in length. This uncommon little ichthyosaur has a thin, pointed rostrum, armed with numerous needle-sharp teeth, and has relatively large orbits, like most ichthyosaurs. Similar in appearance but larger in size is *I. tenuirostris*, named for its long thin rostrum. In contrast is the fourth species, *I. breviceps*, whose short rostrum gives it a bird-like appearance and makes the orbit appear enormous.

Temnodontosaurus is similarly represented by four species.[23] The commonest, which is also the largest, is *T. platyodon*. It is the species to which Mary Anning's impressive first ichthyosaur belongs. *T. platyodon* reaches lengths of up to 9 m, which is only marginally smaller than the Triassic genus *Cymbospondylus*. Like *Cymbospondylus* it has a relatively long and robust body, and its long slender rostrum is armed with a battery of sharp teeth. This was one of the largest ichthyosaurs of the Jurassic, and was probably a formidable predator. We have no direct evidence of what these ichthyosaurs fed upon. A wide range of prey animals were available, including the various squid-like molluscs that abounded in those warm Jurassic seas, fishes, and also other marine reptiles. Perhaps they preyed upon plesiosaurs, or upon other ichthyosaurs.

The most likely candidate as a hunter of other ichthyosaurs is *T. eurycephalus*, a species that is unfortunately represented by only one specimen: an isolated skull. The rostrum is very short, very much like that of *Ichthyosaurus breviceps*, and the skull is correspondingly deep. The teeth are large and well spaced and have bulbous roots, which suggests that they were firmly anchored in the jaws. These features are indicative of a powerful

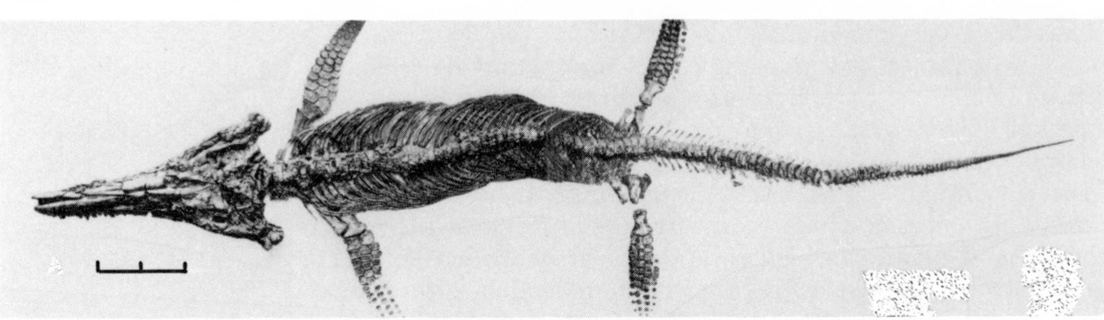

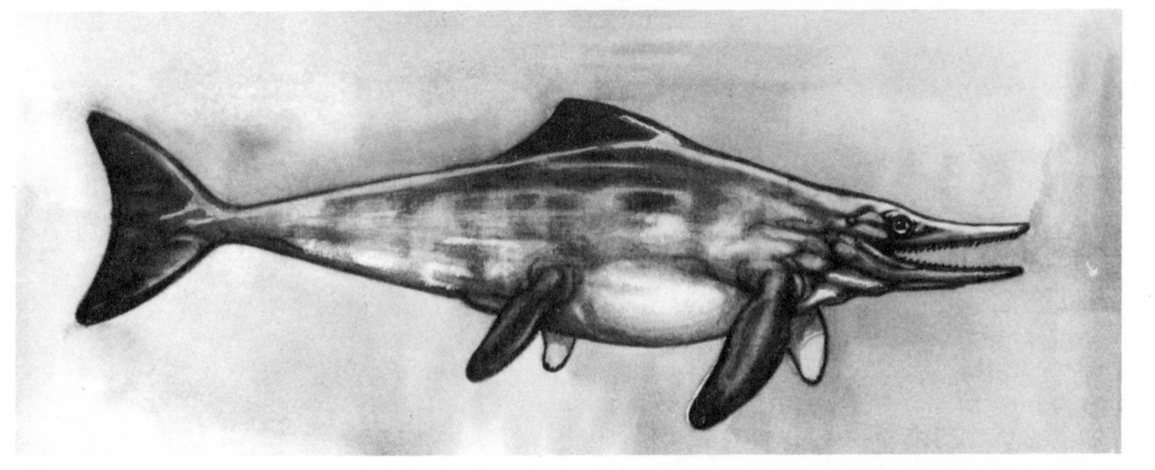

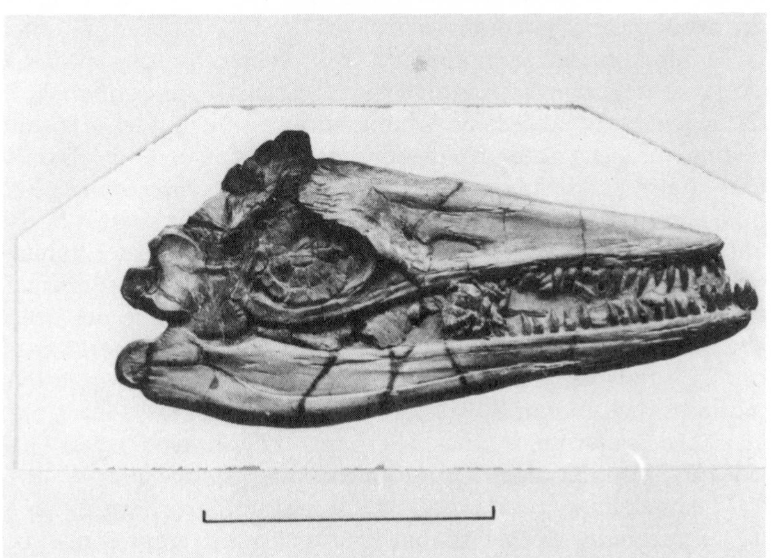

This complete skeleton of the giant English species **Temnodontosaurus platyodon** *(top) has been dorsoventrally compressed, straightening the tail bend, but its position is revealed by close inspection of the skeleton; scale measures 25 cm; Lyme Regis, Dorset. The fins are relatively larger than in* **Ichthyosaurus communis**, *the tail somewhat smaller, as shown in the restoration (middle).* **Temnodontosaurus eurycephalus** *(bottom), known only from this isolated skull, was a deep-jawed form which may have hunted other ichthyosaurs—scale measures 50 cm; Lyme Regis, Dorset.*

crushing apparatus, and remind us of similar adaptations that we have seen in the giant flesh-eating dinosaurs. This particular individual has a basisphenoid bone clenched between its teeth; one of the bones from the base of the skull. It is likely that this element was displaced from its natural position during preservation, but it is possible that it does not belong to this animal but to some unfortunate victim.

Neither of the other two species of *Temnodontosaurus* is well known. *T. risor,* which is represented by three isolated skulls, appears to be very similar to *T. platyodon* but is somewhat smaller. The fourth species, *T. longirostris,* is of moderate size, probably not exceeding 3 m, and is characterized by a long and slender rostrum that appears to have few teeth.

While the majority of early Jurassic ichthyosaurs found in England are from the southwest, a few other localities have been productive. All of these lie upon a band of Liassic rocks that runs diagonally across the country from the Dorset coast in the southwest, to the Yorkshire coast in the northeast. One of the more important localities is near the town of Whitby, in Yorkshire, where cliffs of Liassic age look out over the sombre North Sea. These exposures belong to the upper division of the Liassic and are therefore slightly younger than the Lower Liassic strata of Lyme Regis and Street.

Ichthyosaurs are not the only fossils that have been found along this stretch of the Yorkshire coast. Ever since Roman times people have searched the cliffs for jet, a semi-precious form of coal, which was once prized for making jewellery. The jet industry, which was centred on Whitby, disappeared long ago, and, perhaps because the cliffs are no longer being searched for jet, ichthyosaurs are seldom found. Whitby has yielded relatively few ichthyosaurs compared with Lyme Regis, and most of these are housed in the delightful museum which graces the town. Although there are several complete skeletons, the preservation is rather poor and the material is consequently not well known. The bone is hard, black, and glossy, much like Whitby jet, and the specimens all appear to belong to the same species, *Leptopterygius acutirostris*.[24] These are large ichthyosaurs, at least as large as *T. platyodon*, which they strongly resemble. More research is needed on the relationships among the various genera of ichthyosaurs, and this might show that the differences between *Leptopterygius* and *Temnodontosaurus* are so minor that they should be referred to the same genus.

Our first glimpse of Jurassic ichthyosaurs presents us with as wide an array of types as we saw in the Triassic. In contrast to their Triassic ancestors, the Jurassic ichthyosaurs all had a pronounced caudal fin, and their teeth were set in a groove instead of being set in individual sockets. Most Lower Jurassic ichthyosaurs found in England are Lower Liassic in age, relatively few

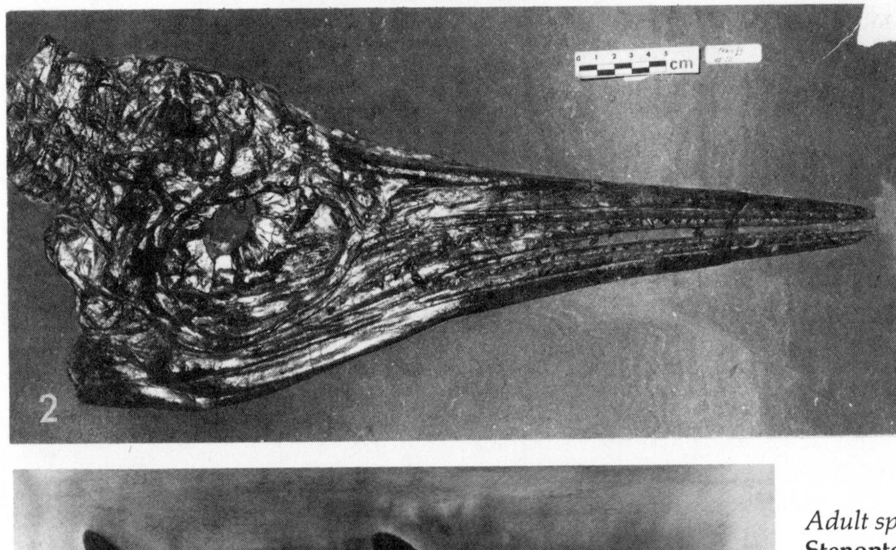

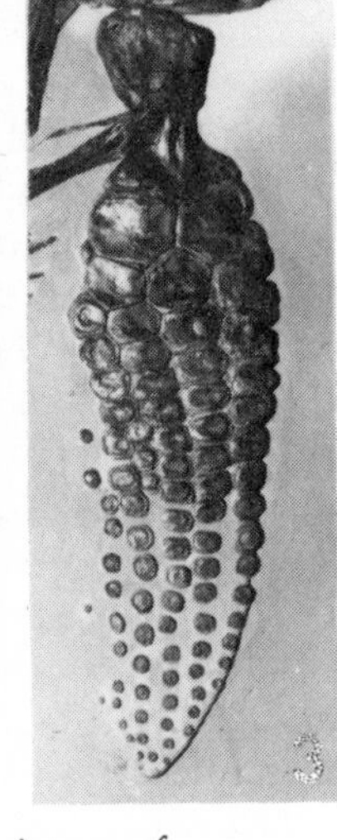

Adult specimens of **Stenopterygius quadricissus**, *the commonest German species, are unusual for being almost completely devoid of teeth; Holzmaden, West Germany. The caudal fin is especially large, as depicted in the restoration.*

having been collected from the geologically younger Upper Liassic strata. In Germany, however, the situation is reversed, and the Upper Liassic quarries of Holzmaden have actually yielded more ichthyosaur skeletons than all the other localities put together.

Quarrying has long since ceased in the English localities, but many of the quarries in southern Germany are still active, and about a dozen skeletons are added to the growing collections every year. The major natural history museums of the world have at least one Holzmaden ichthyosaur in their collection, and

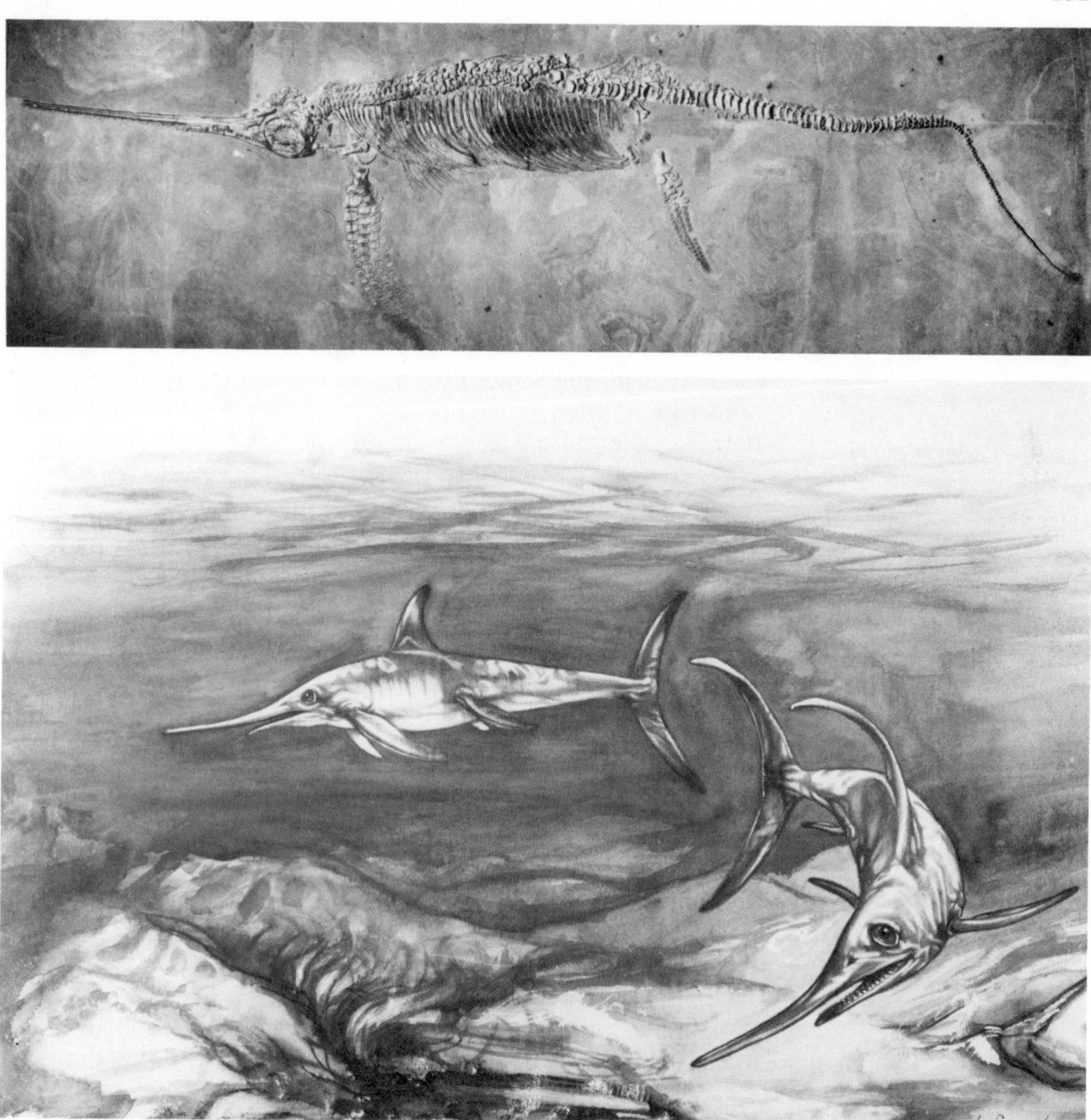

Eurhinosaurus huenei, *one of the largest German species, is unusual for the abbreviated lower jaw. The slender paired fins and tail, depicted in the restoration, suggest speed.*

some have more. (I estimate that about 600 ichthyosaur skeletons or partial skeletons have been collected from the Holzmaden area over the years.)

With a few interesting exceptions, the German species are much like their English counterparts.[25] Three genera are represented: *Stenopterygius*, *Leptopterygius*, and *Eurhinosaurus*. *Stenopterygius*, a dolphin-sized ichthyosaur, is very similar to its English equivalent, *Ichthyosaurus*, and several species are recognized, differing from one another in shape and size. The most common species, *S. quadriscissus*, is unusual in that, although the juvenile specimens have numerous well developed teeth, the adults are almost, if not completely, toothless. Another species, *S. hauffianus* (which also occurs in England), has an abbreviated rostrum, and in this respect is similar to the English species *I. breviceps*. *Leptopterygius*, as we have seen, is a large genus similar to the English genus *Temnodontosaurus*. The largest species, *Leptopterygius burgundiae*, reaches lengths of just over 9 m. The third genus, *Eurhinosaurus*, which is easily as large as *Leptopterygius*, is a most unusual ichthyosaur—quite unlike any other. The fore and hind fins are both long and narrow. The tail is steeply downturned and in life must have supported an immense crescentic tail. The most remarkable feature, however, is in the skull. The rostrum is drawn out into an enormously long and slender process, but the mandible stops short, and is only about one-third the length of the rostrum. The rostrum is armed with teeth throughout its length. So, too, is the mandible, and the appearance of the skull is much like that of the modern swordfish *(Xiphias)*. The swordfish uses its long rostrum for making sideways slashes at fishes as it swims through a school; then having injured a number of them, it swims back again and swallows them. Perhaps *Eurhinosaurus* used its long rostrum in a similar fashion.

This latest glimpse of the evolutionary history of the ichthyosaurs, which spans from the Lower Liassic to the Upper Liassic, covers an interval of about 4 million years and presents us with a wide variety of species. We do not know whether these species were restricted to England and Germany during this period, or whether they were widely distributed, but the available evidence suggests that ichthyosaurs, like many present-day whales and dolphins, were widespread.[26] It is fortunate that this view of life was so extensive because we do not get another glimpse until the Upper Jurassic, some 40 million years later, and for this we have to journey to the southeast of England.

The ancient kingdom of East Anglia has been swept by many waves of invasion and emigration during its history. The Flemings brought weaving skills. The marauding Vikings robbed and raped. The Icelanders brought a knowledge of the sea and how to fish. But the pragmatic Romans set to work digging drainage ditches and building roads. At the time of the Roman conquest, much of East Anglia lay under water and settlements were confined to a few low hills that rose above the swamps. This damp, cold land, often shrouded in mist, was probably the least popular billeting with the Roman soldiers. Several factors contributed to the poor drainage. The land was flat, much of it lying at, or below, sea-level, and the heavy clay soil prevented the water from passing through it. The drainage ditches and causeways the Romans built to link their garrisons lowered water levels, but when the Romans left England the works fell into disrepair and water levels rose again. No serious attempts to resolve the problem were made until the 17th century, when the assistance of the Dutch was obtained. Long experienced in land reclamation, they built an efficient drainage system that was the forerunner of the present system of ditches, canals, and pumping stations.

Today, the clay that was once the undoing of the land is used in the manufacture of bricks. Referred to as the Oxford Clay, it was formed in the sea that covered Britain during the Late Jurassic and is rich in fossils. Peterborough, a sprawling town 100 km to the north of London, is one of the major centres of the brick industry, and has yielded enormous quantities of vertebrate fossils, mainly ichthyosaurs and plesiosaurs, together with some crocodiles. Much of the material passed unnoticed, and was therefore destroyed, but considerable amounts were saved and a major portion of this material was acquired by the British Museum (Natural History). The brickworks in the adjacent county of Bedfordshire have also been productive, as have a number of quarries in the county of Cambridgeshire. Several other localities, including some in Dorset, have also yielded material, and there is consequently no shortage of Upper Jurassic ichthyosaurs. However, this wealth of material is disappointing because it comprises largely isolated vertebrae, fin elements, and skull bones, with relatively few associations (bones belonging to one individual) and probably no complete skeletons.

Upper Jurassic ichthyosaurs are not confined to England, their remains having been found in many parts of the world including Europe and the Americas, but the material is again largely incomplete. The incomplete nature of the specimens, however, was no deterrent to the palaeontologists who first studied them, and more than 20 species have been described. The practice of naming new species on the basis of isolated scraps of bone, common in 19th century palaeontology, has cluttered the literature with hundreds of meaningless names.

A study of the Upper Jurassic ichthyosaurs has shown that almost all the specimens belong to the same genus, *Ophthalmosaurus*.[27] The North American ophthalmosaurs have traditionally been referred to a separate genus, *Baptanodon*, but there seems to be no valid reason for doing this, and all should be referred to *Ophthalmosaurus*. A number of species of this genus have been described, but the differences between them are minor and further research might reveal that there are only two Upper Jurassic species, the English *O. icenicus*, and the American *O. discus*.

Like many of its Lower Jurassic predecessors, *Ophthalmosau-*

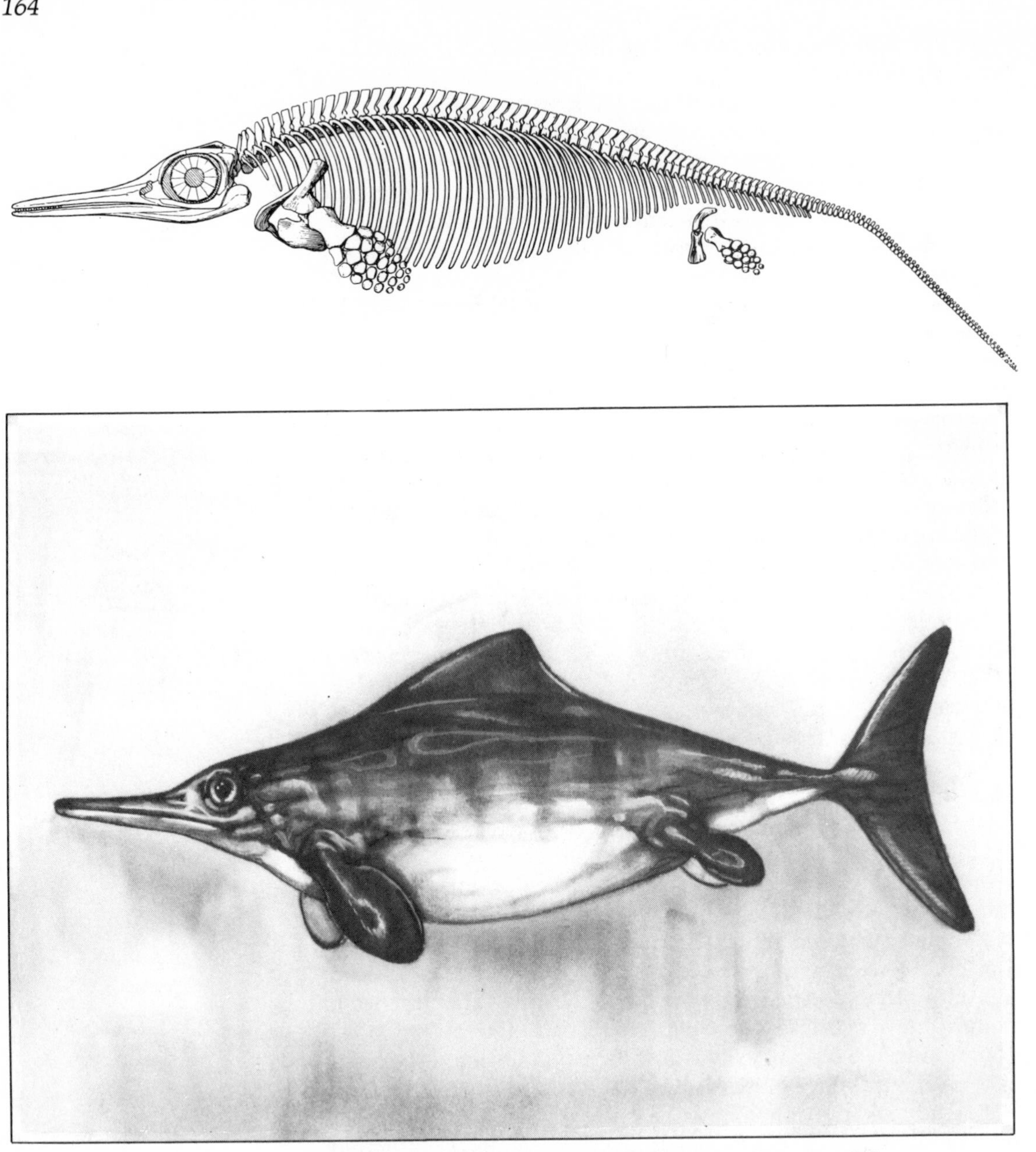

Top: Andrew's reconstruction of the Upper Jurassic ichthyosaur **Ophthalmosaurus**. *Although fragments of this ichthyosaur are very common, associated remains are rare. In the artist's restoration,* **Ophthalmosaurus** *is depicted as a short-bodied form with large tail and rounded fins.*

rus is a dolphin-sized ichthyosaur, reaching a length of about 4 m. The fore and hind fins are both broad, but much rounder than in earlier forms. The individual bones of the fins are round rather than angular, and barely make contact with one another.

This is in marked contrast to the closely packed arrangement of most Lower Jurassic fins. Consequently, it is almost impossible to put a disarticulated fin back together again, and very few have been found in an articulated condition.

One of the striking features of *Ophthalmosaurus* is the relatively enormous size of its orbit. The rostrum is fairly long and slender and is nearly, or completely, devoid of teeth. Judged from the many hundreds of bones that have been identified, *Ophthalmosaurus* was a common ichthyosaur. It was also widespread, both geographically and geologically, having been found in France, Argentina, Wyoming, and in the Canadian Arctic, and spanning from the Upper Jurassic to the Lower Cretaceous.

The Upper Jurassic lasted for about 20 million years, and our impression of ichthyosaur life during this period is one of abundance but little diversity. This contrasts with the early part of the Jurassic, when the seas thronged with a wide variety of species. Were ichthyosaurs really less diverse at this stage of their evolutionary history, or is this lack of diversity merely a reflection of the vagaries of the fossil record? We can never be sure, of course, but it looks as though the reduction in diversity is real, because our samples have been drawn from a number of different localities. Furthermore, when we move up the geological series to the Cretaceous Era for our last glimpse of the ichthyosaurs, we find even less diversity, and it seems that the ichthyosaurs were at their peak during the early part of the Jurassic.

Immortalized in song by Vera Lynn during World War II, the white cliffs of Dover are part of an extensive wall of chalk that forms part of the coastline of southeastern England. These cliffs are actually the exposed edge of a large block of chalk that reaches a thickness of 500 m, and gives rise to the well-drained and gently undulating countryside of southern England. The word Cretaceous comes from the Latin word for chalk. Thomas Henry Huxley, defender of the Darwinian faith, delivered a famous lecture, "On a piece of chalk," to a working men's group in 1868. He described how this familiar rock was formed in the seas tens of millions of years ago by the accumulation of the skeletons of microscopic organisms which became cemented together. Chalk cliffs have always been popular with fossil-hunters and a number of ichthyosaurs have been found in them over the years, but these are mainly fragmentary. The time period covered by the chalk, which is Upper Cretaceous in age, is about 30 million years. Ichthyosaurs also occur in the Lower Cretaceous, of course, and many specimens, mainly isolated bones of the skull and fins, have been found in sediments that are referred to as the Greensand.

We have seen that *Ophthalmosaurus* survived into the Lower Cretaceous, and it appears to be represented by a single species, *O. cantabrigiensis*, which seems smaller than its Jurassic prede-

Platypterigius, *last of the ichthyosaurs, is found in Cretaceous rocks throughout most of the world. Top: Skull of* **P. americanus**, *Upper Cretaceous, Wyoming. Left: Fin of* **P. australis**, *Upper Cretaceous, Northern Queensland. Right: Restoration based upon several specimens. The relatively small tail, which contrasts with Jurassic forms, may have been modified for cruising rather than for sprinting.*

cessors, but the material is very incomplete and our knowledge correspondingly limited. Most Cretaceous ichthyosaurs can be identified with a single genus, *Platypterygius*, which is widely distributed in both space and time. *Platypterygius* extends throughout the Cretaceous Era and has been found in North and South America, England, Continental Europe, Russia, India, and Australia. A complete fossil record would probably confirm a world-wide distribution. At least 15 species have been described, but most of these were founded on inadequate material and there are no more than five recognizable species.[28] Even these are based largely on incomplete material, and the most adequately known species, *P. australis*, is represented by only a few skeletons. If we had several complete skeletons for each of the five species, we might find so much overlap among them that we would not want to recognize as many as five species. For the present, though, we must content ourselves with noting that *Platypterygius* was probably not a very variable genus, certainly not nearly as variable as most of the Lower Jurassic genera.

What sort of an ichthyosaur is *Platypterygius*? First, it is fairly large—about 7 m long, which is larger than *Ophthalmosaurus*. The skull is long and slender and, unlike that of *Ophthalmosaurus*, armed with fairly large teeth. The orbit is relatively much smaller than in *Ophthalmosaurus*, and is not set as far back along the skull, and both of these characters appear to be primitive. Like *Ophthalmosaurus*, *Platypterygius* has broad fins, but the individual bones are rectangular and tightly packed rather than round and widely spaced, and are arranged in regular columns, or fingers, numbering up to eight. The fins are robust and the large size of the pectoral and pelvic girdles to which they are attached suggests that they may have been used for paddling as well as for steering. The down-turned segment of the tail appears to be relatively short compared with the length of the body, which suggests that the caudal fin was only of modest size. Lower Jurassic ichthyosaurs, in contrast, had relatively huge caudal fins.

Investigations into the relationships between the area of the caudal fin and swimming performance in fishes have shown that large tail areas are associated with rapid acceleration, and small areas with steady cruising.[29] For example, the pike, a voracious predator that ambushes other fishes by lunging at them from the seclusion of the vegetation, has a relatively large tail area that generates a rapid acceleration. Because of its large area the tail generates a very large drag force, and the pike is unable to keep up its fast swimming speed for very long. The mackeral, a pelagic fish (of the open sea) that spends most of its life cruising at a relatively high speed, has a relatively small tail that generates a relatively small drag force. The mackeral does not have as rapid an acceleration as the pike but is able to maintain its swimming almost indefinitely. We might infer from this that the Lower Jurassic ichthyosaurs, with their relatively enormous tails, were modified for acceleration, whereas *Platypterygius*, with its relatively small tail, was modified for cruising.

Platypterygius seems to have been the sole representative of the ichthyosaurs during the latter part of the Cretaceous and therefore had the dubious honour of being the last of its kind.[30] The fact that it was not a very variable genus confirms our suspicion that there had been a marked decrease in the diversity of the ichthyosaurs during the latter part of their history, and

The lower Jurassic quarries, near the town of Holzmaden, southern Germany, are still being worked for slate today.

this occurred some 100 million years before their final disappearance at the close of the Cretaceous Period.

Our extensive excursion through space and time has acquainted us with the geological history of the ichthyosaurs, but we have not yet considered them as animals. To do this, we will return to the Lower Jurassic quarries of Holzmaden, in southern Germany, the last resting place of the most perfectly preserved of all ichthyosaurs.

Germany, like many countries, is dependent on the Middle East for oil, and when these supplies were cut off during the two world wars, she desperately sought other sources of supply. A type of slate that had been quarried for centuries in the south had long been known to contain oil and bitumin, up to 20%, and this resource was hurriedly developed as a vital part of the war effort. Now, the layers that are rich in bitumen are also the layers where the best preserved ichthyosaurs have been found—the ones in which the body outline has been preserved. This is no coincidence, and experiments with extracted bitumin and present-day specimens of skin have shown that it does function as a preservative.[31] The body outline of these remarkable ichthyosaurs is not formed of the actual skin, but is represented by a

Some of the ichthyosaurs from southern Germany have the body outline preserved as a carbonaceous film.

very thin carbonaceous film. Analysis has shown that the film consists mainly of hydrocarbons (compounds formed of hydrogen, carbon, and oxygen) and amino acids (the components of proteins), together with small amounts of fatty acids.

A careful examination of these "skin specimens" has shown that it is only the lower surface of the body that has the film. There is no such preservation of the upper surface. This suggests that when a dead ichthyosaur settled on the soft seabed its underside became embedded in a bituminous slime and was preserved, while the soft tissues of the upper surface rotted and were swept away. It is exceedingly rare to obtain any indication of the body outline of an extinct animal and these unusual specimens provide us with some unique information.

Ichthyosaurs were recognized as being very fish-like from the pioneer days of Conybeare and De la Beche, but the full extent of this resemblance was only realized with the discovery of the skin specimens. These specimens revealed that ichthyosaurs had a dorsal fin and a deep crescentic caudal fin, both similar in shape to those of fishes. Because of the tailbend, the presence of some sort of caudal fin had long been suspected, but the discovery of a dorsal fin was a complete surprise for there is no internal skeleton to hint at its existence. The paired pectoral and pelvic fins appear to have had wide bases, which suggests that they were primarily used as hydroplanes for adjusting the swimming level, rather than as paddles to row the animal through the water. The body outline is beautifully streamlined, with the deepest part of the body occurring less than half way along its length, just ahead of the dorsal fin. A streamlined shape is seen, not only in the bodies of most vertebrates that swim or fly well, but also in cross sections of their fins and wings. Man has utilized this shape in a wide variety of applications, ranging from ships and aircraft to bridge supports and turbine blades. To understand the significance of streamlining we have to know something about the forces that act on a body moving through a fluid. This knowledge will also enable us to interpret the features we have seen in the ichthyosaurs.

When a body moves through a fluid, whether air or water, it experiences a force called drag, which opposes its forward motion. The size of the drag force varies with the size and shape of the body and its speed, and with two properties of the fluid, its density and its viscosity. Density is a fairly familiar quantity. It is the weight of a given volume of substance compared with an equal volume of water. Viscosity is a measure of how easily a fluid flows, and, it follows, how readily it flows around an object that passes through it. Treacle is far more viscous than water and therefore pours much more slowly. Swimming in treacle would be laborious as well as messy because of its sluggish flow over the body.

The drag force acting on a body is a combination of two forces: pressure drag and friction drag, which are proportional to the fluid's density and viscosity, respectively. Visualize a marble falling to the bottom of a tall glass cylinder filled with treacle. The total drag force acting on the marble is large enough to slow the marble down so that we can watch its descent. To sink, the marble has to push a pathway for itself through the treacle, just like a commuter forcing his way to the door of a crowded subway car. The treacle closes in again behind the marble so that there is no permanent tunnel, just as the crowd closes in again in the wake of the battling commuter. The marble is actually pushing particles of treacle out of its way, and they, in their turn, are resisting this push with their own inertia (inertia is the tendency for an object to stay where it is). The struggling commuter is doing exactly the same thing; he has to push against the inertia of the other people, and his progress is obviously easier if his fellow travellers are 25 kg children rather than 100 kg adults. The inertia force exerted by the fluid is the pressure drag, and it increases with the density of the fluid. The pressure drag acts at right angles to the surface of the marble and has its greatest effect at the leading face, falling off to zero at the circumference. The force also acts on the trailing surface of the marble, and since it acts here in the direction of motion it actually assists its descent. In a similar way the people falling back into place behind the commuter exert a small force that helps to push him on his way. In the example we have chosen, the size of the pressure drag is relatively small compared with the size of the friction drag, because of the high viscosity of the fluid.

The friction drag acts at right angles to the pressure drag, that is, parallel with the surface of the body, and always opposes its

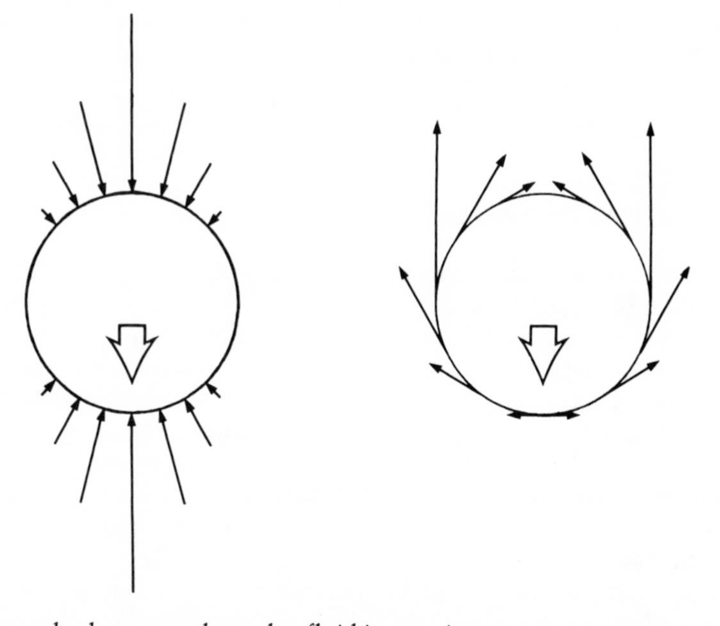

When a body moves through a fluid it experiences two components of drag: pressure drag (left) which acts at right angles to the surface, and friction drag, which acts tangentially. Lengths of the arrows depict relative effect of the two components upon the progress of the body. At high Reynolds numbers the fluid actually breaks away from the posterior surface of a sphere, so that this diagram is somewhat simplified.

motion. Friction drag is ineffective at the leading face of the marble but rises to a maximum at the circumference. Friction drag arises because of the viscosity of the fluid, whose particles are reluctant to slip past each other as the object pushes them aside. Our frustrated commuter would find it far more difficult to push his way through the crowd if they linked arms, because this would increase their resistance to being jostled (their "viscosity").

The relative magnitudes of the pressure drag and friction drag vary according to the shape and size of the body and the density and viscosity of the fluid. A useful expression of this relationship is the Reynolds number, used extensively in aeronautical and marine engineering:

$$\text{Reynolds number} = \frac{\text{density x speed x length}}{\text{viscosity}}$$

where density and viscosity refer to the fluid, and speed and length refer to the body moving through it. Suppose we want to work out the Reynolds number of a dolphin 2 m long swimming at a speed of 10 m/s. It is important to work in the same units and we will work in SI units (Système International; metre, kilogram, second). The density of water is 1000 kg/m^3, the viscosity 1.304×10^{-3} newtons/m^2 (at 10°C).[32] The speed is 10m/s, and the length of the body is 2m. Reynolds number therefore equals:

$$\frac{1000 \times 10 \times 2}{1.304 \times 10^{-3}}$$

= 15337423, or approximately 15.3×10^6.

This is a fairly high Reynolds number. Very small animals such as planktonic organisms, swim only slowly and have Reynolds numbers of less than 10. Movements at low Reynolds numbers are dominated by viscosity forces, and the greatest drag force is therefore friction drag. This is irrespective of whether the fluid has a high or low viscosity. Water, for example, has a fairly low viscosity, but when we see minute animals swimming in a droplet of water, viewed under a microscope, they appear as if they are swimming in a very thick fluid. At high Reynolds numbers, the situation is reversed; pressure drag is the main force, and viscosity, and hence friction drag, can be almost ignored.

Drag forces rob a moving object of large quantities of energy, and any steps that can be taken to reduce these forces are advantageous. There is little that can be done to reduce friction drag, but pressure drag can be eliminated by streamlining. Pressure drag is only important at high Reynolds numbers, consequently we only see streamlining in bodies that move at high Reynolds numbers, and these include aircraft, ships, submarines, fast cars, birds, whales, and most fishes. Ichthyosaurs are included in this group, together with their contemporaries, the plesiosaurs and mosasaurs. We do not expect to find streamlining in microscopic organisms, nor in animals that move relatively slowly. The seahorse, for example, is a small and slow-moving fish and is not streamlined, whereas the salmon, a fast swimmer, has a streamlined body. Streamlining is a very familiar word, and has been used to describe a number of different things from fibre-glass fairings on the fronts of motor cycles to Olympic swimmers with shaved heads. We will only use the word, however, with reference to the tear-drop shape seen in most bodies that move at high Reynolds numbers. To understand how this shape reduces pressure drag we have to consider the forces that act on a streamlined body moving through a fluid.

The pressure force, which acts at right angles to the surface of the body, has its greatest effect at the front end, the leading edge, where it opposes progress head on. The effect of the pressure force diminishes as we pass farther back, and, by the time we reach the widest part of the body, the shoulder, it no longer opposes the forward motion. As we pass back from the shoulder, along the trailing edge, the direction of the pressure force

The seahorse (left), a slow swimmer, is not streamlined whereas the salmon, a fairly fast swimmer, is streamlined.

changes. It is now towards the front and actually assists the forward motion. We saw this in the example of the marble falling in treacle, but in a streamlined shape the trailing edge is far more extensive than the leading edge and therefore makes a much greater contribution to the forward motion than it does in a spherical body.

The overall effect of the pressure drag depends upon the relative lengths of the leading and trailing sections of the body; if the trailing edge is long and gently tapering, the pressure drag can be completely eliminated. However, we never get something for nothing; pressure drag is always accompanied by friction drag, and this acts along the surface and always opposes forward motion. It follows that increasing the length of the trailing edge increases the size of the friction drag. At high Reynolds numbers, the friction drag is small compared with the pressure drag, but it cannot be entirely dismissed. It has been found that a good compromise is to have the shoulder placed about one-third of the way back from the front of the body.

Little was known about streamlining during the early days of aeronautics, and the wires used for supporting the wings generated enormous drag forces. If we measured the drag forces on a piece of wire and on a streamlined strut of similar thickness, we would find that the drag on the wire was about nine times higher. Stated another way, a strut could be about nine times as thick as a wire before it generated a similar drag force.[33] With the development of the wind tunnel and a scientific rather than trial-and-error approach to flying, the importance of streamlining was realized and struts replaced wires.

Before returning to the ichthyosaurs we have to consider one more aspect of fluid dynamics: the flow of fluid over surfaces. When a fluid flows over a body, the layer in contact with the surface is stationary; above this is a zone of transition where the velocity of adjacent layers increases to that of the fluid stream. This whole region of transition, from stationary to free flowing fluid, is called the boundary layer. The thickness of the boundary layer varies with the Reynolds number. At the high Reynolds numbers of modern aircraft, the boundary layer is only

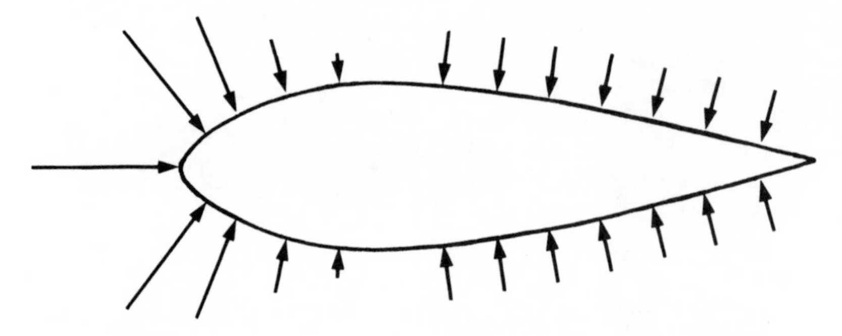

The streamline shape reduces drag by capitalising on the beneficial effect of the pressure drag component acting on the trailing surface. Lengths of the arrows depict relative effect of the pressure drag upon the progress of the body.

about as thick as a sheet of paper, whereas in microscopic animals, which move at a very low Reynolds number, the boundary layer is so thick compared with the body that it is meaningless to talk about one.

We can see the relationship between the thickness of the boundary layer and the Reynolds number every time we drive a car in the rain. At low speeds the Reynolds number is low and the boundary layer is correspondingly thick. The beads of water that form on the windows lie within the boundary layer and are therefore not displaced by the air flowing over the car. As the speed of the car increases, the thickness of the boundary layer decreases, until it is thinner than the beads of water. At this point the beads project beyond the boundary layer and are consequently swept back by the air flow. The largest droplets are the first to move, and the car has to be travelling very fast before the smallest ones are swept away. Since the beads project beyond the boundary layer they offer resistance to the airflow, thus increasing the drag, but because they are very small and are not fixed to the surface their effect is negligible. However, fixed projections, such as wing mirrors, door handles, and roof racks do generate a significant drag force, especially at high speeds, and this is well known to the designers of high-speed vehicles.

Since the boundary layer of a modern aircraft is less than one millimetre thick, the rivets that secure the skin to the airframe have to be flush with the surface (take a look next time you board an aircraft) whereas the rivets on the surface of a bus or on the hull of a ship are not flush-fitting and yet lie well within the boundary layer. Fast-swimming fishes have smooth bodies, which are usually covered in small scales, and are sometimes scaleless.[34]

Seals and their relatives have smooth fur, cetaceans have a smooth skin, and birds have a well-tailored coat of contour feathers. Smooth bodies reduce drag not only by eliminating the resistance that projections generate but also by maintaining a smooth flow of fluid over the surface. When fluid flows gently, without any swirling movements the flow is called laminar; it generates the least drag. Under certain circumstances, such as increasing speed, laminar flow breaks down. Swirling motions are set up in the fluid and the boundary layer starts to break away from the surface. This pattern of flow is described as turbulent, and it usually creates far more drag than laminar flow. Furthermore, because the boundary layer separates from the surface over much of the body, the beneficial effect of the pressure drag acting on the trailing edge in the direction of motion is lost. We see examples of laminar and turbulent flow every day without always realizing it. When a tap is partly turned on the flow is laminar and the water column looks as smooth as glass. As the tap is opened more fully, a point is reached at which the flow becomes turbulent, and the glassy column is replaced by a rough cascade. Since turbulent flow generates much drag, animals that move at relatively high Reynolds numbers have evolved smooth bodies and streamlined shapes to promote laminar flow, and these same strategies have been developed in the design of our own vehicles. When a dolphin or fish is moving slowly, the water flow is laminar over most of the body, but, as the speed is increased, separation begins to occur, starting at the posterior end of the body and moving forward towards the head. The most efficient streamlined bodies are those that can maintain laminar flow over the greatest area, and dolphins and whales appear to be the masters of this art.

The high swimming speeds of porpoises have always impressed us, but an observation made by biologist, Sir James Gray, in 1936, was completely baffling. Gray timed a porpoise during a burst of speed and found that it reached 10.3 m/s, which is about 20 knots. This was not altogether surprising, but when Gray calculated the magnitude of the drag force he was amazed to find that it was considerably less than it should have been for a body of this shape and size. The only other possible explanation was that the porpoise was developing considerably more power than any other animal of similar size.

This puzzle has become known as "Gray's paradox". Experiments with life-sized models and dead porpoises towed behind boats gave fairly large drag forces. If the drag force on a living porpoise was this large, the porpoise's muscles would have to generate a power output that seemed unreasonably high, and this seemed unlikely. The research effort was concentrated on determining how cetaceans could reduce the drag forces well below predicted levels. Naval departments naturally took a keen interest, and the United States Navy invested large sums of money in cetacean research. One of the findings was that the outer layer of the skin of cetaceans is particularly soft and resilient, and has the microscopic structure of a fluid-filled sponge. This layer, which is only about 1.5 mm thick, has been suspected of being capable of damping out the effects of localized high-pressure zones, thereby delaying the onset of turbulent flow.[35] The effectiveness of this mechanism was not altogether clear, and various experiments were conducted with artificial skins. The United States Navy investigated the effect of coating the surfaces of a submarine with a resilient skin to see whether the drag force was reduced, but it seems that the results were not very promising. It was also suspected that the waterflow over the body of a porpoise may not be horizontal from snout to tail, but rather that it may pass obliquely upwards and backwards. If this were the case the effective length of the animal would be less than its body length, and since friction drag increases with body length (though, at high Reynolds numbers, it is far less important than pressure drag), it follows that the actual drag would be somewhat less than the expected drag.

There is, however, another possible solution to Gray's paradox. It concerns the power output of a cetacean. Gray's deduction of the maximum power output of the porpoise he timed was based upon a weight for weight comparison with man. Unfortunately, Gray chose the maximum power output a man can maintain for a 15-minute period, but his porpoise was clocked during a burst of activity that lasted for only seven seconds. A human athlete can generate more than one horsepower during a burst of activity lasting six seconds, but this falls to half of this value if the activity is sustained for a minute. Gray therefore grossly underestimated the power output of his porpoise during its rapid burst of activity. Some more recent experiments conducted upon trained porpoises have shown that the drag force acting on the body is no less than would be expected in a rigid model of similar shape and size. The power output, however, was calculated to be about 50% higher than that of a human athlete.[36] There is obviously much more to be learned about the hydrodynamics of swimming animals, but we now have a sufficient grasp of the fundamentals to be able to return to the ichthyosaurs and interpret the structures we see.

One of the most striking features of the ichthyosaur specimens whose body outline has been preserved is that they have a beautiful streamlined shape. As we might have predicted, the deepest part of the body occurs in the front half, a strategy for reducing the magnitude of the pressure drag. If we look closely at the paired fins, and at the lower lobe of the caudal fin, we can see that the leading and trailing edges both have areas that are unsupported by the internal skeleton. The unsupported areas

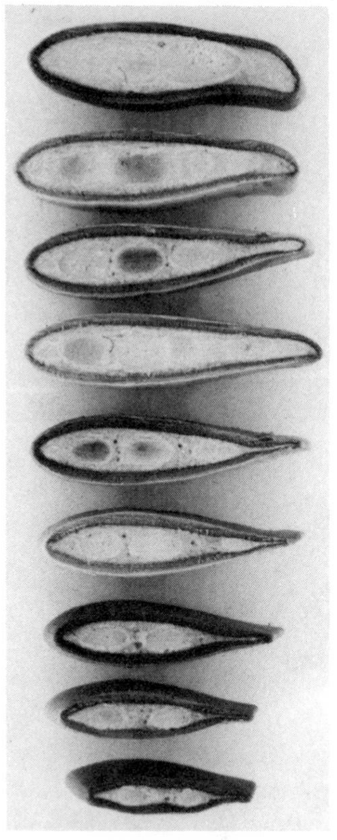

The cast of the forefin of a Jurassic ichthyosaur (left) when sectioned, reveals a streamlined shape. Compare this with the sectioned dolphin fin (far right). Leading edge is to the left in each case.

are much wider on the trailing than on the leading edges, and we can conclude that the trailing edge was thinner and more gently tapering than the leading edge. We can get a good idea of the actual cross-sectional shape of the paired fins by cutting sections across them and examining them in profile. We do not need to damage an actual ichthyosaur fin, because a cast can be made and this can be sectioned. The sections all have streamlined profiles that compare closely in shape with a variety of other structures, ranging from porpoise fins to ships' rudders. The strategy is the same in each case: to reduce the magnitude of the pressure drag. As neither the upper lobe of the caudal fin nor the dorsal fin has an internal skeleton, we cannot determine their profiles, but we would predict that they were streamlined, like the tail flukes and dorsal fin of cetaceans, which also lack an internal skeleton. Their streamlined body and fins probably gave ichthyosaurs a low pressure drag, and most of the drag was probably attributable to friction. This in turn was minimized by their smooth, scaleless skin. All the evidence suggests that ichthyosaurs were streamlined swimmers, and we now need to consider how they generated forward thrust and controlled their position in the water. This will allow us to interpret the functions of the tail, the dorsal fin, and the paired fins, which are all based on the same principle, the behaviour of inclined planes moving through a fluid.

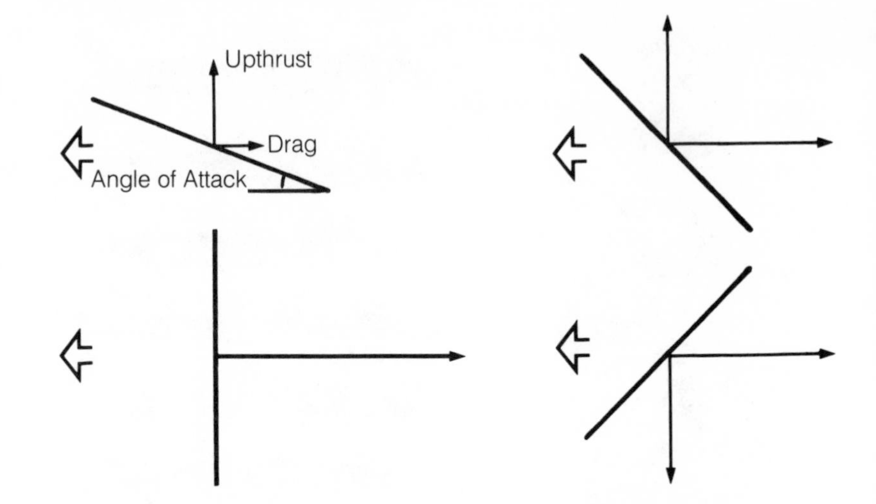

When an inclined plane moves through a fluid at a small angle of attack (top left) it experiences an upthrust and a drag force. With increasing angle of attack (top right) the magnitude of both forces increases. At right angles (bottom left) only a drag force is experienced, while at angles greater than 90° (bottom right) the drag is accompanied by a downthrust. The magnitude of the forces are indicated by the lengths of the arrows.

When I was small, the family vacation was always spent at Littlehampton, on the Sussex coast, and one of my favourite outings was the boat trip around the harbour and up the River Arun. The *Littlehampton Belle* was a pleasure craft of modest size, but to me she was an ocean liner, and I recall being overwhelmed when invited to take a turn at the wheel. Equal to the excitement of the occasion was the profound mystery of how a turn of that spoked wheel could cause the *Littlehampton Belle* to change direction. I pondered the problem for some time before coming to the conclusion that the wheel must have been connected to some large weights that pressed down on one side of the boat, causing it to turn. I did not yet know about the behaviour of inclined planes, but if I had there would have been no mystery.

When a plane, that is, a flat surface, is inclined at a small angle and moved through a fluid, it experiences an upthrust. This is because the plane deflects the fluid away from its surface and therefore generates an equal and opposite force. The propeller of an aircraft is an adapted inclined plane, and the thrust it generates is due to the stream of fast-moving air that it drives behind it. If the angle of the plane, called the angle of attack, is gradually increased, the magnitude of the upthrust increases. The drag on the plane also increases, and when the angle of attack is 90° there is no longer any upthrust, just a very large drag force. If the angle is increased beyond 90°, that is, if it is inclined downwards, there is a downthrust. The rudder of a ship is a vertical plane that can be inclined to one side or the other. When the rudder is moved so that its trailing edge moves to the right, the thrust is to the left. This pushes the stern to the left, which in turn swings the vessel around, pointing the bows to the right. Water skis also act as inclined planes, and the upthrust produced by the small angle of attack the skis make with the surface equals the weight of the skier.

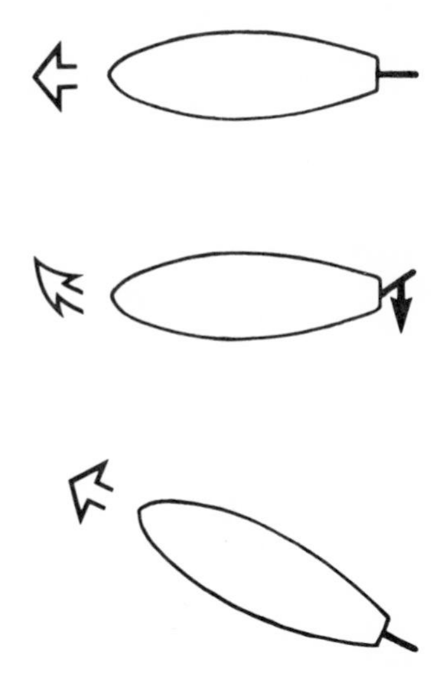

The rudder of a ship functions as an inclined plane. The force generated causes the ship to rotate about its center of gravity, pointing the bows in the desired direction. Top: Sailing a straight course. Middle: Rudder moved so as to turn the ship to the right. The thrust generated by the inclined plane displaces the stern to the left, causing the bows to swing to the right. Bottom: Sailing on the new course.

The efficiency of an inclined plane can be expressed by the ratio of the lift force to the drag force. If the plane has a streamlined profile, the magnitude of the drag force is minimized and the lift-to-drag ratio is therefore maximized. The lift force increases with increased area, but so does the drag force, so we cannot improve the ratio by increasing the size of the plane. However, if we use a long narrow plane instead of a square one, we find that the lift-to-drag ratio is improved. Therefore if we take two planes of equal area, one square and the other long and narrow, we will find that the second plane generates a greater lift force for a given drag than the first one. The shape of a plane is expressed by the aspect ratio which is the ratio of the length to the width. A plane 10 cm long and 10 cm wide has an aspect ratio of one, whereas a plane 20 cm long and 5 cm wide has an aspect ratio of four. One of the reasons why planes and wings with high aspect ratios give a higher lift-to-drag ratio is that they generate less of a vortex at the tips. These vortices, termed wing-tip-vortices, are caused by the swirling of fluid from the high-pressure zone beneath the wing to the low-pressure zone above it.

A variety of devices function as inclined planes for producing a forward thrust from fish tails and penguin flippers to the rubber fins worn by scuba divers. Each varies in the way it is moved, but the principle is the same in every case. The tail of a fish is stiff, but its point of attachment to the body is a flexible joint. As the whole structure is wagged from side to side the joint adjusts so that a small angle of attack is always maintained between the tail and its direction of movement. When the tail is moved to the left the left side presses against the water. The water pressure it experiences causes the whole tail to flex about the joint, so that the posterior edge trails behind. As a consequence, the whole tail is inclined to its direction of motion, at an angle of attack that is less than a right angle, and the thrust experienced is directed towards the head. A similar movement occurs when the tail moves to the right. Every stroke of the tail is therefore a power stroke. In whales the tail is moved up and down, and the down stroke is the most powerful movement, the upstroke being largely a recovery stroke. When penguins or turtles are swimming, the angle of attack of the fore flippers is maintained by rotating the whole structure about the joint. The

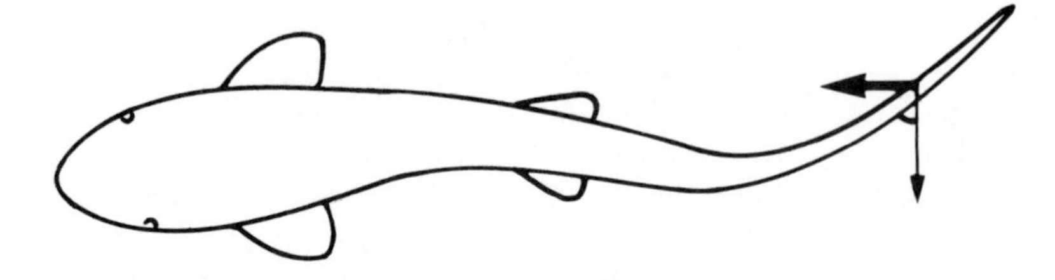

As the tail of a fish moves from side to side it is deflected by the resistance of the water, and therefore functions as an inclined plane, giving a net upthrust toward the head at every beat.

downstroke is made with the leading edge tilted below the trailing edge, the upstroke with the leading edge tilted above the trailing edge.

The role of the dorsal fin is similar to that of the flight feathers of an arrow, or the tail fin of an airplane—to maintain stability. If the body yaws (swings so that the head turns to the left or right) the dorsal fin, which lies largely behind the point of balance (centre of gravity) becomes an inclined plane and the thrust produced brings the body back into line.

We return now to the ichthyosaurs and complete our interpretation of their swimming structures. The paired pectoral and pelvic fins were probably kept in an extended position, just as they are in cetaceans (which only have pectoral fins), functioning as hydroplanes for adjusting the swimming level rather than as flippers for producing thrust. The ichthyosaurs' fins, however, may occasionally have served as flippers, as they do in many cetaceans, especially during slow swimming. When the pectoral fins were set at a small upward angle of attack, the upthrust generated would have lifted the front end of the body, causing the animal to rotate around its centre of gravity, depressing the tail. This would enable the ichthyosaur to rise in the water. The pelvic fins may have acted in consort with the pectoral fins, their upthrust, acting behind the centre of gravity, lifting the tail and reducing the pitch of the ascent. Diving could be effected by setting the pectoral fins at a downward angle of attack.

Although the tail is approximately symmetrical, it can be seen that it is not internally symmetrical because the lower lobe is supported by the downturned portion of the vertebral column. The vertebral column probably made the lower lobe stiffer than the upper one. Consequently, when the tail was swept from side to side the resistance of the water probably deflected the upper

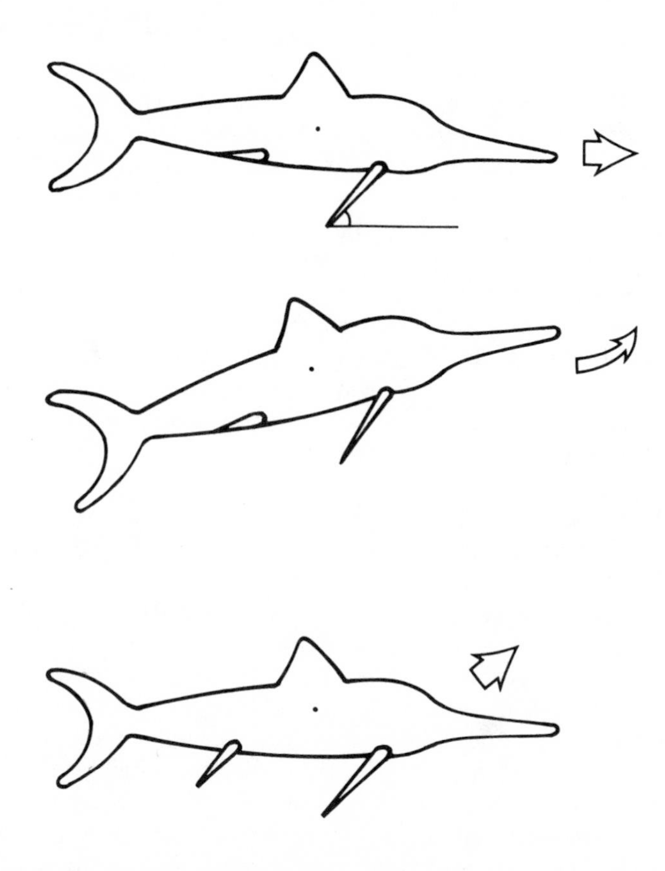

The pectoral fins of the ichthyosaur probably acted as hydroplanes to adjust the swimming level. If during level swimming the angle of attack was set at an acute angle (top) the upthrust generated would pitch the head upwards (middle). This force acting in front of the centre of gravity might be balanced by the pelvic fins (bottom) acting behind the centre of gravity, but this is all entirely speculative.

lobe more than the lower lobe. This would therefore function as an inclined plane moving in a horizontal direction, producing a net downthrust.[37] It is therefore possible that the tail of an ichthyosaur generated a downthrust that tended to rotate the body about the centre of gravity, raising the head. This downthrust would be balanced by a downthrust produced by the pectoral fins, in front of the centre of gravity, and would have facilitated diving. This is speculative, of course, and may well be an oversimplification of the true situation. The tail of the shark, for example, has a far more complex action than was formerly believed.[38]

Lower Jurassic ichthyosaurs had particularly large tails, with fairly high aspect ratios. The aspect ratio of the tail of *Stenopterygius megacephalus*, for example, is much higher than that of the salmon, but probably not as high as that of the speedy swordfish. In *S. hauffianus*, however, the tail is slender and has an aspect ratio easily as high as that of the swordfish. The other fins, similarly, have high aspect ratios, suggesting that *S. hauffianus* was a fast swimmer. *Eurhinosaurus* has exceedingly long and slender fins and although we have no specimen in which the body outline has been preserved, we can be fairly confident that these fins had high aspect ratios. Furthermore, the steeply downturned tail suggests a high aspect ratio caudal fin, and it may reasonably be concluded that *Eurhinosaurus* was among the fastest of ichthyosaurs. Most ichthyosaurs appear to have been adapted for speed and speed is often associated with a predatory way of life.

Almost all specimens of ichthyosaurs have a dentition consisting of numerous, fairly sharp, pointed conical teeth. The teeth are so closely spaced that when the jaws are closed they mesh together, leaving no gaps. This type of dentition suggests a diet of fish, and is seen in such connoisseurs of fish as the dolphin and the seal. Fish are difficult to catch, but once apprehended they slip down the throat very easily and require no chewing. Fish-eaters therefore need jaws that have a swift snapping action, without necessarily any crushing ability, and this is just what we find in the majority of ichthyosaurs. The evidence for this conclusion lies in our ability to detect and interpret areas where muscles were once attached to the bone. The attachment areas of the muscles that closed the lower jaws are marked by various bony ridges and roughenings, and these are all placed close to the jaw joint. Consequently, the smallest movements in these muscles would have brought about a large movement at the tip of the jaws, just as a slight movement with the finger and thumb can bring about a large movement at the tips of a pair of tweezers. Since muscles can contract through short distances almost instantaneously, the jaws were probably able to close very rapidly. Our suspicion that ichthyosaurs were active predators is confirmed by the remains of stomach contents preserved in the abdominal region of many specimens. Fish scales can be recognized, together with large numbers of hooklets belonging to various species of cephalopods, animals allied to the squid. In addition to finding gastric contents, a number of coprolites (fossilized faeces) have been found which, on the evidence of their chemical and geological composition, are believed to have belonged to ichthyosaurs.[39] Whereas ichthyosaur gastric contents contain large numbers of cephalopod hooklets (small hooks, once part of the suckers on the tentacles), the coprolites contain mostly fish scales. Assuming that the coprolites do indeed belong to ichthyosaurs, the evidence suggests that ich-

Jurassic ichthyosaurs had large tails with high aspect ratios. The aspect ratio in **S. megacephalus** *(top) is higher than in a salmon (second from the bottom) but lower than in the swordfish (bottom).* **S. hauffianus** *(second from top) probably had an aspect ratio as high as that of the swordfish.*

thyosaurs fed upon fishes and cephalopods, but that the hooklets were retained within the stomach and not allowed to pass through the rest of the digestive tract. A similar situation occurs in the sperm whale, which feeds largely on squid. Beaks and other hard parts of the squid are retained within the stomach, and are periodically coughed up, presumably so as not to damage the delicate lining of the intestine. Cephalopods, like fishes, are wary animals that avoid capture, and this brings us to the question of how ichthyosaurs located their prey.

Most ichthyosaurs have a remarkably large orbit. A good estimate of the actual size of the eye can be obtained from the sclerotic ring, which is frequently preserved. This thin bony structure consists of a number of overlapping plates that were embedded in the white of the eye. Many present-day birds and reptiles have sclerotic rings, and the function appears to be to maintain the shape of the eye. The function of the sclerotic ring in ichthyosaurs is usually said to be to withstand the pressure experienced during diving, but since the vertebrate eye is fluid-filled, and since fluids are incompressible, this cannot be so. Many whales dive to great depths but their eyes are without a sclerotic ring, and the function of this structure in the ichthyosaurs may have been to maintain the shape of the front part of the eye. There is little doubt that the majority of ichthyosaurs had large eyes, and the evidence from an endocranial cast shows that the optic lobes were probably also large. Both pieces of evidence suggest that sight was the dominant sense. Experiments with captive cetaceans have shown that they also have keen eyesight, but for finding food and avoiding obstacles in the water their sense of hearing is far more important. Their acute hearing is part of an elaborate echo-location system that involves the emission and reception of short bursts of high-frequency sounds. Echo-location is also used by bats, and both systems have been subjected to considerable investigation. The question naturally arises whether ichthyosaurs also echo-located, but this can only be examined when we have an understanding of how the system works.

When the sound waves emitted by a dolphin strike an object in the water, the rebounding waves are received by the ears and the impulses are transmitted to the brain where they are analysed. Humans cannot echo-locate, but are able to determine the direction from which a sound is coming. We probably achieve this by detecting the slight differences in signal strength reaching the left and right ears, and also perhaps by the slight time difference between reception of the sound at the two ears. A sound to the right of our head, for example, not only sounds slightly louder to the right ear, but also reaches that ear slightly before it reaches the left ear. Our ability to detect these slight differences between right and left sides hinges upon the fact that the two sound receptors, the inner ears, are isolated from one another, each being surrounded by a bony capsule, the otic capsule. Most of the sound waves that fall on the head are reflected away, because of the large difference in density between flesh and bone, and air. The only sound waves that reach the inner ear structures are those that pass down the bony canal running from the ear flap to the ear-drum. When the head is placed underwater, however, the situation is changed, because water has about the same density as the body and most of the sound waves falling on the head pass straight through. There is now hardly any difference in signal strengths or arrival times between the two inner ear structures. Consequently, we cannot detect the direction of a sound. This can be confirmed by conducting simple experiments in a swimming pool. Whales have overcome this problem by surrounding each otic capsule with a layer of spongy tissue that insulates it from the rest of the skull so that there is no direct bone-to-bone contact. (As the cetacean otic capsule is not firmly attached to the rest of the skull, it frequently falls away from the body during decomposition. Being of dense bone, it is readily preserved, and otic capsules are fairly common fossils.)

Examination of an ichthyosaur skull reveals that the two otic capsules are firmly braced against the cranium, and it appears that there was no room for an intervening layer of insulation. It is therefore doubtful that the capsules were insulated from one another, which is a count against ichthyosaurs having directional hearing, and hence of being able to echo-locate.

The ability to echo-locate requires not only directional hearing, but also ears that are sensitive to sound. Sound travels through air in the form of waves, much like the movement of ripples across a pond after a stone has been thrown into it. The speed of the waves is fixed for a particular fluid at a particular temperature, and is about 330 m/s (730 m.p.h.) in air, and 1450 m/s (3200 m.p.h.) in water. The distance between wave crests, the wavelength, is related to the pitch or frequency of the sound. High-frequency sounds, like the squeak of a mouse, have a short wavelength, while low-frequency sounds, like the roar of a lion, have a long wavelength. We can easily calculate the wavelength of a given sound from the relationship:

$$\text{wavelength} = \frac{\text{velocity of sound}}{\text{frequency of sound}}$$

Middle C, for example, has a frequency of 256 Hz(hertz—cycles/s) and the wavelength of this sound, when passing through air, is $330 \div 256 = 1.29$ m. When sound waves strike an object that has a density different from that of the fluid in which they are being conducted, they rebound, forming an echo, but only if the object is sufficiently large.

It is easy to obtain an echo by shouting in front of a large brick wall, but impossible by shouting in front of a lampost. It has been found that, in order to obtain an echo from an object, the object needs to be about as wide as the wavelength of the sound. Stated another way, high-frequency sounds can be reflected by smaller objects than low-frequency sounds. You can demonstrate this for yourself without even moving from your chair.

Assuming you are reading this book in a quiet room, cup one hand to your ear as if you were hard of hearing. Can you hear a high pitched hissing sound? Now add your other hand, doubling the size of your ear trumpet. Notice how the pitch of the hissing sound drops. With one hand you are reflecting sound waves into your ear that have a wavelength of about 8 cm, which corresponds to a frequency of about 4000 Hz. When the size of your reflector is doubled, sounds with a wavelength of twice the original length are being reflected, so you hear sounds with only half the frequency. Experiments with animals that echo-locate have shown that they are able to detect very small objects. Bats flying in total darkness can avoid thin wires, and blindfolded dolphins can avoid ropes strung across a pool. This remarkable resolution is possible because these animals use very high-frequency sounds, too high for us to detect. In mammals, the part of the ear that is sensitive to sound is called the cochlea, and this is a small tapered tube, coiled like a snail. The cochlea is completely surrounded by the bone of the otic capsule, and it is such a tight fit that we are able to get a good idea of its shape by examining the impression it leaves in the bone. Reptiles do not possess a coiled cochlea but have, instead, a less elaborate uncoiled structure called a cochlear duct. We know that many reptiles are sensitive to sound, but they may not be able to detect very high-frequency sounds, as mammals do. If we compare the bony otic capsule of an ichthyosaur with that of a mammal we see that the impressions left by the sensitive part of the ear are far less elaborate, with no evidence of a coiled structure. Drawing conclusions on negative evidence is hazardous, but it seems that ichthyosaurs may not have had an acute sense of hearing. This, together with the fact that the otic capsules were braced against the cranium, strongly suggests that they were unable to echolocate.

We have learned a great deal about ichthyosaurs because their fossil remains are so well preserved. Perhaps the most remarkable instance of fine preservation in ichthyosaurs is the occurrence of individuals with embryos in their abdominal cavities.

The discovery of this unusual occurrence was reported in 1846 by an Englishman named Chaning Pearce.

> In developing an *Ichthyosaurus* which I took up from the rock, so as to lay bare that surface which was downwards in the quarry, I removed the clay with great care and exposed to view an *Ichthyosaurus communis* about eight and a half feet long, lying on its back in the highest state of preservation. . . . In cautiously lifting the laminae of clay between the two hinder paddles, my attention was first arrested by a series of small vertebrae lying on three or four posterior ribs; on removing another portion of the clay, ribs, the rami of the jaws, and the other parts of the head were visible.[40]

A female ichthyosaur with her offspring. While this mother may have died at the very moment of giving birth, it is more likely that the embryo was expelled from its mother after her death. See text for details. This specimen, from Holzmaden, Germany, is on public display in the Staatliches Museum für Naturkunde, Stuttgart.

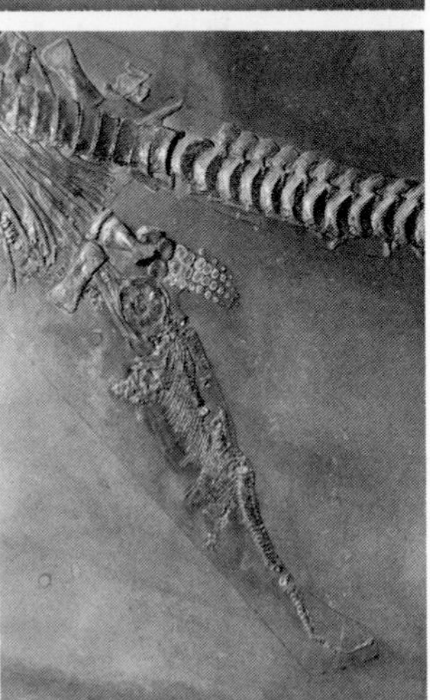

He went on to describe how the tiny skeleton lay in the body cavity of the larger individual, completely surrounded by bone, with its head towards the tail, and reported that, "while the posterior two-thirds of the little animal is within the pelvis, the head appears to protrude beyond it, and apparently in the act of being expelled at the time of death." As the smaller specimen was surrounded by the bones of the larger one, it was apparent that it had not been incorporated accidentally during preservation. The possibility that the small individual had been swallowed was discounted because "so delicate a structure would have been dissolved by the gastric juice", and he arrived at the inescapable conclusion that he was seeing an unborn ichthyosaur lying within its mother's body cavity.

Such a singular discovery had to be treated with extreme caution, and Pearce wrote to the highest authorities in the land: Professor Richard Owen and the Reverend Dr. William Buckland. Both men gave their assurance that there was no reason why ichthyosaurs should not have been viviparous (live-bearing). Twelve years later the great German geologist Friedrich Quenstedt made a similar discovery, but instead of concluding that the smaller individual was an embryo, he decided that it had been devoured by the adult. As the quarries of Holzmaden continued to yield more and more ichthyosaurs, additional skeletons were discovered that contained small inclusions. Parent or predator? A controversy sprang up that continued well into the 20th century. In 1907 the German geologist Wilhelm Branca made the valid point that the two alternatives were not mutually exclusive.[41] He suggested that those small inclusions that lay with their heads facing forwards had been grasped by the tail and swallowed tail-first, whereas those that faced towards the adult's pelvis were embryos, their long snouts being particularly suitable for engaging the narrow birth canal. Branca's fellow countryman, Fritz Drevermann, agreed in principle but argued that, while a fleeing youngster would initially be grasped by the tail, it would then be flipped around and swallowed head first, which is just what dolphins do with fishes.[42] Inclusions that faced towards the pelvis of the adult were consequently interpreted as food items, while those that faced the other way were believed to be embryos, birth normally occurring tail first as in the cetaceans. The debate continued for many years and was largely between German palaeontologists. Wilhelm Leipmann questioned the significance of the orientation of small individuals within the bodies of adults, pointing out that, in domestic animals, tail-first births were almost as common as head-first births.[43] Drawing from human obstetrics, he also noted that embryos can be displaced into the stomach region after the death of the mother, and that birth can even occur after death. He believed this last possibility to be the most plausible explanation for the occurrence of ichthyosaur skeletons that had been preserved during the actual process of birth.

Birth after death has been observed in whales that have been stranded on the shore. In 1974, for example, a school of false killer whales was stranded on a sandy beach on the north coast of Tasmania.[44] After initial examination, the bodies were buried in the sand, but when the site was revisited some months later the bodies were found to be lying on the surface again because they had not been buried deeply enough. Four of the females were found to be pregnant, and in two cases a foetus was partly protruding through the genital slit, presumably because of the mounting gas pressure. Whales are normally born tail first, but in three of the dead females the offspring were in the head-first position. The relative position and orientation of a small individual within the body of another is therefore not an infallible guide to whether it is an embryo, so how can we reach a decision in the case of ichthyosaurs?

Each case has to be judged on its merits, after a number of factors have been taken into account. The size of the inclusion can be a useful guide; young ichthyosaurs are only available as food after they have been born, therefore very small individuals must be embryos. If the inclusion is very scattered it is likely to have been devoured, especially if it is associated with stomach contents such as cephalopod hooklets. The orientation is probably of little significance, but the engagement of the head or tail in the birth canal, or the close proximity of either to the pelvic region, suggests an embryo. Conversely, an inclusion that lies towards the front of the body cavity of the adult, especially if its head is pointing backwards, is more likely to be an item of food than an offspring. Although several ichthyosaur skeletons containing inclusions have been found since Chaning Pearce's day, they are fairly rare. I believe I have seen most of the available material, comprising only eleven specimens, eight of which I concluded to be pregnant females.

The identification of embryos within the body cavity of an extinct animal is not only extremely unusual but is also very useful. First, it establishes the sex of the adult beyond any reasonable doubt. There have been several accounts of dinosaurs where males have been distinguished from females, but none of these can be proven. The identification of several female ichthyosaurs also allows us to look into the question of sexual dimorphism, that is, the differences between males and females. Many animals are sexually dimorphic, and many species, including our own, have slight skeletal differences that enable us to identify the sex of the individual. The evidence at present available suggests that ichthyosaur skeletons are not sexually dimorphic.

As we saw in Chapter 2, we have no way of distinguishing biological species in the fossil record simply because we cannot apply the yardstick of interbreeding. Therefore, even when two fossils look very similar, we can never be sure that they were capable of interbreeding and thus were members of the same biological species. Pregnant ichthyosaurs, however, provide us with a unique opportunity of identifying individuals that unquestionably belong to the same biological species. Furthermore, by comparing the skeleton of the infant with that of its mother, we obtain a lot of information about the changes that occur during growth. For example, young ichthyosaurs, like young humans, have a head that looks far too big for the body.[45] Ichthyosaurs appear to have continued growing after reaching sexual maturity, and we therefore encounter large size ranges among individual members of a given species. The fact that juveniles differ markedly from their parents raises serious problems when we try to identify individuals with their species. The study of pregnant females, however, has helped to resolve this problem. We know that these adults are unquestionably mature, and the differences between them and their offspring are almost entirely attributable to differences in maturity. We are therefore able to recognize features that can be used as indicators of maturity.[46]

9
The Incredible Flying Machine

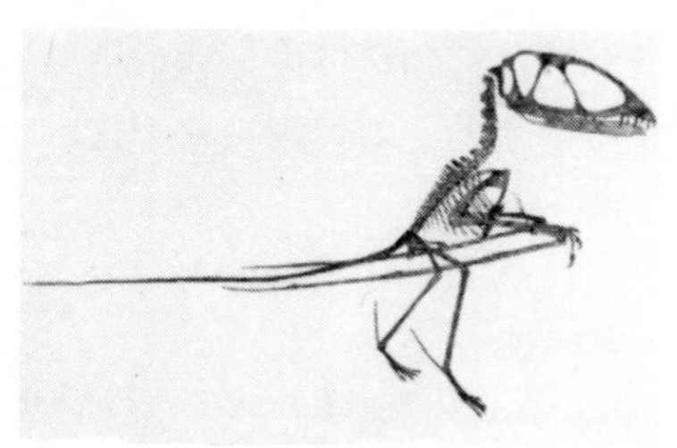

Anyone familiar with opening nights knows that something always has to go wrong. During the last frenetic months before the dinosaur gallery was opened at the Royal Ontario Museum, everything seemed to go awry. Most of the dinosaurs were being mounted in a Mesozoic setting, and the reconstruction of the flora of those times became a major problem. Attempts to fabricate a giant tree fern that would stand up under its own weight engendered a deeper respect for nature than we had before, as did our efforts to duplicate palm fronds in plastic. Painted landscapes of the Mesozoic environment added a dimension of reality to the setting, but also a false sense of completeness. We were dismayed to find that the Cretaceous sky, that now canopied the recently completed *Lambeosaurus* skeleton, was marred by an ugly air vent. It was out of the question to relocate or close off the vent, and the gaping hole, which seemed to grow larger with time, defied all attempts to disguise it. Then someone had a brilliant idea. Why not make a model of the giant pterosaur *Pteranodon* and place it right in front of the offending orifice? A life-like model of this flying reptile was hurriedly constructed, and preparations made to install it. The plan was to place the model right in front of the vent, with its body almost vertical, completely concealing the vent. However, the technician at the top of the ladder, a former Luftwaffe pilot, could not bring himself to place *Pteranodon* in such an aerodynamically unstable position. As a result, *Pteranodon* not only does not conceal the air vent, but actually draws attention to it, because everyone looks up to get a good view of the model, which is the only life-like reptile in the whole gallery!

It is not surprising that *Pteranodon* attracts so much attention. It is a most unusual animal. Walking through the gallery one day, I could not help overhearing a teacher addressing her class: "The pterosaurs became extinct because their wings became so large that they could no longer fly properly." The attention of the class was directed to the wire-and-fabric replica as the point was pressed home—the wings were certainly very long, some eight metres from tip to tip. According to the teacher they were far too long for the good of its owner, and extinction was the inevitable outcome of this folly of nature. Without realizing it, the teacher and her attentive class had just dismissed one of the most perfectly designed and engineered gliders the world has ever known. The glider apparently had such a low flying speed that it

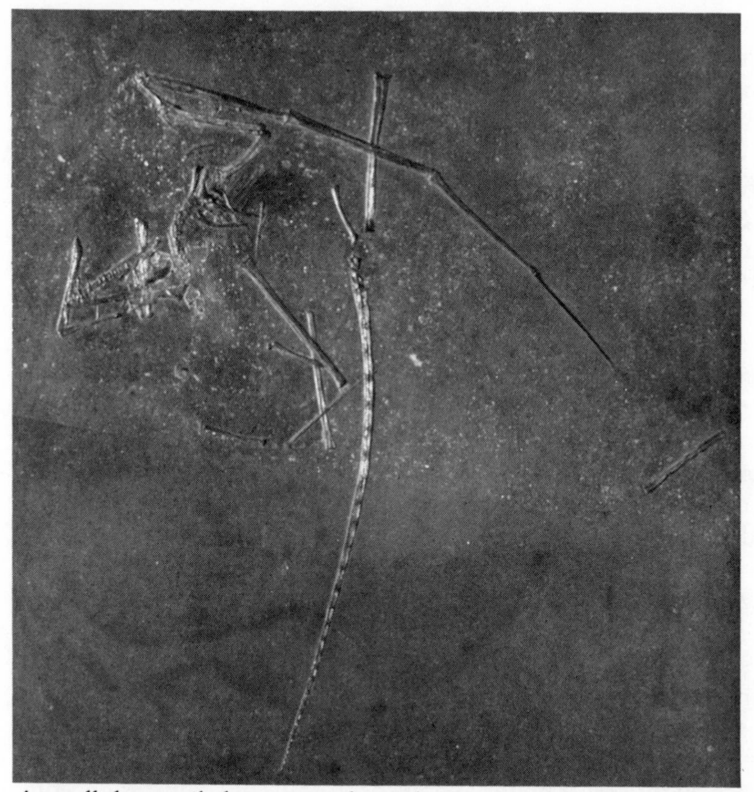

A small, long-tailed pterosaur from the Lower Jurassic of Holzmaden.

could become airborne on a breeze, turn in less than its own wingspan, and sink at a lower rate than the best modern gliders.

The pterosaurs first appeared in the fossil record towards the end of the Triassic Period, about 200 million years ago, and they flourished until the close of the Cretaceous Period, nearly 140 million years later. Many of the Jurassic species were fairly small—about the size of a thrush—and some had long bony tails that appear to have terminated in an expanded flap, probably used as a rudder. The long-tailed kind apparently did not survive into the Cretaceous Period, which was dominated by large tail-less pterosaurs, exemplified by *Pteranodon*.

The pterosaurs had many features in common with birds and bats, which is not surprising since all three were highly modified for flight. They are frequently referred to as flying dinosaurs but this is erroneous, and, as we saw in Chapter 1, there is some doubt regarding their classification—perhaps they should be placed in a class of their own. The smaller pterosaurs probably flew by flapping their wings, like bats and most birds, but the large ones were primarily gliders. The wing was membranous, like that of a bat, but, instead of being supported by most of the hand, it was supported by only one finger. This finger, the fourth, was remarkable for its enormous length, which far

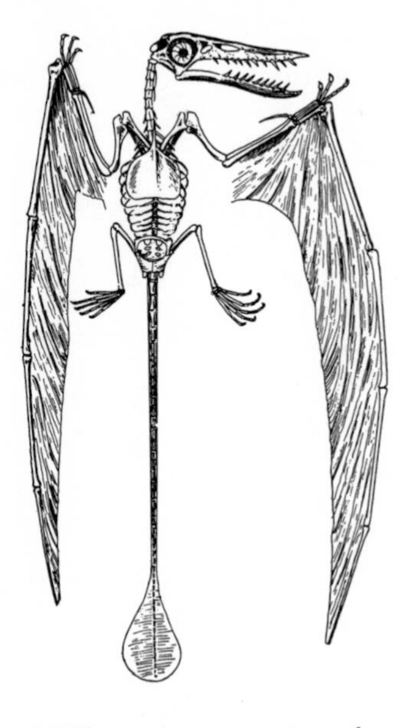

Williston's restoration of the long-tailed pterosaur **Rhamphorhynchus**.

exceeded that of the rest of the front limb, and formed the leading edge of the wing. The thumb, index finger, and middle finger all terminated in sharp claws and were probably used for grasping and climbing. The fifth digit was lost early in their history,[1] although some palaeontologists, for example von Meyer, have suggested that the pteroid bone, a small element that arises from the wrist and probably supported a small membrane on the leading edge of the wing, may represent the fifth digit.

The Jurassic and Triassic pterosaurs had sharply pointed teeth, and most of them were probably beasts of prey, but teeth were sparse or absent in the large Cretaceous pterosaurs. *Pteranodon*, for example, had no teeth at all. Almost all the pterosaur skeletons that have been collected were found in marine deposits. This suggests, but does not prove, that most of them lived in close association with the sea.[2] The larger pterosaurs probably fed mainly on fish, and at least two specimens of *Pteranodon* have fish remains preserved in the stomach region[3].

As is frequently the case in palaeontology, most of our material is fairly localized, both geographically and geologically. The best-preserved material comes to us from the famous Holzmaden quarries of southern Germany and from the equally famous quarries of Solnhofen, some 100 km to the east. Both deposits are Jurassic in age and have therefore yielded the smaller species. Large quantities of material have been collected from Cretaceous deposits, but this is fragmentary in nature and the most completely known representative of this period is *Pteranodon*. *Pteranodon* has been found in many parts of the world, but the best material is from the western United States.

The flying mechanism of the gliding pterosaurs is simpler and better understood than the flapping flight of their smaller relatives, and consequently this chapter will be devoted to *Pteranodon*. Before delving into the flight mechanisms of this ancient aeronaut, however, it is necessary to review the principles of flight.

All heavier-than-air flying machines, from stag beetles to Boeings, rely upon the principle of the airfoil to keep themselves airborne. The major difference among aircraft, both living and man-made, is in the power source used to generate the forward thrust that is necessary to make the airfoil work. Most flying animals use muscle power to flap wings to produce thrust, while others, the gliders, extract energy from moving air currents. Most man-made flying machines use various types of heat engines to generate thrust, but others soar effortlessly on moving air currents.

Our knowledge of the airfoil principle dates back more than two centuries, to the work of Daniel Bernoulli. He found that when a fluid flows over a curved surface its velocity is increased, causing a reciprocal decrease in pressure. This can easily be demonstrated by means of a pair of coloured glass balls of the sort used to decorate Christmas trees. If the balls are held about 1 cm apart and air is blown through the gap between them, they will move together and touch. The explanation is that the air that flows over the two curved surfaces experiences a reduction in pressure, and, since the rest of the air surrounding the two balls is at normal pressure, they are forced together. The airfoil, which usually takes the form of a wing, exploits Bernoulli's principle by having a convexly curved upper surface and a flat or concave lower surface. When the airfoil is moved through the air, the flow over the two surfaces produces an area of reduced pressure next to the upper surface, and an area of increased pressure next to the lower surface. As a consequence the airfoil experiences an upthrust, or lift. This lift increases with the speed and eventually exceeds the weight of the aircraft, at which point it becomes airborne. When the speed of the air over the airfoil slows, the air begins to separate from the surface. Separation begins at the trailing edge and moves forward, and as it does, the lift decreases. As the speed decreases further (or if the angle of attack is increased), a point is reached when there is a rapid decrease in lift, and the airfoil is then said to have stalled. The airspeed (the speed of the airfoil relative to the air) at which the airfoil stalls is called the stalling speed. If the airspeed of an aircraft is allowed to fall below the stalling speed it rapidly descends.

The performance of an airfoil is largely determined by the shape of its cross section, and improvements in design during the pioneering days of flying were generally obtained by the method of trial and error. Needless to say, there were many errors! A significant landmark in the history of aeronautics was the use of the wind tunnel to test models of airfoil sections. The Wright brothers were among the first to use a wind tunnel, and they were able to resolve most of their problems on the ground.

It was found that the lift force, which acts at right angles to the direction of the motion of the airfoil, was always accompanied by a drag force, which acts in opposition to the direction of motion, that is, at right angles to the lift. The combination of the two forces is called the total reaction, and it acts through a point called the centre of pressure. The size of the lift force can be improved by increasing the camber of the airfoil, that is, its thickness relative to its width, and also by inclining the whole section at a small angle of attack. (As we saw in the previous chapter even a simple flat plate experiences a lift if it is inclined to the direction of motion.) Increases in lift, however, are accompanied by increases in drag that make it progressively more difficult to push the wing through the air, thus decreasing its efficiency.

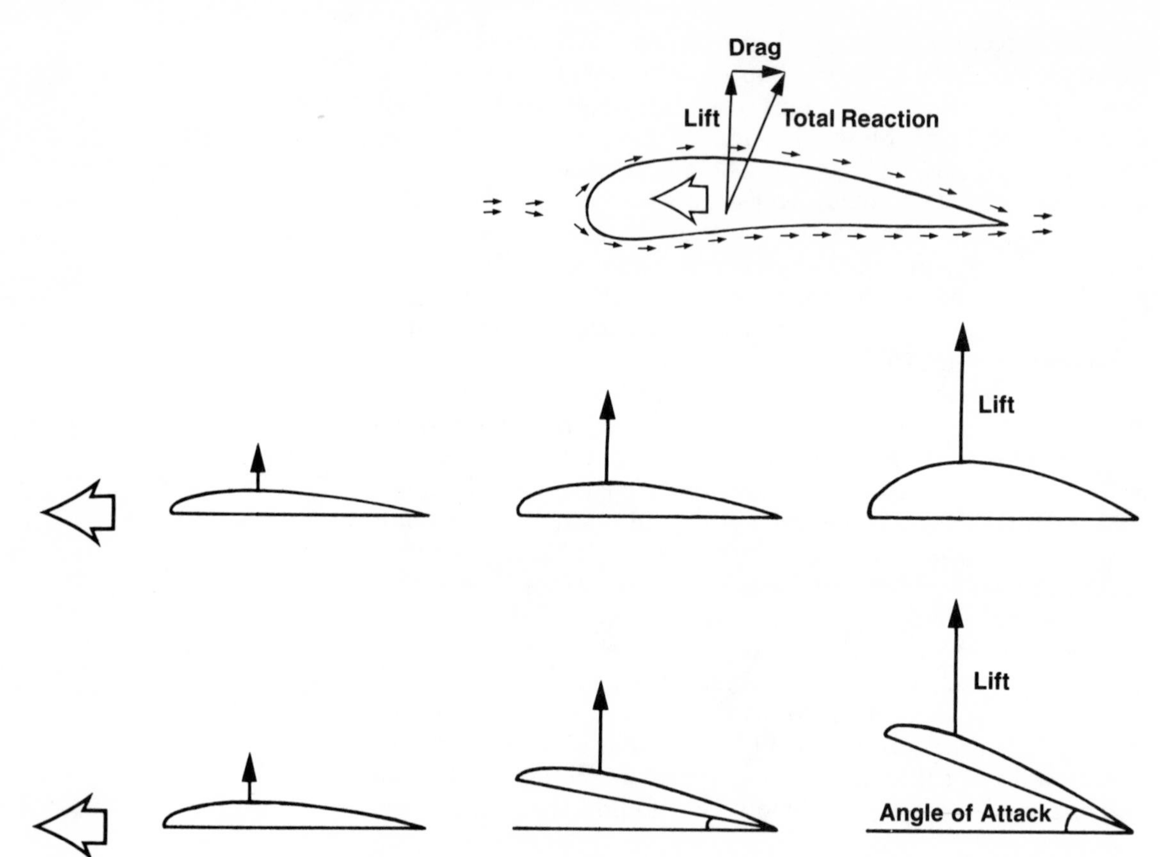

Top: When an airfoil moves through the air it experiences two forces: lift and drag, which act at right angles to one another. The resultant, the total reaction, acts through a point called the centre of pressure. The lift force generated by an airfoil can be increased both by increasing the camber of the airfoil (middle), and by inclining it at a small angle of attack (bottom). Increases in the lift force, however, are accompanied by increases in the drag force. The magnitude of the forces shown here are indicated by the lengths of the arrows.

A useful measure of the efficiency of a wing is the ratio of lift-to-drag, which varies with the shape of the section. The shape of the whole wing also affects the ratio of lift-to-drag, and it has been found that long narrow wings (that is, wings with high aspect ratios—a term encountered in the previous chapter) have a higher ratio than short wide wings. (The width of a wing is measured along its chord, that is, a line drawn through the wing section parallel to the direction of motion, and usually at its widest part.) Wings that have a high aspect ratio not only give a higher lift-to-drag ratio but also have a higher stalling speed, which means that higher speeds have to be maintained to prevent stalling. The wing of the albatross has a high aspect ratio

Birds of prey (top) have low aspect-ratio wings but the albatross has high aspect-ratio wings.

that enables it to remain aloft with the minimum of effort, but the relatively high stalling speed prevents it from flying as slowly as some other birds. Birds of prey usually have a very broad wing with a low aspect ratio, which allows them to fly very slowly. Slow flying speeds give the enhanced manoeuvrability that enables them to make tight turns as they soar above an intended victim. Their wings also have a high camber which gives them good lifting ability for carrying off their prey.

Weight also has a considerable influence on flying performance, and is measured in terms of wing loading, that is, the total weight, divided by the surface area of the wings. Aircraft with low wing loadings tend to be more manoeuvrable, to have shallower gliding angles (the least angle at which an aircraft can glide) and lower stalling speeds, and to require less power.

The relationships between aspect ratio, wing loading, power, and flying performance may be demonstrated by comparing two famous fighter aircraft of World War Two: the Messerschmitt 109 and the Supermarine Spitfire.[4] Apart from the Messer-

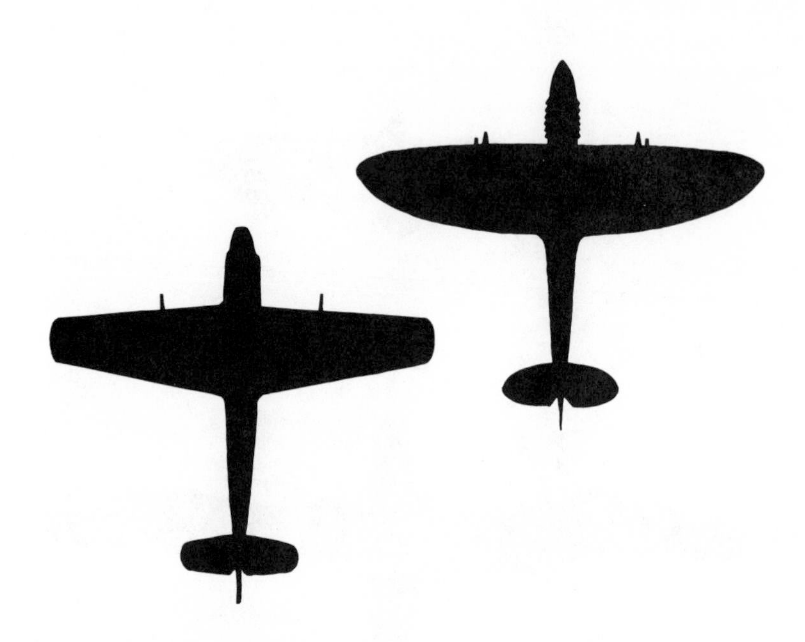

The Spitfire (right) had relatively broader wings than the Messerschmitt, and they were slightly larger. Both aircraft weighed about the same, consequently the Spitfire had a lower wing loading, hence greater manoeuvrability.

schmitt's slightly shorter wingspan (9.8 m compared with 11.3 m) and marginally greater weight (2,500 kg compared with 2,400 kg), the two aircraft were very similar in size. The most striking difference between them was the shape of the wings. The Spitfire had much broader wings, giving it a lower aspect ratio and a wing area almost 40% greater than that of the Messerschmitt. As a consequence, the wing loading of the Messerschmitt was considerably higher than that of the Spitfire (by 33%), requiring its Daimler-Benz engine to deliver 1,100 horse power (hp), compared with the modest 800 hp of the Spitfire's Rolls-Royce power plant. The Messerschmitt could climb and dive faster than the Spitfire and had a higher operational ceiling, but it was much less manoeuvrable. Because the Spitfire could fly slower, it could make tighter turns, and one of the defensive strategies of its pilots was to put their machines into tight spirals , making it almost impossible for the faster and wider-turning adversary to get in a good shot.

Most birds are capable of both flapping and gliding, and a continuous spectrum connects flapping flyers such as sparrows, which do little gliding, with birds like the albatross, which spend most of their time gliding, and which usually flap their wings only on take-off. In flapping flight almost all the power required for keeping aloft is supplied by the muscles, and it is therefore an energetically expensive means of flying. A more economical way of flying is to extract energy from moving air currents. There are basically two ways in which this can be done: by exploiting vertical and by exploiting horizontal air currents, described as soaring and gliding.

Soaring on rising air currents is the most effortless form of flying, and most vertical movements are caused by columns of warm air called thermals. Thermals usually result from differences in warming and cooling rates of different parts of the Earth's surface, and sail plane pilots learn to recognize where thermals are likely to occur. I once flew over Wyoming in a small aircraft on a bright spring afternoon. Much of the snow had melted, leaving dark patches of exposed ground. As these patches had absorbed much more heat from the sun than the surrounding snowy areas, they were the centres of rising columns of warm air, and as we flew over them the aircraft was lifted up, only to drop down again over the snow. Rising air columns can also be caused by updrafts, as when on-shore winds strike a sea cliff. The familiar association between wheeling seagulls and rugged cliffs brings this to mind. Most accounts of soaring flight emphasize that rising air columns are often only a few metres in diameter, so that soaring birds have to keep circling in order to stay within the column and so remain airborne.[5] The wheeling flight of vultures and their relatives, a familiar sight in western movies, certainly seems to support this conclusion. However, a careful study of vultures and their allies, made in India during the early part of this century by a meticulous observer named E.H. Hankin, has shown that circling is only a small part of the flying repertoire of soaring birds. Hankin found that soaring birds often travel for miles in a straight direction without any discernable wing movements, and appear to be free to change course at will.

> It is difficult to understand how anyone could see cheels and eagles playing together in the air and still believe that soaring flight is due to birds having to hunt for and take advantage of chance ascending currents. The complicated movements of the cheel as it glides in any direction to meet or avoid the other birds are only explicable on the view that every minute portion of soarable air is as ready as every other portion to yield energy for its flight.[6]

Hankin was unable to determine just what quality of the air it was that permitted birds to soar. He could discount the wind because birds soar just as well on perfectly calm days as they do on windy days. Soaring was found to occur only during the daytime, and then only after the sun had been shining for some time. (Soaring birds are grounded at night.) He observed that the time at which the air became "soarable" varied according to the size of the birds. Those with smaller wing loadings became airborne before birds with higher wing loadings. The order in which the different kinds of birds became airborne was therefore the same each morning. Flapping was required for take-off, but once airborne the birds seldom flapped their wings. Sometimes the sky became so overcast that soaring flight was interrupted and the birds had to resort to flapping, or return to the ground. Hankin rejected the idea that soaring flight is caused by large masses of rising air, one of his reasons being that vertical currents usually cannot be detected in soarable air. He noted that the movements of aerial seeds and isolated feathers, which are often seen floating in the air, are as random during the day when the air is soarable as they are after sunset when the air no longer supports soaring flight. Much progress has been made in aviation since Hankin's time, but we are still a long way from understanding the underlying mechanism of soaring flight.

Gliding flight, as exemplified by the albatross, is better understood than soaring flight. It exploits differences in horizontal wind velocities. As air flows over the surface of the Earth, it is slowed by friction, and the bottom layer of 20 cm or so is essentially stationary—this is well known to sunbathers on windy beaches; lying in relatively still air, one becomes aware that it is windy only on sitting up. There is, therefore, a velocity gradient, the slowest moving air being at the bottom. The albatross makes a shallow dive from about 20 m with the wind at its back, and as altitude is lost ground speed (speed relative to the ground) is gained. At the bottom of the descent, which is just above sea-level, a turn is made into the wind, and the ground speed is so high that the bird ascends rapidly. As the altitude increases the ground speed decreases, but because the air encountered is moving progressively faster the air speed does not diminish very rapidly. As a consequence, the bird continues to climb even though its ground speed is very low, and it reaches a sufficient altitude to enable it to repeat the process. Coming ashore only to breed, the albatross spends almost all its life on the wing, covering thousands of lonely miles, feeding on squid and fish.

In flight, the albatross is the most graceful of birds. Its effortless gliding requires only an occasional wing movement, and therefore a minimal expenditure of energy. Once on land, however, it undergoes a transformation into one of the clumsiest of animals, earning it the epithet of "gooney bird." Its heavy body and big feet give it an awkward, waddling gait, and its efforts to become airborne are both laborious and undignified.

The grounded bird faces into the wind and runs as fast as it can, with outstretched wings flapping frantically. The flight muscles can barely produce sufficient power to get it off the ground, and take-off attempts do not always meet with success.

The largest species, the great Wandering Albatross, has a wingspan of 3.3 m and weighs about 8 kg, which may approach the limit for powered take-offs.[7] The reason why there is a limit is that the weight of a bird increases approximately in proportion to the cube of its length, whereas the power generated by the muscles only increases approximately with the square of the length (that is, with the area of their cross section)[8]. Very large and heavy aircraft have been possible only because of great improvements in engine design. The jet engine can deliver several times more power than a piston engine of the same weight. There has, of course, been no such improvement during the evolution of birds in the power output of flight muscles. It is extremely unlikely that an albatross could sustain flight for any length of time by wing-flapping, and its dependence on the wind explains why it is grounded on calm days.

If the albatross, with a 3.3 m wingspan, is close to the upper size limit for flight, how do we rationalize the occurrence of *Pteranodon* and its allies, which had wingspans of more than 8 m? These great pterosaurs were simply too large to fly, but fly they did, and a careful study of the skeleton of *Pteranodon* reveals a truly remarkable piece of aeronautical engineering.

Few relics from the past have excited our imaginations or confounded our powers of reason more than *Pteranodon*. Ever since its discovery in the 1870s,[9] palaeontologists have speculated on how such large and frail animals could have become airborne. Could they flap their wings? Did they launch themselves from cliffs? Would a grounded individual ever be able to become airborne again? These, and many other questions, went largely unanswered until the 1970s when *Pteranodon* became the subject of a joint investigation between a palaeontologist, C.D. Bramwell, and an aeronautical engineer, G.R. Whitfield.[10] Before assessing the results of their study, however, we need to become familiar with the anatomy of *Pteranodon* and see how it compares with other flyers.

An observer examining *Pteranodon* for the first time is usually struck by three things: the unusual crest that projects from the back of the skull, the thinness of the bones, and the large size of the wings. The humerus is a short bone, and, like the other bones of the skeleton, it is hollow and thin-walled like a bird's. Because of its fragility, it has undergone compression during preservation, and the various shapes occurring in different specimens led early palaeontologists to believe that they belonged to different species.[11] In many vertebrates the articulation of the head of the

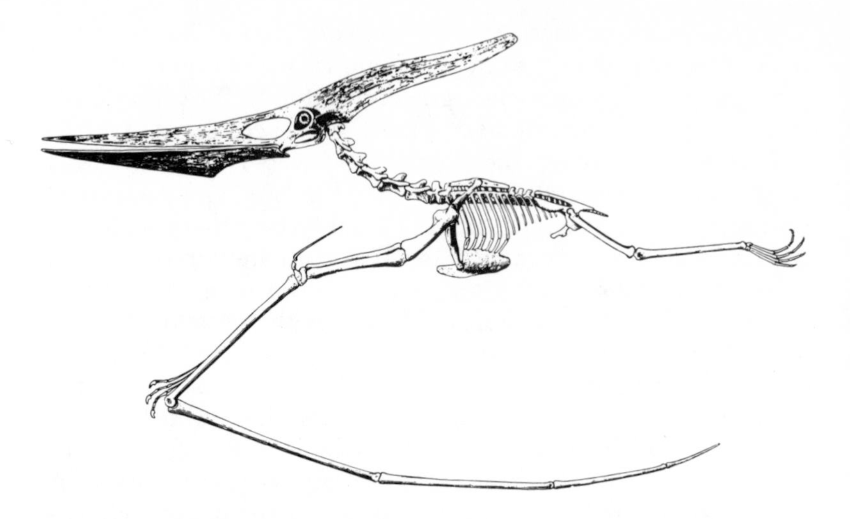

Eaton's restoration of the large Cretaceous pterosaur **Pteranodon**.

humerus with the shoulder girdle is a ball-and-socket joint, but in *Pteranodon* it is essentially a hinge joint. This joint appears to have permitted an up-and-down flapping movement of the wing and a small amount of twisting, but the wing tended to remain in a locked position, with the humerus inclined at an angle of about 20° above the horizontal and about 20° towards the rear. This was probably the normal position of the humerus during flight, and the locking joint, which is unique among flying animals, is reminiscent of the leg joint of the horse, which permits it to sleep in a standing position.

The bones of the forearm, the radius and the ulna, are almost twice the length of the humerus, and the elbow, like our own, is a hinge joint but far more restricted in its movements. As in other tetrapods, the wrist comprises a number of small bones, the carpals, which articulate with a series of four metacarpal bones that correspond to those in the palm of the human hand. All four metacarpals are exceedingly long—almost twice the length of the forearm. The first three, which articulate with three clawed digits, are very slender, but the fourth, which articulates with the wing digit, is as stout as the radius and the ulna. This fourth metacarpal is jointed at the wrist so that it can be rotated forward, depressing the leading edge of the wing, but it is prevented from rotating the other way by a bony stop. The bones of the forearm are connected to the wrist in such a way that bending the elbow causes the fourth metacarpal to swing backwards and upwards. This movement probably allowed the wing to retract partially while the animal was in flight. The individual finger bones (phalanges) of the clawed digits have normal proportions, but those of the wing finger are very wide and extremely long, and together constitute more than half the

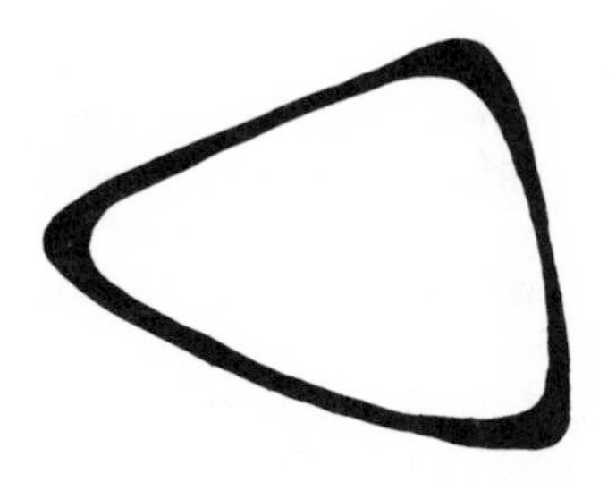

The walls of the wing bones of **Pteranodon** *are not of uniform thickness. Transverse sections across the bones show that they are thickened in areas of maximum stress.*

length of the wing. The first (proximal) phalanx articulates with its metacarpal in a very mobile pulley joint, which permitted the wing to be folded across the back of the animal when it was not being used for flying. There is evidence that the wing was prevented from being folded back during flight by a thick tendon extending from the humerus to the end of the metacarpal bone. The presence at one time of such a tendon is suggested by the occurrence of notches in both of these bones. The thin-walled structure of the bones, which has been compared with the thickness of blotting paper, is particularly obvious in the bones of the wing. So that maximum strength could be achieved with minimum weight, the bone material was concentrated in areas of highest stress, and this strategy is revealed when cross sections of the bones are examined. The thickness of the walls is not uniform, being greatest at the angles. The ends of bones were probably subjected to the greatest stresses, and in birds these regions are strengthened by fine internal struts. A similar situation probably occurred in the pterosaurs.

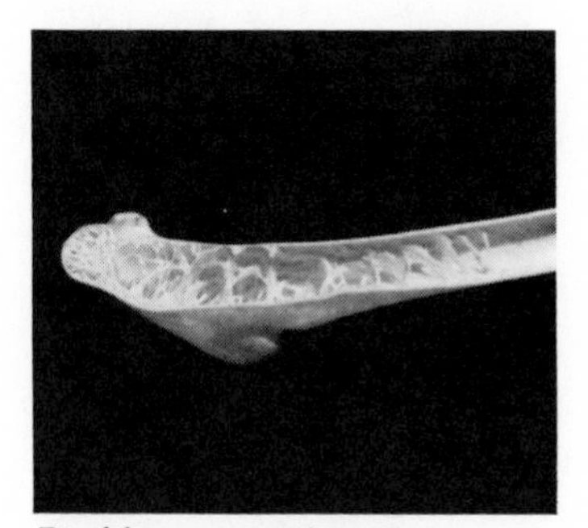

Bird bones combine strength and lightness by having thin walls which are braced by internal struts. A similar strategy is used in aircraft design.

We do not know the shape or structure of the wing membrane in *Pteranodon*, but an approximation can be made by reference to certain Jurassic specimens in which the outline has been preserved, and by analogy with the bat. The membrane was probably thin and elastic, as in bats, so that any modifications in the configuration of the wing finger during flight would not cause the wing membrane to be thrown into folds. It is believed that the wing membrane extended from the sides of the body, as it does in the bat, but its attachment to the hind limbs is a point of contention. Some palaeontologists, no doubt influenced by the fact that, in bats, the membrane extends down the leg as far as the foot, have suggested an extensive attachment to the legs. Others reject this possibility, pointing out that there is no evidence for it in any of the specimens in which outlines of the membrane have been preserved; we will be returning to this point later. There is some evidence that a small membrane may have been attached to the inside edge of each leg, extending as a narrow strip to the base of the tail.[12] There was probably a small membrane in front of each wing, extending from the shoulder region and supported by a small bone, the pteroid bone. This may have had a function similar to the alula of the bird wing, which is an anti-stalling device.

The birds' alula, which is supported by the thumb, is like a small wing and can be extended so that it protrudes from the leading edge of the wing. When the wing is nearing a stalling condition, that is, when the lift is no longer sufficient to support the body weight, the alula flicks out and directs the airflow over the surface of the wing. This can be seen particularly well in the pigeon when it is coming in to land, because the wing movements are sufficiently slow to enable the careful observer to catch an occasional glimpse of the alula being deployed. In aeronautical terminology, the alula is a leading edge slot, and the device was used on the wings of aircraft in the early days of flight, by Handley-Page, to prevent stalling at low speeds. The Messerschmitt 109 had an automatic leading edge slot that was extended in near-stalling conditions.

The pectoral girdle is similar to that of a bird, comprising an upper element, the scapula, fused with a lower element, the coracoid, the two forming an L-shaped structure with the socket for the humerus at its centre. Several of the anterior dorsal vertebrae are fused together, and a bony plate is formed that has a socket on either side to receive the ends of the scapulae. This fused structure, peculiar to the pterosaurs, is called the notarium. It provided a firm anchorage for the scapulae. Most birds, similarly, have fused anterior dorsal vertebrae, but the scapula is braced against the ribs rather than attached to the vertebrae. The notarium, particularly long in *Pteranodon*, has eight vertebrae. The ends of the coracoids articulated with a pair of sockets on the sternum, so that the whole pectoral girdle was rigidly braced, forming a firm anchorage for the wings. In carinates (flying birds) the sternum is a large, saucer-shaped bone with a deep median keel that provides a large area of attachment for the powerful flight muscles. In *Pteranodon*, however, the sternum is relatively smaller, and does not have such a well-developed keel as in many carinates. This suggests that the flight muscles were not as large relative to the body as they are in carinates. It must be pointed out, though, that bats do not have a very extensive sternum but nevertheless have extensive flight muscles (the left and right sets of muscles pull against each other and the sternum functions mainly as an anchor).

The similarity with the birds extends to the pelvic region, because the sacrum is very avian in appearance.[13] So, to a lesser extent, is the pelvis. The hind limbs, however, have a greater overall resemblance to those of a bat than a bird. The similarity to bats extends beyond the proportionality of the individual bones of the leg and foot to the unusual nature of the hip joint. In birds, dinosaurs, and mammals, the head of the femur is set off from the shaft so that when it locates in its socket in the pelvis the leg lies vertically beneath the body. In bats and pterosaurs, however, the head of the femur has a more terminal position so that the leg sprawls out from the side of the body rather than lying vertically beneath it. The extreme sprawling gait depicted in some restorations of pterosaurs, however, is probably an exaggeration. This sprawling posture of the hind limbs, in bats, is correlated with the fact that the wing membrane is attached to the legs. Having the legs projecting from the sides of the body permits the shape of the wing membrane to be adjusted simply by moving the legs up or down. This posture, however, is a disadvantage when the animal is moving on the ground. Bats walk on all fours, using their thumbs to prop up the front part of the body, and although some of them, including the vampire bat, are agile and can even leap into the air, most of them are rather ungainly on the ground.[14]

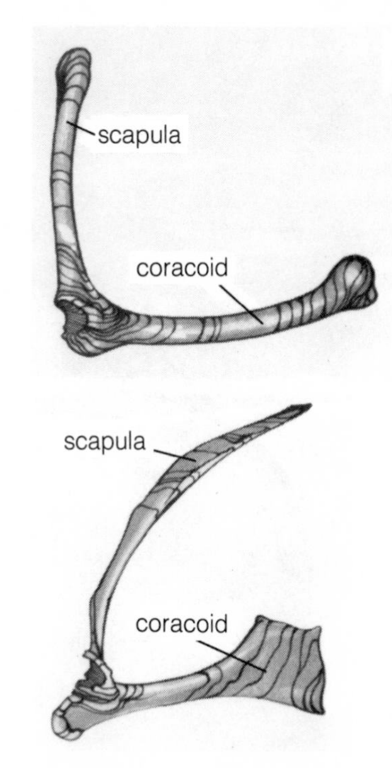

The scapulocoracoid of **Pteranodon** *(top) is very similar to that of a flying bird.*

The smaller pterosaurs may have been quite agile when they walked, but *Pteranodon* might have been rather awkward. It has even been suggested that grounded individuals propelled themselves along on their bellies with rowing movements of the hind legs,[15] or perhaps by pulling themselves along by their front claws, but recent studies refute this. The hind feet of pterosaurs are much like those of bats, with long toes ending in sharp claws and it is likely that they used them for hanging upside down to roost, like bats. While the small pterosaurs may have roosted in trees, *Pteranodon,* with its eight metre wingspan, probably avoided trees with the determination of a kite-flyer.

Pterosaurs, like birds (and bats), have thin-walled bones, but birds are unusual in having the hollow spaces inside their bones continue into the cavities of the lungs. Our own lungs, like those of other vertebrates, are closed sacs connected to the throat by the trachea. In birds, however, the lungs are connected with several thin-walled sacs, the air sacs, which connect in turn with the hollow cavities of the bones—a most bizarre situation! Birds can shunt air in and out of this system during breathing, and it seems that one of its functions is to help them lose excess body heat. The avian air-sac system is revealed by the occurrence of fairly large openings, called pneumatic foramina, which communicate with the hollow cavities of the bones. Pterosaurs have similar openings, which suggests that they, too, may have possessed an air-sac system. Bats do not have such a system.

The most striking features of *Pteranodon* is its enormous head, half of which is formed by the crest. The crest reminds us

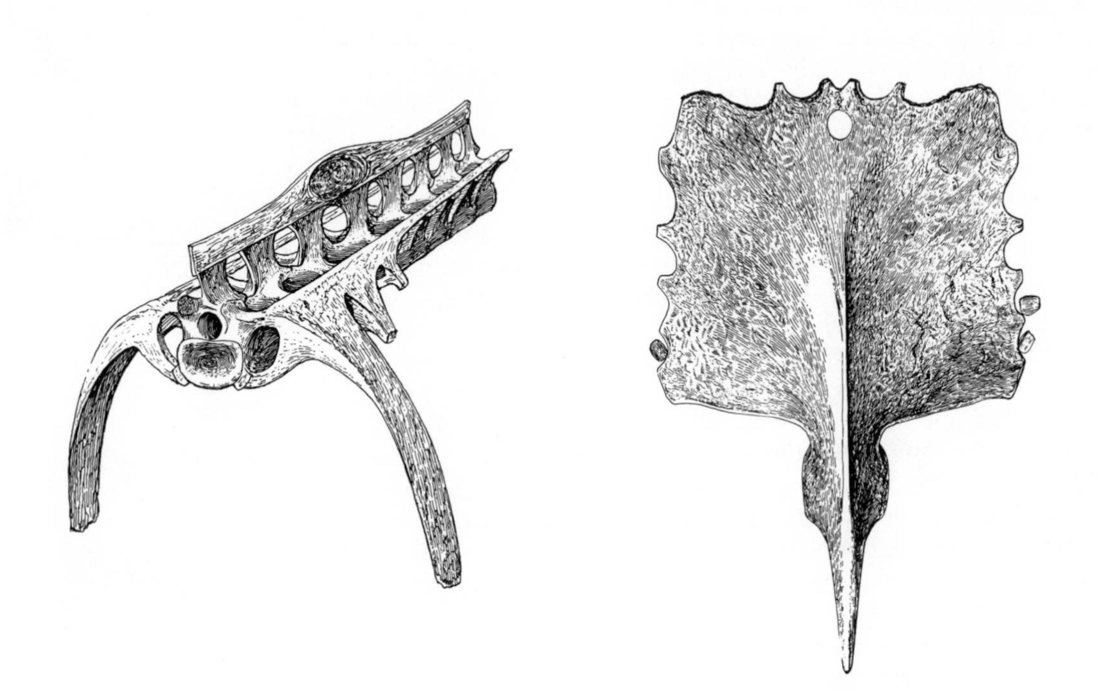

A restoration of the notarium (left) and sternum of **Pteranodon**.

of the crested dinosaur *Parasaurolophus* (see Chapter 4), but the resemblance is only superficial because its crest had no connection with the nares and was only a few millimetres thick. Teeth are entirely absent, and the long sharp bill which has a distinctly avian appearance, may have been provided with a horny beak. The jaw joint has a most unusual structure, quite unlike that of any other reptile, and gives a valuable clue to the method of feeding. The articular surface (on the quadrate bone) for the mandible bears a spiral groove that has a left-handed thread on the right side of the skull, and a right-handed thread on the left side. The articular surfaces of the mandible are correspondingly grooved to match these two spirals. Consequently, when the mouth was opened, the left and right halves of the mandible was forced apart by the tracking action of the jaw joint, apparently increasing the width of the gape. There is little doubt that *Pteranodon* fed on fish because, as mentioned earlier, fish remains have been found in the stomach region of some specimens.[16] In one specimen remnants of fish and crustacea were found just beneath the mandible and this has suggested to some palaeontologists that they may have had a throat pouch, like that of a pelican.[17] The evidence, however, is circumstantial.

Although the skull is large, it is lightly constructed and nearly every part is excavated by pneumatic canals that may have connected with an air-sac system. The significance of the long crest and lightly built skeleton lies in the flying mechanism, and our ability to interpret this reflects the advanced state of aeronautical engineering.

Aeronautics has come a long way since the days of Orville and Wilbur Wright, and has evolved from the realm of trial and error to a sophisticated technology with a high level of predictability. Long before the first Boeing 747 was built, its flying characteristics were precisely known, and these can be determined for any flying machine, given sufficient data. Gliders are simpler than powered machines, and such information as maximum speed, stalling speed, minimum turning circle, sinking rate, and gliding angle can be deduced for them given the weight, and wing configuration.

Pteranodon, like the albatross, appears to have been too large to have been able to sustain flight by wing-flapping and we conclude that it was primarily a glider. Starting from that premise Bramwell and Whitfield[18] modified a computer program designed for analysing the performance of man-made gliders and used it for deducing the probable flight characteristics of *Pteranodon*. Estimates had to be made for the body weight and area, and for the shape, profile and area of the wings. The details of how these estimates were made need not concern us here, but we do have to discuss one of the basic assumptions they made, namely the shape of the wing membrane. We have seen that there is some disagreement among specialists as to whether the wing membrane attached to the legs in pterosaurs. Bramwell and Whitfield assumed that it did, but K. Padian, who has made an extensive study of the problem, has presented evidence that it did not, at least in the Jurassic pterosaurs that he studied.[19] If the wing membrane of *Pteranodon* did not extend to the legs, how would this affect the results obtained by Bramwell and Whitfield? Obviously, their estimate for the wing area would be too high, giving a wing loading which would be low. Low wing loadings, as we have seen, are correlated with low stalling speeds, enhanced maneouvrability, shallow gliding angles and the consumption of less power. If Bramwell and Whitfield were wrong about the extent of the membrane, which seems likely, then *Pteranodon* would not have such a good performance in these regards as their results suggest. We will now examine the results of their study, noting parenthetically, how these would compare if the data were re-evaluated using a smaller wing area.

As was seen earlier, the weight of a bird tends to increase in proportion to the cube of the wingspan (this is what would be expected, because volume, and hence weight, is proportional to the cube of the length, as discussed in Chapter 5), and it was calculated that a bird with a wingspan similar to that of *Pteranodon* would weigh about 100 kg. But the highest estimate for the weight of *Pteranodon* was less than a quarter of that—giving a low wing loading, hence a low sinking speed and correspondingly shallow gliding angle.[20] The best flying speed, that is, the speed that gave the slowest sinking rate, was found to be about 28 km/h or 15 knots (underestimate). At this speed, the animal would sink at about 0.4 m per second or 1.5 km/h, (underestimate) which is about half the sinking rate of a falcon, albatross, or man-made glider, and the gliding angle was only about 1 in 18, or 3° (underestimate). The stalling speed was calculated at about 24 km/h or 32 knots (underestimate). The unusually slow flying speeds, attributable to its small body weight and large wing area, conferred outstanding manoeuvrability, and it was calculated that *Pteranodon* could turn in a radius of only about 5 m (underestimate), banked at an angle of about 60° (overestimate). In a tight turn like this, the wing tip on the inside of the turn would move through a radius of only about 3 m (underestimate). Such tight turns would enable *Pteranodon* to keep within fairly narrow thermals and updrafts if necessary. The low flying speeds suggest that it probably did not use differential wind velocities to glide, the way the albatross does, because it would not have been able to make much progress against strong winds.

The remarkably low stalling speed resolves the problem of how *Pteranodon* could have become airborne. All that was needed was a wind brisker than the (underestimated) 24 km/h stalling speed, which is only a light breeze. If it faced into the wind with the wings outstretched, the lift generated would suffice to raise the animal into the air. As its movements on the ground may have been laboured, it was probably vulnerable and most likely avoided landing on the ground preferring to roost in high, inaccessible places such as cliff faces, from which it could become airborne by just letting go.

Was *Pteranodon* able to take off on calm days, by flappings its wings to become airborne? The wings were certainly mechanically capable of being flapped up and down, and the minimum amount of power required of the muscles is that needed to overcome the rate of sinking. The required power has been calculated to be about 68 watts (underestimate).[21] The estimated weight of the flight muscles of *Pteranodon* was 3 kg,[22] and if it is assumed that these muscles were capable of generating the same power per unit weight as those of birds, then they were just sufficient (insufficient) for sustained flapping flight. While flapping flight may have been used on occasions, as it is in the flight of the albatross, *Pteranodon* presumably spent most of its flying time gliding effortlessly on outstretched wings.

In order to fly successfully, an aircraft must be able to compen-

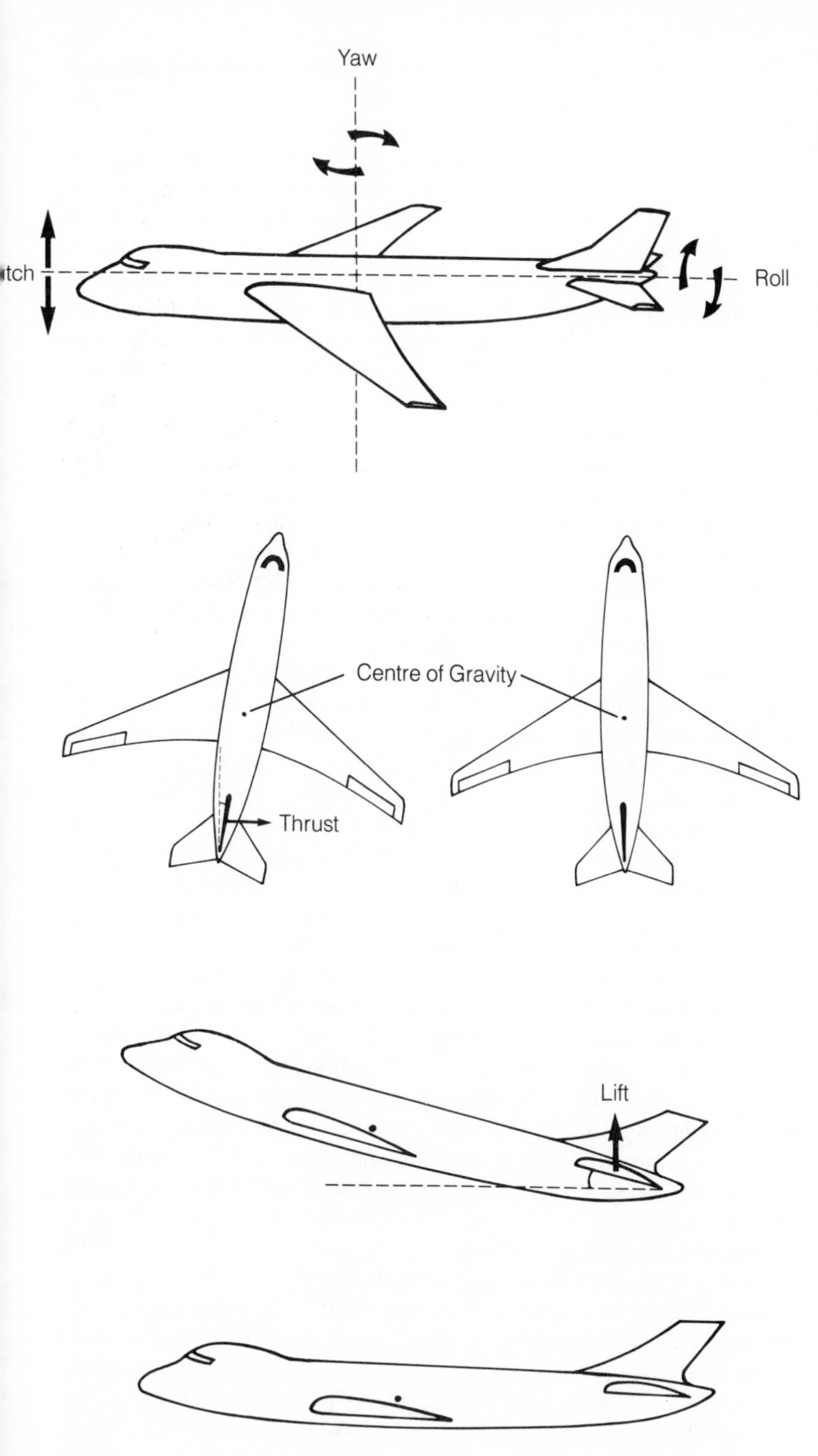

Top: Movements in the three planes of space are pitch, yaw, and roll. Middle: When an aircraft yaws (left) the rudder becomes an inclined plane and the thrust generated swings the tail back in line again. Bottom: When the nose pitches up, the horizontal stabiliser becomes an inclined plane and the lift generated raises the tail.

sate for alterations in its flight path caused by air movements, and it must be able to change course at will. There are three basic movements that can occur during flight: Yaw, pitch, and roll. Yaw is a side-to-side turning movement about a vertical axis, pitch an up and down movement about a horizontal axis, and roll is a turning movement about a longitudinal axis. All three movements are corrected for during the flight of an aircraft by the action of inclined planes. Yaw is corrected by the action of the rudder. When an airplane is flying on a straight course, the rudder cuts through the air in the direction of travel, but when the machine begins to yaw the rudder becomes inclined at a small angle of attack and the deflection force that it generates brings the airplane back onto a straight course. Control of pitch is brought about by the action of the horizontal stabilizer. The flight feathers of a dart similarly correct for yaw and pitch, and if a dart is thrown with a wobble it can be seen to correct itself very rapidly and to fly straight. In addition to correcting for yaw and pitch, the tail of an airplane has adjustable control surfaces that can cause it to yaw (turn) and pitch (dive or climb). Roll is corrected, and effected, by the ailerons, which are elongated flaps on the trailing edges of the wings, placed towards the wing tips. By increasing the angle of attack of a given aileron, an additional lift can be given to the wing on that side, causing the aircraft to roll towards the other side.

Although birds have tails, these are used mainly in landing, and almost all in-flight manoeuvres are effected by movements of the wings. These movements are very difficult to see, and it takes considerable time and experience before the subtle movements that cause changes in the flight path can be detected.[23] Upward pitch is caused by moving both wings forward so that their lift force is moved farther ahead of the centre of gravity, thus raising the head. Downward pitch is achieved by the reverse action. Upward pitch can also be achieved by raising the wings above the level of the body (positive dihedral)—an adjustment that capitalizes upon the drag acting on the wings. Raising the point of application of the drag force above the centre of gravity causes a rotation around the latter, which raises the head. The reverse action is achieved by placing the wings below the level of the body, in the negative dihederal position. Yaw can be produced by the partial retraction of one wing. The resulting reduction in drag causes it to travel faster, turning the bird towards the other wing. Roll is effected by increasing the force of the downbeat of one wing; this generates greater lift on that side, rolling the body towards the other wing. Turning is probably always accompanied by a roll, the wing on the outside of the turn beating more powerfully than the other. Several of the birds Hankin studied could rotate their wing tips, producing a negative angle of attack. This not only depresses the adjusted wing but also increases its drag; consequently, the bird rolls, turning towards the twisted wing. The wing tips therefore function as ailerons, and a similar mechanism probably exists in other birds. The head is small relative to the body in most birds and appears to have no role in steering.

Pteranodon, being tail-less, had to effect most of its control movements by adjustments of the wings. The head, with its long crest, was probably also an important control surface. Roll might be controlled by changing the profile of one of the wings. By depressing the wing (fourth) finger on one side, the leading edge of the wing membrane could probably be lowered, increasing its lift (and drag) and causing the body to roll over towards the opposite side. According to this suggestion roll to the left could be effected by lowering the right wing finger with or without raising the left wing finger. Pitch could probably be controlled by swinging the leading edge of the wings forward, advancing the centre of pressure (the point through which the combined forces of lift and drag act) of the wings in front of the centre of gravity, thus raising the head. If there were membranes attached along the inside edges of the hind legs, as suggested for Jurassic pterosaurs, they might have functioned as important control surfaces. If both legs were lowered together, a symmetrical lift would be generated, pitching the head down, whereas lowering one leg would produce an asymmetrical lift, causing roll as well as pitch. This, of course, is speculative, as are all of our discussions on the flight of *Pteranodon*. Yaw may have been controlled by the partial retraction of one wing, as it is in birds, or perhaps by movements of the head, which was relatively large. The lift force produced by the inclined head would cause the body to steer to the same side. The head was pivoted on the neck, and, when the head was inclined during flight, the beak, acting as an inclined plane, generated a deflection force which, acting in front of the pivot, tended to rotate the head farther in the same direction. The long crest, which had about the same area as the beak, also generated a deflection force, but this was behind the pivot and therefore tended to rotate the head in the opposite direction, thus counteracting the turning effect of the beak. Inclination of the head during flight did not, therefore, result in the head being twisted round farther. Instead, the head was stabilized, and the resultant deflection force turned the whole body towards one side. Without the crest, *Pteranodon* would have required large neck muscles to prevent the head from being twisted right round. (*Pteranodon*'s crestless contemporaries might not have used their heads for steering).

When birds are flying they often retract their wings momentarily, and this can be seen particularly well in house sparrows. The sudden decrease in wing area reduces both the lift and the drag, and the bird dives, gaining speed. This action is particu-

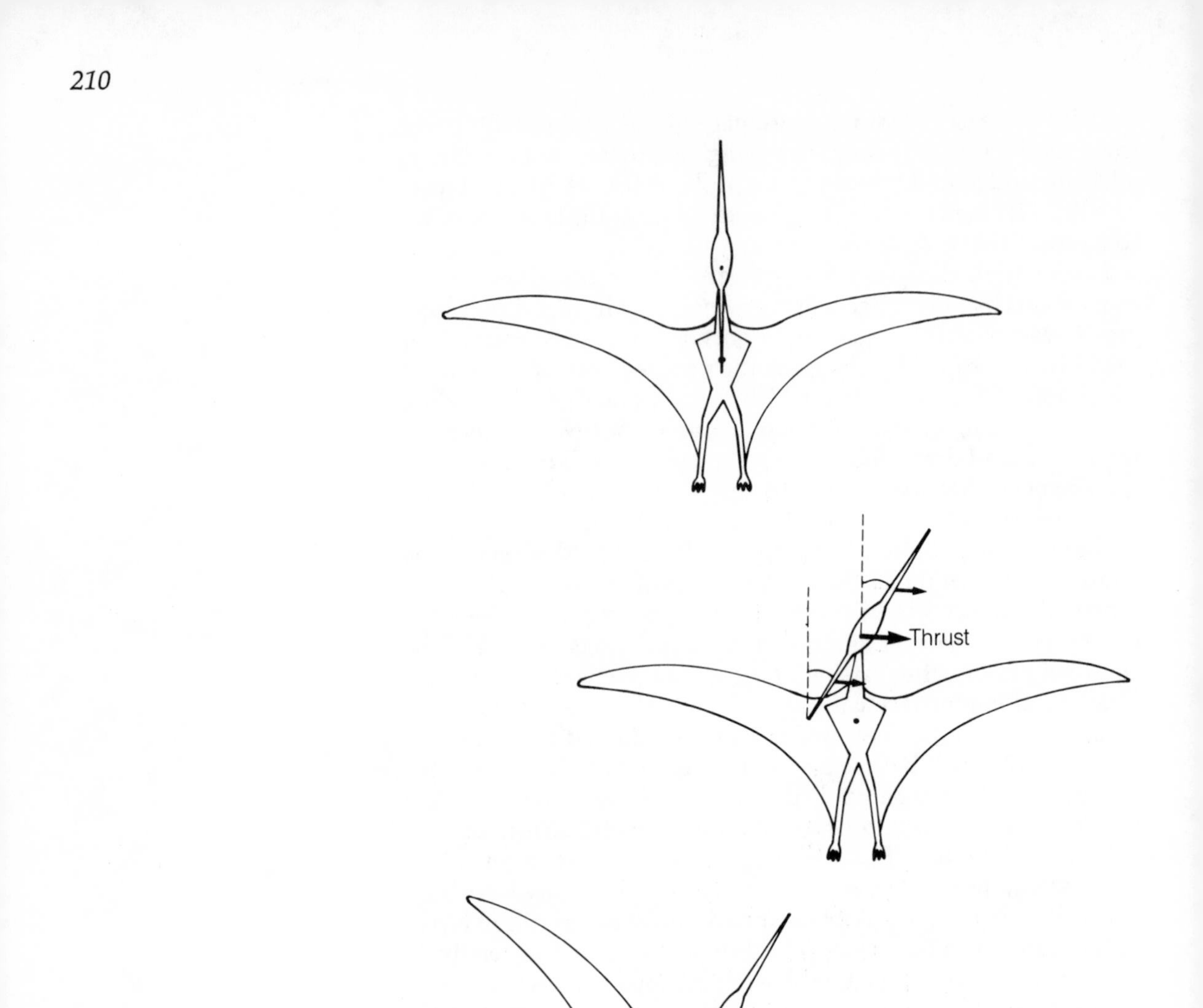

When flying a straight course (top), a rotation of the head to the right (middle) would have generated a thrust to the head which would have caused the body to yaw onto a new course (bottom). Note that **Pteranodon** *is depicted as having a membrane which attached to the legs—this may not have been so (see text for details).*

larly dramatic in diving birds, such as brown pelicans and gannets, which fall into the sea like stones in order to catch fish. Partial retraction of the wings commonly occurs in soaring birds, and enables them to increase their flying speed. We saw earlier that the wing of *Pteranodon* was probably capable of partial retraction during flight, and this would allow for steeper and faster descents, but the skeleton was probably far too lightly built to withstand very steep dives.

Landing, the most critical part of any man-made flight, is often seen as an almost insurmountable problem for the lightly built pterosaurs. The stalling speed of *Pteranodon*, however, was sufficiently low to minimize the hazard. In preparation for landing, the profile of the wing was probably set to its maximum camber, for maximum lift and drag. This could presumably be accomplished by lowering both wing fingers, depressing the leading edges. The leading edges of the small pteroid membranes may also have been depressed, further increasing the camber of the wing. Similar changes can be seen in the wing profile of an airplane preparing to land. Just before the heart quickens at the sound of the undercarriage being lowered, the leading and trailing edge flaps are extended, increasing both the camber and the area of the wing.

Pteranodon, far from being an evolutionary failure, was a highly specialized and successful glider. We may visualize that most of its life was spent on the wing, probably flying over the sea, feeding on fish and other marine organisms. Like many marine birds, it may have seized its prey while flying close to the surface, avoiding alighting on the sea. In contrast to its flapping predecessors of the Jurassic, most of the energy required for flight was extracted from moving air currents, and the expenditure of energy was probably low. It follows from this that its food requirements may have been modest.

It was long believed that *Pteranodon* was the largest flying animal that ever existed, but the remains have been found in Texas of a pterosaur with an estimated wingspan of 15 m, comparable to that of an executive jet.[24] We do not yet know much about this unbelievable animal (provisionally called *Quetzalcoatlus*[25]) because the material is rather incomplete. In contrast to most finds of pterosaurs, the remains were not in a marine deposit, but more than 400 km from the nearest shoreline. This suggests that the animal may have been terrestrial rather than marine, which raises some interesting problems regarding its feeding habits and roosting places. Apart from its gigantic size, it is unusual for its remarkably long neck, which suggests that it may have been a carrion feeder. (The material was associated with the remains of sauropod dinosaurs; this has been interpreted as additional evidence that these pterosaurs may have been feeding on carrion.) The vulture uses its long neck for probing deep into carcasses, and it is conceivable that this giant pterosaur, similarly, used its long neck for thrusting deep into the putrefying hulks of dinosaurs. If they were scavengers, they would have had to feed on the ground, which would present serious problems in taking off again. The large size appears to rule out any possibility that it was able to generate sufficient muscle power to achieve lift-off by flapping its wings. Even large vultures, which are considerably smaller than this reptilian giant, have great difficulty in becoming airborne when disturbed during a meal, especially when gorged with flesh. The only conceivable way for the great pterosaur to become airborne would be to launch itself into the wind with outstretched wings. Could the carcass of a dinosaur have provided a suitable launching site? Perhaps the hind legs were in some way specialized for take-off. Perhaps it was not a carrion feeder after all. Until more information becomes available, this unusual animal will remain a mystery.

No period in the history of the Earth has spawned so many incredible creatures as the Mesozoic Era, and these giant aeronauts are among the most unusual of all.

10
The End of an Era

For six months of the year Canada is a land of ice and snow, and most of her inhabitants look forward to winter as they might look forward to a severe head cold. There are driveways to be shovelled and cars to be dug out of snowdrifts, and the daily ritual of getting young children into and out of their thick winter clothes can drive the most rational mother to the brink of insanity by winter's end. So it is hardly surprising that Canadians throw themselves into the pleasures of summer with the enthusiasm of children released from school. Summer is a time for trips. Trips to the cottage, trips to the lake, camping trips, canoeing trips, and fishing trips. Westerners take to their cars and drive east, while easterners pack up their campers and head for the west. At the height of summer the Trans-Canada Highway is reminiscent of a wagon trail in pioneer days.

The trip across Canada is an exhilarating and rewarding experience, and for a traveller from the east one of the most memorable moments must be rounding a bend in the road, just beyond Calgary, and seeing the Canadian Rockies. Having spent the previous few days driving across the flat country of the prairies, that first glimpse of the mountains is unforgettable. Rising to heights of more than 3,000 m, the peaks are always snowcapped, and the summer meltwaters feed countless rivers and streams that cascade through the foothills and wend their way across the great plains of the interior. Many of the rivers pass through the badlands of southern Alberta, whose sandstone fabric has been eroded into the strangest of shapes. The Red Deer is one of the largest rivers, and it has carved a deep valley through this wasteland. It is a land of sagebush and cactus, the home of jack rabbits and rattlesnakes. It is also dinosaur country, and probably the richest collecting area in the world.

Since the latter part of the 19th century collectors have combed these hills and gullies for bones weathering out of the laminated sandstones, and few of them were disappointed. Approximately 500 specimens, many of them complete skeletons, have been found over the years, and more are being exposed as the rocks slowly weather away. Drumheller is one of several small towns that stand beside the Red Deer, but is distinguished from the others by having become the focal point of the dinosaur cult. Hundreds of visitors descend upon the town each summer, and the good people of Drumheller provide for their needs with dinosaur jewellery, dinosaur handicrafts, and even dinosaur burgers. Just outside the town is a signpost marked "Dinosaur Trail," and many visitors take this road

Dinosaur Provincial Park, in the Alberta Badlands, is one of the richest dinosaur collecting localities in the world. Weathering has carved the sandstone rocks into these odd shapes, called hoodoos. Prickly pear comes into bloom in early summer, adding colour to the arid terrain.

through the badlands to prospect for their own pieces of dinosaur bone. The Red Deer flows on beyond the town, and about 100 km to the southeast it makes a detour through a richly fossiliferous locality that has been designated Dinosaur Provincial Park. Here the visitor is actively discouraged from collecting or interfering with any bones he may see. Dinosaurs are still to be found and there has been a recent resurgence of collecting activity, largely due to the efforts of the Provincial Museum of Alberta. Perhaps we are to see another golden age of dinosaur hunting like the one at the turn of the last century.

The name Sternberg is synonymous with dinosaur hunting,

and any account of the history of dinosaur collecting in western Canada deals mainly with the industry and successes of this famous family[1]. Charles Hazelius Sternberg, who was born in the state of New York in 1850, worked for many years as a field assistant to pioneer palaeontologist Edward Drinker Cope. Sternberg had three sons, Charles, George and Levi, and from about the turn of the century they joined him in the field. Levi subsequently joined the staff of the Royal Ontario Museum, where he spent the rest of his working life, helping to build one of the world's major collections of dinosaurs.

The Sternbergs collected hundreds of specimens, and in 1936, 20 years before Dinosaur Provincial Park was founded, Charles spent a summer relocating and identifying more than 100 of the dinosaur quarries he and his father had excavated. These quarries are marked by permanent stakes driven into the rock[2].

The rocks in the park belong to the Oldman Formation, which is part of the Campanian, the penultimate epoch of the Cretaceous Period. Radiometric dates give an age of about 72 million years. If we journeyed up the Red Deer valley, some kilometres north of Drumheller, we would find geologically younger rocks belonging to the Edmonton Formation, which are part of the Maestrichtian, the last epoch of the Cretaceous, hence of the Mesozoic Era. Dinosaurs were still plentiful in the Maestrichtian, but crested dinosaurs were becoming scarce, and towards the close of the Cretaceous the most abundant genus was the horned dinosaur, *Triceratops*.[3]

One of the best places to see the last chapter of the Mesozoic Era as it was written in the rocks is Hell Creek, in the adjacent state of Montana. The end of the Cretaceous is conveniently marked by a coal seam (designated the Z-bed), one of many found throughout the western interior. Below this seam dinosaur bones are quite common, but above it—nothing. Nothing, that is, that can be identified as dinosaur remains. The small mammals that had shared the Mesozoic world with these great reptiles were now the predominant tetrapods.

In geological terms, the transition from a world dominated by reptiles to one ruled by mammals is sudden. The sense of sudden change is particularly apparent to an observer at Hell Creek, who can literally stand with his feet in the Mesozoic Era and the rest of his body in the Tertiary Era. In terms of time, however, this transition may have taken as long as two million years or it might have been considerably less.[4] We are unable to be precise about the duration because of the limitations of our dating techniques. Individual radiometric dates for Cretaceous sediments have intrinsic errors of at least plus or minus one million years, which is about the length of the interval we are trying to measure.

The Cretaceous-Tertiary boundary may be seen in many other

The end of the Age of Reptiles is marked by the band of coal, the Z-band (arrow), seen here in Makoshika State Park, eastern Montana.

parts of the world, and the available evidence suggests that individual boundaries are essentially contemporaneous. Not only do we fail to find dinosaurs in sediments of Tertiary age, but their reptilian relatives—the pterosaurs, ichthyosaurs, plesiosaurs, and mosasaurs—are also absent. So, too, are a number of other groups of animals and plants, including the ammonites and belemnites, marine cephalopods related to present-day squids.

This great wave of extinction that swept the world at the close of the Mesozoic Era has been recognized since the early days of palaeontology, and no effort has been spared in the search for a cause. The extinctions affected so many different groups of organisms that it was natural to seek an answer that would account for each and every case. Changes in climate, intense competition from the mammals, widespread disease, spillover of low salinity Arctic water as Greenland separated from Eurasia, and extraterrestrial catastrophism are just some of the hypotheses that have been proposed. Each has its merits, and its disadvantages, but the search for a single cause presupposes that there was a single wave of extinction. Some palaeontologists argue that so many groups of reptiles had become extinct long before the close of the Cretaceous that the end of the Age of Reptiles cannot be attributed to a single event. One of the questions we will have to examine, therefore, is whether there was a single reptilian extinction event.

When tackling other palaeontological problems we have been able to make reference to modern animals, but we clearly cannot do that on the question of extinction. Another difficulty is that most of the evidence we shall be assessing is negative evidence; the extinction of a particular group of animals is established on the absence of that group from post-Cretaceous sediments. Negative evidence is notoriously unreliable as witnessed by the discovery of a coelacanth fish off the coast of South Africa in 1938. The coelacanths were believed to have become extinct at the close of the Cretaceous because no post-Cretaceous fossils were known, but here was living proof that the group had not become extinct. There are several other examples, and all serve as warnings to us. Lastly there is the problem that our dating techniques lack the precision we require to determine the duration of the wave of extinction.

Dr. Dale Russell, head of the Division of Palaeontology of the National Museums of Canada, has for several years been pursuing the problem of extinction. In the winter of 1976 he convened a meeting of specialists from various branches of science to discuss the problem of the Cretaceous-Tertiary extinctions, and the results were published the next year.[5] Russell assessed the total numbers of genera, both plants and animals, that were living during the Cretaceous and Tertiary periods. He found that the numbers fell by about 50% across the boundary. Freshwater organisms were virtually unaffected, but marine forms suffered a significant decline in their diversity. Terrestrial vertebrates, especially the reptiles, also suffered a marked decline, but other terrestrial animals were barely affected. Reptilian genera declined from 54 at the close of the Cretaceous, to 24 at the beginning of the Tertiary, while the number of mammalian species increased slightly, from 22 to 25. Another interesting point is that no terrestrial vertebrates that were heavier than about 25 kg appear to have survived the transition.

Russell made the point that the scale of the extinctions that swept the world would be impressive even if it took place over an interval of several million years, but he was persuaded that the interval was much less. In his beautifully written and attractively illustrated book on the dinosaurs of western Canada, Russell gave an estimate for the interval of about 10,000 years, and this was based on sedimentation rates.[6] If the extinctions did take place in such a short period of time, a mere blink of the eye in geological terms, then it is probable that they were correlated and probably attributable to the same cause.

Russell concluded that a cosmic catastrophe was responsible, and of the several possibilities that have been proposed by various authors[7] he favoured a supernova. A supernova is an exploding star that sends considerable amounts of radiation far into space during its death throes. Supernovae have apparently been observed eight times during the last 2000 years, and the chance of a star having exploded close enough to the Earth at some time during its long history to have a deleterious effect on the environment is probably high.

The Earth is under continuous bombardment by radiation from the sun and from space, but is shielded by its own magnetic field and by the ozone layer of the upper atmosphere. It has been established that the Earth's magnetic field undergoes reversals, which occur about once every 100,000 years. After a reversal, the polarity of the north and south poles is switched, so that a compass that formerly pointed north would point south. We know that reversals have occurred because they are recorded in the rocks. The Earth's magnetic field is relatively weak, but it is strong enough to imprint itself onto the rocks, and the reversals have been permanently recorded in the Earth's crust. Magnetic reversals take anything up to about 4,000 years to complete, and during this time the shielding effect of the field is lost. It has been argued that, if the Earth were subject to a burst of increased radiation during this period (whether from a supernova or some other cosmic event), the effects on life could be sufficiently devastating to cause widespread extinctions.

The supernova hypothesis, however, has now been largely eclipsed by an alternative cosmic event proposed by physicist L.W. Alvarez and his co-workers.[8] During a study of the chemical composition of a clay sample from the Cretaceous-Tertiary boundary of Italy they discovered an abnormally high concentration of iridium. Iridium is a rare element in the Earth's crust, occurring in concentrations of about one-tenth part per billion, but the Italian clay sample contained concentrations of nine parts per billion. Although this may not sound very high, it was about 30 times higher than the average concentration measured for several Cretaceous samples they collected beneath the clay. The analysis was repeated on Cretaceous-Tertiary samples from other parts of the world with similar results: samples from Denmark and New Zealand showed increases in iridium concentrations of 160 and 20 times. Similar findings have been reported from south-east Spain and New Mexico.[9] These investigations suggest that there was a sudden, world-wide increase in the levels of iridium at the close of the Cretaceous. Where did the iridium come from?

Alvarez and his colleagues could find no satisfactory explanation for the increase in terms of processes occurring on the Earth, but noted that iridium is found in high concentrations in extraterrestrial material (meteorites and the like). They therefore proposed that the Earth had been hit by a large asteroid at the close of the Cretaceous. The impact of the collision was said to have sent up a great shower of dust which enveloped the Earth, cutting out the sun for several years. Photosynthesis was arrested, killing plants and causing widespread extinctions. The asteroid, they said, would need to have been about 10 km in diameter to effect such widespread change, and this would have left a crater up to 200 km in diameter.

Is there any evidence for such an event? There is no question that asteroids of this size do come close to the Earth, and there is no reason to doubt that collisions have occurred in the past. It has been estimated that such collisions occur with a periodicity of tens of millions of years[10], therefore the suggestion that the Earth collided with an asteroid is perfectly possible. No large crater has been found, but this could be because the impact occurred at sea (2/3 of the Earth is covered by sea).

Some specialists who study craters have argued that the concentrations of iridium reported by Alvarez and others are too high to be attributed to an asteroid impact. A more serious objection to the asteroid hypothesis is the fact that iridium abundance anomalies have been recorded in Tertiary sediments for which neither an asteroid impact, nor extensive extinctions, have ever been suggested.[11] How can the abnormally high levels of iridium be accounted for in boundary sediments if there was no asteroid impact? The Earth is constantly being showered with meteoritic dust from disintegrating meteors, and this material, which is high in iridium, becomes incorporated into the sediments.[12] If there were a temporary decrease in the sedimentation rate for particles originating on Earth—and such does seem to be the case at the close of the Cretaceous—there would obviously be an increased concentration of meteoritic material, hence of iridium.[13] The iridium abundance anomaly, then, does not necessarily support an extra-terrestrial catastrophe. If such an event had occurred, though, could it have accounted for the widespread extinctions seen at the close of the Cretaceous?

A catastrophic extinction event would have caused all the affected groups to become extinct at the same time. What evidence is there that the extinctions which affected so many different organisms were synchronous? The junction between the end of the Cretaceous and beginning of the Tertiary is often clearly marked, both by changes in the geological appearance of the sediments and in changes in the contained fossils, but how can we be sure that the junction we can see in Hell Creek, Montana, is synchronous, say, with the junction we can see in the Waipara River valley in New Zealand? Radiometric dating, lacking sufficient precision, is of no avail, but there is a promising possibility in the phenomenon of magnetic reversals. Since a reversal would affect the whole Earth at the same time, it is conceivable that the magnetic "stripes" preserved in the rocks can be used as time-markers. By recognizing a particular reversal at the Cretaceous-Tertiary boundary at one locality, it should be possible to determine whether the boundary occurs at the same time zone at other localities. In theory this should provide a way of testing the catastrophe hypothesis, but in practice it is not so straightforward. Only certain types of rocks retain a magnetic record, and this may have been completely disrupted during the formation of the sediments by the action of burrowing organisms, by the upwelling of carbonates, or by overprinting with other magnetic fields. The application of magnetic reversals is therefore limited and does not appear to have resolved the problem one way or the other.

We have discussed the Cretaceous-Tertiary boundary as if there were a continuous fossil sequence across the junction, but this is probably seldom true. Most studies on the boundary have been made in North America, and Hell Creek is probably one of the few known areas with a more or less continuous sequence. Elsewhere there are gaps between the occurrence of the last Cretaceous fossils and the appearance of the first Tertiary one, ranging from between one and two million years in the southern United States, to about fifteen million years in Africa. Because of these gaps during this critical period of Earth history we cannot be absolutely sure that the extinction of the dinosaurs and the other reptilian groups, not to mention all the other animals and plants that succumbed, occurred at the same time throughout the world. Indeed there is evidence that the great wave of plant extinction at the close of the Cretaceous was not synchronous with that of the dinosaurs.[14]

There have been reports that some of the reptilian groups that appear to have become extinct at the end of the Cretaceous have actually been found in Tertiary deposits, but these can probably all be dismissed.[15]

At this point it will be useful to summarise our findings so far:

1. There was a marked reduction in the total number of plant and animal genera at the close of the Cretaceous Period. This was most marked in marine organisms and in large terrestrial vertebrates.
2. The interval of time during which the Late Cretaceous extinction occurred may have been as short as a few years or as long as several million years.
3. It has been suggested that a cosmic event that either showered the Earth with radiation (supernova) or enveloped it in dust (asteroid) was responsible for the extinctions. If this is true, then the extinctions must have been synchronous.
4. The synchrony of the extinctions of the various groups of organisms cannot be established, and there is evidence that some extinctions were actually not synchronous.

5. Because of numerous gaps in the fossil record between the end of the Cretaceous and the beginning of the Tertiary, we cannot be absolutely sure that all the dinosaurs (and all of the other groups we believe to have become extinct) did in fact become extinct at the close of the Cretaceous.

One of the major objections to the catastrophe hypothesis is that some organisms, and not others, were affected. Why were dinosaurs extinguished, but not their archosaurian relatives, the crocodiles? Why did pterosaurs perish but not birds? Why did ammonites and belemnites die out but not their relatives, the squids? Why were marine organisms more affected than freshwater ones? If all the mammals had died out, or all the vertebrates, or all the animals, then the supernova hypothesis would be promising, because the sensitivity of organisms to radiation increases with their complexity. It is lowest in the microscopic organisms, which includes planktonic forms, and highest in birds and mammals.[16] Furthermore, since aquatic animals would have been largely shielded from radiation, why were so many marine organisms extinguished, including so many planktonic ones?[17] Russell has pointed out that the largest terrestrial organisms to survive were of the size order of 25 kg. Does this suggest that only those animals small enough to seek shelter from harmful radiation, or other unfavourable environmental conditions, were spared? In the light of the above discussion, this appears to be a very tenuous argument.

What about the asteroid hypothesis? If the Earth had been enveloped in a cloud of dust that blocked the sun and halted photosynthesis, we would expect it to have affected all plants alike. However, it did not. Freshwater organisms, as we have already seen, were virtually unaffected, and the extinction of land plants was also very uneven. In western North America, for example, between 70 and 80 percent of the terrestrial species became extinct, but in the tropics the number of extinctions was so small as to be statistically insignificant.[18] Furthermore plant extinctions of a similar scale have been reported for the Paleocene-Eocene boundary, where no catastrophic event has ever been postulated.[19]

A less serious objection to the catastrophe hypothesis, but one that weakens the case, is the fact that many reptilian groups had become extinct, or had declined to small numbers of genera, long before the end of the Cretaceous. We must remember, however, that we are basing an argument on negative evidence. *Stegosaurus* and its plated allies were primarily Jurassic dinosaurs and became extinct before the Upper Cretaceous; only two of the eight sub-families of sauropods survived into the Upper Cretaceous; and most of the iguanodon dinosaurs became extinct before Upper Cretaceous times;[20] so too had most of the ichthyosaur genera.

The problem with assessing diversity by counting genera in fossil organisms is that few groups have been sufficiently studied to determine whether the genera that have been recognized have any significance. Hundreds of the genera have been founded on inadequate scraps of bone, and any discussion on diversity based upon such material is obviously meaningless. The nomenclature of ichthyosaurs has been extensively studied so it is a fairly reliable group in which to study diversity.

As we saw in Chapter 8, there were six ichthyosaur genera in the Upper Triassic. Although none of these appears to have survived into the Jurassic, the diversity of the group was not diminished because there were five Lower Jurassic genera, most of which have a number of referred species.[21] By late Jurassic times, however, the number of genera had been reduced to three. One of these genera, *Ophthalmosaurus*, survived into the Lower Cretaceous, but it does not appear to have survived into the Upper Cretaceous, where only one genus is known, *Platypterygius*.[22] There was, therefore, a real decline in the diversity of this reptilian group during the later part of the Mesozoic Era. The decline was more marked, however, at the end of the Lower Jurassic, when the number of genera was halved, and again at the end of the Upper Jurassic, when the number was halved again, than at the end of the Upper Cretaceous, when only one genus became extinct. As far as the diversity of the group is concerned, the final extinction at the close of the Cretaceous was far less significant than the earlier extinctions. However, we naturally place more importance on the event that was responsible for extinguishing one genus at the close of the Cretaceous, because it marked the final extinction of the whole group of organisms.

Dinosaurs also appear to have undergone a decline in diversity long before their final disappearance from the fossil record. There were 36 genera of dinosaurs living in North America during the Campanian Epoch, which ended about 11 million years before the close of the Cretaceous Period. By the Maestrichtian, however, the final epoch of the Cretaceous, they had dwindled to 17.[23] Russell believes that this decline in the number of genera is apparent, not real, and that it is due to bias in the sample resulting from the intensity of collecting. He points out that 563 dinosaur specimens have been collected from the Campanian of North America, compared with only 194 from the Maestrichtian. His argument, which has some validity, is that if more Maestrichtian specimens had been collected more genera would have been recognized. In spite of this argument, I believe that the data support a real decline in diversity of the North American dinosaurs before their final extinction.

The fact that some of the groups that did not survive into the Tertiary had already fallen into decline before the close of the

Cretaceous diminishes the importance of the Cretaceous-Tertiary extinction event. Furthermore, since so many other groups, both animal and plant, appear to have been largely unaffected, the possibility that there ever was a sweeping catastrophe at the close of the Cretaceous is diminished. We cannot deny the fact that a large number of species did become extinct, but their extinctions were not necessarily correlated. It has been pointed out elsewhere that extinction is an inevitable outcome of evolution (Darwin made the point himself), and that extinction events are not necessarily correlated with one another.[24]

Relieved of the burden of seeking an Armageddon—one all-embracing solution to the extinction problem—we can now investigate some of the hypotheses that have been proposed to explain the extinction of the dinosaurs.

Extinction is usually interpreted as the ultimate expression of failure, but such value judgments are rather meaningless. The fact that an organism had survived up to the time of its extinction is a measure of its previous success, and we should remember that extinction is the inevitable fate of all organisms. Extinction, in essence, is the other end of the spectrum from speciation, and, like speciation, it only occurs because of change. Without change, within the living organisms or within their environment, there would be no speciation, no evolution, and no extinction.

In our search for possible causes of the extinction of the dinosaurs, we will bear in mind the fact that a surviving species must be well adapted to its environment—otherwise it would not be surviving—and that it will continue to survive unless some changes occur. We saw in Chapter 2 that offspring are usually not identical to their parents, and the variation that exists in each generation ensures that at least some individuals survive to propagate the species. It would be difficult to visualize a change occurring within all of the individuals of a species that would cause them all to be no longer able to survive within their environment. This leads to the conclusion that extinction is probably caused by changes in the environment, rather than in the organisms, changes that are so sudden in terms of the generation time of the organisms, and so drastic in their effects on the individuals, that there is insufficient time for the species to adapt to the new environment through the process of natural selection. A few recent examples will illustrate the point.

During the Industrial Revolution in England, vast quantities of smoke were belched from countless chimneys, causing a gradual blackening of the surrounding land. One of the victims of the blackening of trees and buildings was the grey Peppered Moth which, because of its high contrast with the black background, became a more obvious target for its natural enemies, the insectivorous birds. However, the build-up of soot was relatively slow compared with the generation time of the moths, and the occurrence of an occasional black moth in each brood led to a shift in the relative abundance of grey and black specimens. The Peppered Moth survived in the industrial north. Compare this with the fate of the Passenger Pigeon. This bird was once common in North America and huge flocks were frequently seen in the northern United States and southern Canada. Berries and seeds formed the greater part of its diet, and these were obtained from the forest. With the clearing of the forest for agriculture, the Passenger Pigeon lost much of its food supply and this probably reduced its numbers significantly. A greater threat to its survival, however, was predation by man, for whole flocks were exterminated under hails of lead shot. The Passenger Pigeon population appears to have been in decline for several centuries, but the additional pressures of overhunting brought it to the brink of extinction at the turn of the century, and the last survivor died, in captivity in the Cincinnati zoo, in 1914.

Let us now look at the possible environmental changes during the latter part of the Cretaceous that might explain the demise of the dinosaurs. Environments of the past are reconstructed largely by reference to plant fossils. Plant species are identifiable, not only by their leaves, but also by their pollen grains, these being especially resistant to decay and therefore abundant in the fossil record. Many of the plants found in Mesozoic sediments belong to groups that have survived to the present day, and, since we know the climatic conditions under which they now flourish, we can surmise the climatic conditions under which their predecessors lived. This assumes that the climatic preferences of particular types of plants has not changed over the passage of millions of years, which is a reasonable assumption.

The Jurassic world was warm and lush, and the flora was dominated by cycads, palms, conifers, ferns, and the like—plants that are restricted today to the tropics and subtropics. There were apparently no seasons, a fact that is reflected in the absence of growth rings from the trees, and we may visualize a constant warm climate similar to what is found in parts of our world. There were no flowering plants (angiosperms), and if we were transported back to the Jurassic most of us would find the scenery quite unlike anything we had ever seen.

The Cretaceous Period brought a more moderate climate and the beginnings of seasonality, with winters that became progressively cooler.[25] Flowering plants appeared and spread, and by Late Cretaceous times the climate, and the flora, were reminiscent of parts of the southern states of the United States. For many palaeontologists, the continued cooling trend and the more marked seasonality that characterized the Late Cretaceous provided an obvious solution to the problem of the great reptilian extinction.[26] This explanation appeared all the more promising when it was suggested that dinosaurs were warm-blooded, because large, poorly insulated homeotherms, are potentially very sensitive to rapid deteriorations in climate.

Climatic change appears to be a satisfactory explanation for the extinction of the dinosaurs, and it is likely that this was responsible for the demise of many of them, but why did some of them not migrate to warmer parts of the world? The tropical and subtropical plants did not become extinct at the close of the Cretaceous; they merely became more restricted in range. Those living in North America spread farther south, accompanied by tropical animals, so why did not the dinosaurs, or at least some of them, also migrate southwards? It is likely that they did. Perhaps some of them even lived on in the tropics long after their relatives to the north had expired. There is some evidence that dinosaurs survived in New Mexico after the disappearance of the last dinosaurs in Montana.[27] Some may even have survived into the Tertiary, but the gaps in the fossil record across the Cretaceous-Tertiary boundary have so far prevented verification.

For some palaeontologists, the widespread changes in the terrestrial flora at the close of the Cretaceous were of more significance in the demise of the dinosaurs than the climatic changes that precipitated them. But this does not seem likely, on several grounds. Dinosaurs had already survived one floral upheaval during the early Cretaceous, when the cycads and ferns were largely replaced by the flowering plants, and this change was probably of far greater extent than the change at the close of the Cretaceous.[28] The argument that the shortage of winter fodder would have had serious effects is weakened by the knowledge that conifers were in abundance, and that at least one hadrosaur is known to have fed on conifer needles, from the evidence of gut contents (see Chapter 4). One ingenious suggestion was that the decline in ferns robbed the dinosaurs of a natural laxative and they consequently died, no doubt tight-lipped, of constipation![29] Another hypothesis in similar vein was that dinosaurs were poisoned by eating plants that contained high concentrations of selenium. The reason given to explain why mammalian herbivores were not similarly extinguished was that they were intelligent enough to be more selective in their choice of food.[30]

The dinosaurs shared their Mesozoic world with the mammals, and it is frequently argued that it was competition from the mammals that finally sealed their fate. While it is true that the mammals underwent an explosive proliferation during the early

Tertiary, it seems unlikely that their success was attributable to their having out-competed the reptiles. Indeed, it seems more likely that it was competition from the reptiles that kept mammals very much in the background during the Mesozoic, and that they were only able to undergo their great adaptive radiation after the reptilian empire had fallen. Our evidence for this is that many of the mammalian groups that occupied niches formerly held by reptiles did not appear until many millions of years after the extinction of the occupying reptiles. The ichthyosaurs, for example, barely straggled into the Late Cretaceous seas, and the small dolphin-like forms had disappeared tens of millions of years earlier. But cetaceans did not appear in the fossil record until the Middle Eocene, some 10 million years after the close of the Cretaceous, and dolphins did not appear until the Miocene, about 25 million years later. Ichthyosaurs, quite clearly, were not pushed to extinction by the mammals. However, this does not rule out the possibility that some reptilian groups became extinct because of competition pressure from the mammals; the mammals doubtless had a considerable effect on some of the reptiles.

We know that at least some dinosaurs were hatched from eggs, and observations of living birds and reptiles have shown that this is a critical stage in the life history. The struggle to break through the eggshell is an exhausting process, and for the weaker ones the task is just too great. Crocodiles, as we saw in Chapter 7, have been observed to assist a struggling offspring by breaking the shell in their great mouths, and birds may also assist their young by pecking at the egg. Birds sometimes undergo physiological changes often related to their diet, that cause the shells of their eggs to become so thick that the chicks have great difficulty in hatching out. In other cases the shell becomes so thin that it breaks during incubation, killing the developing embryo.

Professor Heinrich Erben of the University of Bonn has suggested that eggshell thinning may have been a significant factor in the demise of the dinosaurs. He has shown that the eggshell of some Late Cretaceous dinosaurs is relatively thinner than that of earlier ones, and this may be significant. If some physiological or environmental change occurred that caused dinosaur eggshells to become thinner, this would have been a strong selection pressure against the dinosaurs. We have to be cautious in assessing the relative thickness of eggshells, however, because the thickness changes during the development of the chick. Growing bones require supplies of calcium, and this is absorbed from the eggshell, which becomes thinner as the time of hatching approaches. It is necessary, therefore, to ensure that we are not comparing the eggshells of dinosaurs that hatched out with eggshells of infertile eggs.

Another suggestion that has been made regarding dinosaur eggs is that they were more frequently eaten during the Late Cretaceous than during earlier times. There are several modern mammals, reptiles, and birds that have a weakness for eggs, and also for defenceless hatchlings. If the activities of such animals was increased during the Late Cretaceous, this would have placed an additional environmental pressure upon the dinosaurs.

There are probably dozens of other hypotheses that have been proposed to explain the extinction of the dinosaurs and their kin, but none of them adds significantly to our understanding of the problem. It seems likely that extinction is brought about by more than one environmental pressure, as we saw in the case of the Passenger Pigeon, where a combination of food shortages and increased predation pressure by man pushed the species beyond the point of recovery. Since the extinction of each reptilian group probably involved a different set of environmental factors, the probability of being able to account for any particular extinction event is remote. We may search for the causes of the great reptilian extinctions, but we will probably never resolve the problem.

11
The King is Dead: Long Live the King

The southern part of Germany, renowned for its fine wines, strong beer, and unparalleled beauty, is also known for its outstanding Jurassic fossils. The quarries at Holzmaden, Ohmden, and Boll, in the province of Württemberg-Baden have been worked for their slate for several centuries, and have yielded some of the most perfectly preserved fossils in the world. Most notable amongst these, as we have seen, are the ichthyosaurs and pterosaurs. In Bavaria, to the east, are the equally famous quarries of Solnhofen and Eichstätt, noted for the particularly fine-grained limestone that was once used in the printing process and therefore referred to as lithographic limestone. These quarries, however, are more widely known for having yielded one of the most interesting and controversial of all fossil vertebrates: *Archaeopteryx*, the earliest bird.

If ever a fossil conspired with nature to be discovered at the right moment in history it was *Archaeopteryx*. The first specimen, an impression of an isolated feather, was reported in 1861, just two years after the publication of Darwin's *The Origin of Species*. (Some feathered vertebrates were reported from the Solnhofen district in 1820, but the material has been lost.[1]) Less than two months later a second specimen was reported from the same locality and geological horizon. This specimen, an almost complete skeleton with well-defined feather impressions, was studied by the German palaeontologist Hermann von Meyer who named it *Archaeopteryx lithographica*. The specimen was purchased by the British Museum the next year. The fact that *Archaeopteryx* possessed a mixture of reptilian and avian characteristics made it a perfect link between birds and reptiles, and both Darwin's proponents and his opponents seized every opportunity to use the latest discovery to further their causes. The German palaeontologist Johann Wagner, who had not actually seen the specimen himself, declared that *Archaeopteryx* was a feathered reptile, and warned that its initial appearance, of being transitional between reptiles and birds, would be used by Darwin and his followers to support their evolutionary views, but that they would be wrong. With complete disregard for priority he attempted to rename the new fossil *Griphosaurus problematicus*, the puzzling lizard.[2] Owen, the final authority on comparative anatomy, made a detailed study of the specimen and declared that *Archaeopteryx* was a bird,[3] a primitive bird that had certain reptilian characters. He did not discuss the matter further, probably because of his ambivalence towards Darwin's theory.[4] Thomas Henry Huxley, champion of the Darwinian cause, agreed that *Archaeopteryx* was a bird, and discussed its transitional nature in detail, making a strong case for the theory of evolution.[5]

Huxley's study of *Archaeopteryx* revealed a close similarity to the dinosaurs. He therefore proposed that birds had evolved from dinosaurs. For a time this was a widely held view, but it eventually fell into disfavour.

In his book *The Origin of Birds*,[6] which was published in 1926 and which became the standard reference for all subsequent studies, Gerhard Heilmann made detailed comparisons between *Archaeopteryx* and several potential reptilian ancestors. He concluded that *Archaeopteryx* had most in common with the small coelurosaurian (theropod) dinosaurs, but the evidence of a single anatomical feature persuaded him that the dinosaurs were too specialized. The feature in question was the paired clavicles, or collar bones, that form part of the shoulder girdle in most vertebrates. *Archaeopteryx*, and modern birds have a furcula (the wish bone), which is believed to represent a fusion of the clavicles but the coelurosaurian dinosaurs and their theropod allies had lost their clavicles. Heilmann logically argued that as dinosaurs were without clavicles they were too specialized to be ancestral to the birds and proposed that the thecodonts, the group that gave rise to the dinosaurs, were the most likely ancestral stock. The thecodonts remained the favoured common ancestor of the dinosaurs and birds for many years to come.

Since Heilmann's day, however, a number of new coelurosaurian dinosaurs have been discovered, and some of these do have

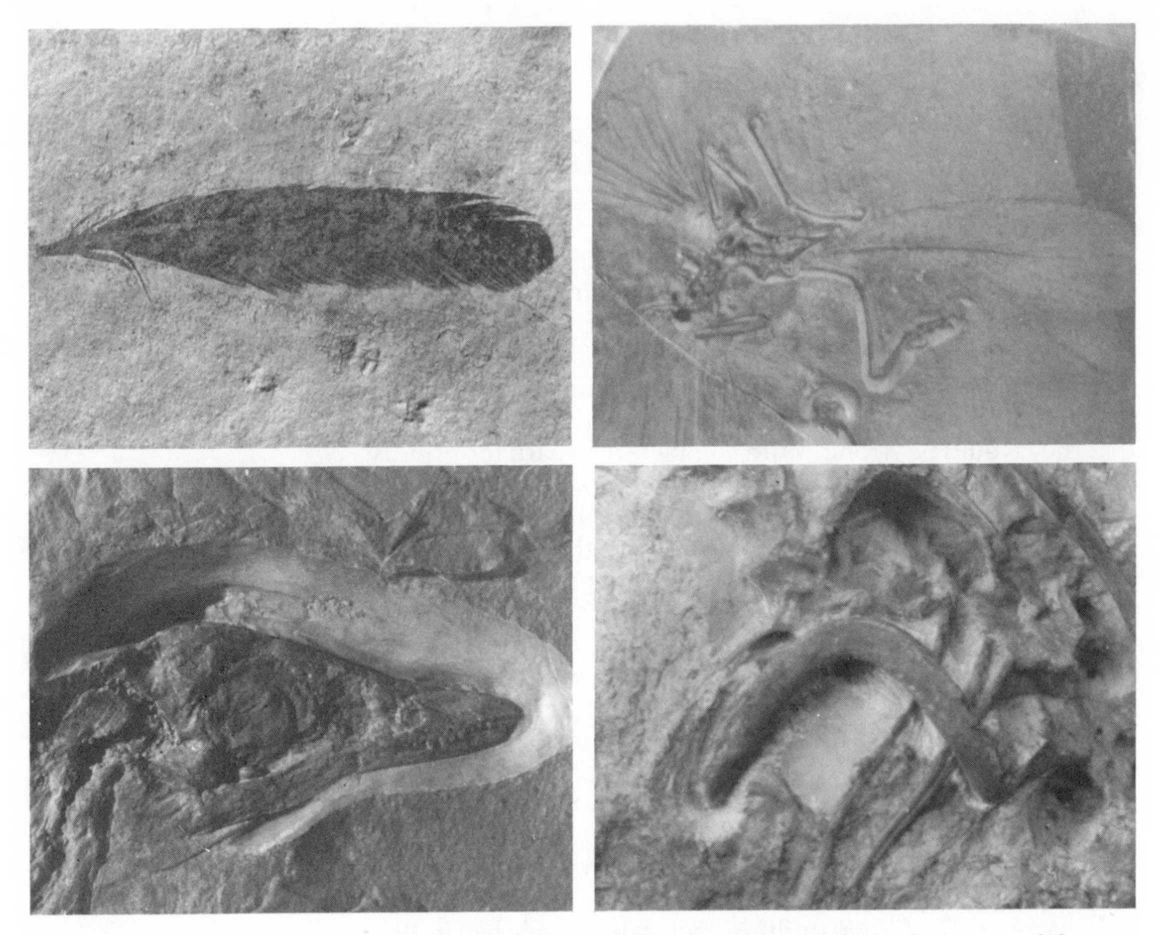

Archaeopteryx lithographica *from the Solnhofen limestone of the Upper Jurassic of southern Germany.* **Top row**, *left to right: The first specimen found, an isolated feather. The London specimen. The Berlin specimen. The Eichstätt specimen.* **Bottom row**, *left to right: The skull of the Berlin specimen. The furcula of the London specimen. The fingers and claws of the wings of the Berlin specimen. The tail of the London specimen.*

clavicles. Heilmann's original objections are therefore removed, and Professor J.H. Ostrom of Yale University has presented a convincing case that *Archaeopteryx*, hence the birds, evolved from dinosaurs.[8] Except for its furcula and the fact that the ischium has an unusual shape, the skeleton of *Archaeopteryx* is virtually indistinguishable from that of a coelurosaurian dinosaur. As we pointed out in Chapter 6, had it not been for the preservation of feather impressions these small differences would probably have been overlooked, and *Archaeopteryx* would have been identified as a small dinosaur.[9]

Is *Archaeopteryx* a bird or a reptile? Whether we regard *Archaeopteryx* as a specialized dinosaur or a primitive bird is

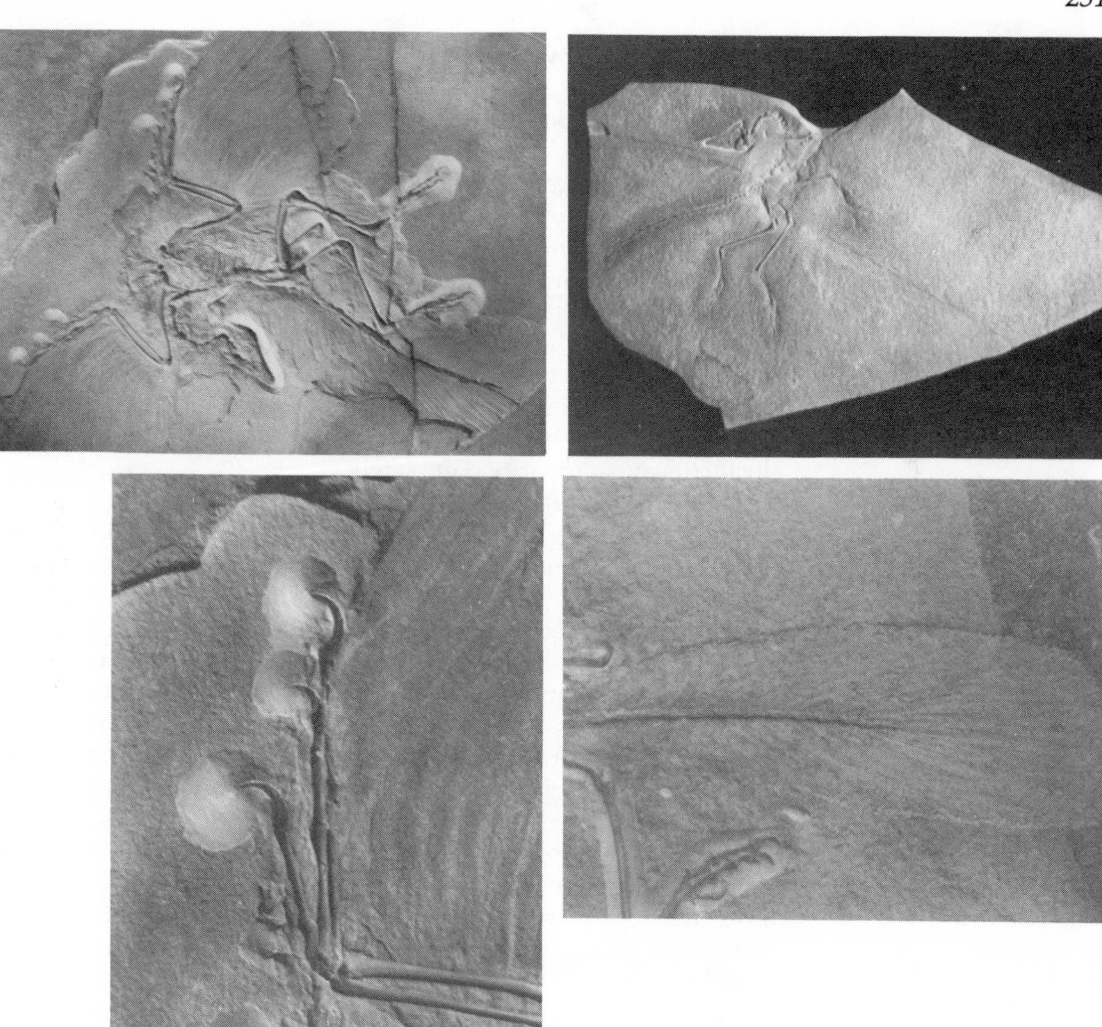

largely a matter of semantics, though many people, especially creationists, would disagree with this. According to Dr. D.T. Gish, an outspoken critic of evolution:

> . . . the so-called intermediate [*Archaeopteryx*] is no real intermediate at all because, as paleontologists acknowledge, *Archaeopteryx* was a true bird—it had wings, it was completely feathered, it *flew*. It was not a half-way bird, it *was* a bird.[10]

Gish then goes on to list the "alleged reptile-like features of *Archaeopteryx* . . .": claws in the wing, teeth, a long bony tail, and the belief that it had a small sternum. As we will shortly see, there is no evidence that *Archaeopteryx* had a sternum, and no bird has a long bony tail, but Gish is correct in pointing out that clawed wings and teeth, both primitive features, do occur in certain birds. However, if he had been familiar with the anatomy of *Archaeopteryx* he would have been able to point out a number of reptilian features that are found in theropod dinosaurs but not in birds. These features include: three free fingers in the hand, a metacarpus comprising three bones, no fusion of the carpals and metacarpals to form a carpometacarpus, a metatarsus which is incompletely fused and which comprises three distinct bones, incomplete fusion of the astragalus and calcaneum with the tibia, a pubic peduncle in the pelvis and the probability that the tibia has a single cnemial crest.[11] Indeed most of the anatomical features of *Archaeopteryx* are dinosaurian and the only truly avian features are the possession of feathers and a furcula. *Archaeopteryx* could hardly be less of a bird without losing its avian identity completely.

While the evolution of a furcula from paired clavicles appears to be a small step, most people consider that the evolution of feathers from a reptilian scale is an enormous jump that cannot be bridged. The problem raises the difficult question of the selective advantages of partially formed structures. Critics of evolution reasonably ask how something that is, say, half way between a scale and a feather can possibly be of any use to its owner. P.J. Regal, who addressed himself to this very question, showed that several tropical lizards have elongated scales, and these are more effective at shielding the animal from solar radiation than conventional scales.[12] He then developed an argument that feathers may likewise have evolved from modified scales as an adaptation to shielding out solar radiation. However, we do not have to construct a hypothetical argument to show that structures intermediate between scales and feathers could be useful to an animal. All we have to do is to look at the wing of a modern penguin, where we can see all shades of grey between regular-looking feathers at the trailing edge, to structures that look like modified scales at the leading edge. The intermediate structures obviously serve a useful purpose and illustrate that the transition from scales to feathers can be bridged by a graded series of imperceptibly small steps. The penguin has the ability to develop a wide range of covering structures, and we should not forget that all birds are able to develop scales—they have them on their legs. An intriguing example of the retention of the ability to develop reptilian features has been provided by some experiments on developing chicken embryos which were induced to grow teeth.[13] These experiments showed that although chickens have lost the ability to develop teeth in the normal way, they have retained the genetic information to do so.

What sort of an animal was *Archaeopteryx*? By avian standards it was fairly large—about the size of a magpie. Like the magpie, it had a long tail, but this was formed largely by the

Left column, *top to bottom: Some lizards, including the Spiny lizards* (**Sceloporus**) *have elongated scales. This shows up particularly well on the tail.* **Right column**, *top to bottom: Close inspection of the wing of a penguin reveals a transition from scale-like feathers on the leading edge, to regular-looking feathers on the trailing edge. See text for details.*

bony vertebral column, which supported a fringe of fairly short feathers. Modern birds, in contrast, have a tail with a number of long feathers attached at their base to the end of the vertebral column. Probably the most striking feature is the clawed fingers, three on either side, on the leading edge of the wing. This primitive feature can be seen today in an unusual bird that lives in the northern forests of South America. Like some remnant from Arthur Conan Doyle's *Lost World*, this bird, which has the Aztec name of Hoatzin, was discovered at the beginning of the 19th century. The adult is about the size of a European blackbird and has no trace of claws, but the newly hatched chicks have two well-developed claws on each wing that they use for clinging to branches as they crawl from their nest. After two or three weeks, the claws disappear. The Hoatzin should not be regarded as a close relative of *Archaeopteryx*, but rather as a bird that retains a primitive feature during its early development. In addition to its clawed wings, *Archaeopteryx* is unusual for the possession of sharp teeth (though teeth are found in some Cretaceous birds), which suggests that it was a predator. Possession of feathers is compelling evidence for endothermy (see Chapter 6), and we may visualize *Archaeopteryx* as a very active animal.

There has been much discussion on the flying abilities of this ancient bird, and the consensus seems to be that it was a poor flier.[14] Modern flying birds, the carinates, have a large keeled sternum, which forms an attachment area for the powerful muscles of flight. In contrast, the flightless birds, the ostrich and its allies, (referred to as ratites) have a keel-less sternum and poorly developed wing muscles. Paradoxically, *Archaeopteryx* appears to have had no sternum[15] but had well-developed flight feathers. This has suggested to some that *Archaeopteryx* may have been incapable of powered (flapping) flight, and only able to glide, but it should be remembered that bats do not have a large sternum but nevertheless have well-developed flight muscles and are powerful fliers.

The study of *Archaeopteryx* naturally raises the question of how flight evolved, which has been the subject of considerable discussion. The American palaeontologist Samuel Williston proposed that flight evolved on the ground, when fast bipedal runners stretched out their feathered arms and leaped into the air. This suggestion was adopted and elaborated upon by Baron Nopsca, who visualized that leaping into the air was an adaptation for increased speed. This suggestion has little merit because as soon as the feet leave the ground the legs are no longer able to thrust the body forward, and, in the absence of powerful flapping movements, a feathered runner would drop back to the ground. An alternate theory, proposed by the American palaeontologist Othniel Marsh, was that flight evolved in the trees, when feathered ancestors of birds leaped and glided from one tree to another. The clawed fingers and backward-pointing big toe, both suited for grasping, were interpreted as persuasive evidence for an arboreal (tree-living) mode of life, and most palaeontologists agree that flight probably originated in the trees. Ostrom, however, proposed a third alternative, suggesting that feathered wings evolved not for flight but for use as a food trap.[16] He visualizes *Archaeopteryx* as a ground-dwelling predator, feeding on small animals such as insects, small reptiles, and mammals. The outstretched wings are believed to have been used to trap these animals, and perhaps also to strike them. While this theory adequately accounts for the evolution of long feathers on the wings, it does not account for the evolution of a long, feathered tail.[17] Furthermore, a close inspection of the wing feathers reveals a feature that strongly suggests that they were adapted for flight. A comparison between the wing feathers of ratites and those of carinates shows that the shaft runs along the middle of the feather in the former but is displaced towards the leading edge in the latter. This suggets that asymmetrical wing feathers are correlated with flying. *Archaeopteryx* has asymmetrical wing feathers, and this has been interpreted as evidence for flight.[18] Regardless of whether flight evolved on the ground or in the trees, there is general agreement that feathers were first evolved as a body insulation and only became modified for flight (or food capture) secondarily.[19]

The possession of feathers, as we saw in Chapter 6, is compelling evidence for endothermy, and Bakker and Galton[20] concluded that high body temperatures and high activity levels were characteristic of birds and all dinosaurs. This belief, together with the fact that birds and dinosaurs are anatomically very similar, convinced them that the two groups should be placed within the same class, for which they proposed the name Dinosauria, with three subdivisions: the subclass Aves containing the birds, the subclass Saurischia containing the lizard-hipped dinosaurs, and the subclass Ornithischia containing the bird-hipped dinosaurs. According to this classification, birds are dinosaurs, and bear a relationship to the other dinosaurs similar to the relationship of bats to the other mammals. While Ostrom[21] appreciated Bakker and Galton's acceptance of his dinosaurian origin for the birds, he did not agree that this justified uniting birds and dinosaurs in the same class. Much of Bakker and Galton's case hinges upon dinosaurs being endothermic, and however convincing the evidence may be for some of the dinosaurs, verification is impossible. Classification systems should be stable and useful, and in these respects Bakker and Galton's classification appears to have no advantages over the present system.

Few biologists are prepared to classify modern birds as dinosaurs, but most would probably agree that birds and dinosaurs are very closely related, and it seems certain that birds are descended from dinosaurs. So there is new hope for the incurable romantics who mourn the passing of the dinosaurs. Dinosaurs probably did not expire at the close of the Mesozoic Era without leaving descendants; their spirit lives on in the form of birds.

THE SUCCESSFUL DRAGONS

Notes

Chapter 1 *Setting the Stage*

1. For an excellent account of the history of the theory of continental drift, see: Hallam, A., 1973. *A revolution in Earth Sciences*, Clarendon Press, Oxford.
2. There are many accounts of dinosaurs. The following are particularly recommended: Colbert, E.H., 1961. *Dinosaurs: Their Discovery and Their World*, E.P. Dutton, New York; Swinton, W.E., 1970. *The Dinosaurs*, George Allen & Unwin, London.
3. Wild, R. 1978. "Die Flugsaurier (Reptilia, Pterosauria) aus der Oberen Trias von Cene bei Bergama, Italien. *Bollettino della Societa Paleontologica Italiana*, volume 17, pages 176–256.

Chapter 2 *Darwin and the Fossil Record*

1. For an excellent historical account of fossils and their place in the development of our ideas in natural history see: Rudwick, M.J.S., 1972. *The meaning of fossils: episodes in the history of palaeontology.* (second edition). Science History Publications, New York.
2. Lamarck's hypothesis of the inheritance of acquired characters, widely rejected by most biologists, recently enjoyed a brief revival. For further information see: Steele, E.J., 1980. *Somatic Selection and adaptive evolution.* Croom Helm, London.
   Brent, L, et al. 1981. "Supposed Lamarckian inheritance of immunological tolerance." *Nature,* volume 290, pages 508–512.
3. Darwin, F. (ed.), 1887. *The life and letters of Charles Darwin*, Volume I, John Murray, London, pages 307–8
4. Darwin, F. (ed.) 1893. *Charles Darwin: his life told in an autobiographical chapter and in a selected series of his published letters.* D. Appleton and Company, New York; page 175
5. Darwin, C., 1839. *Journal of researches into the geology and natural history of the various countries visited by H.M.S. Beagle.*, facsimile reprinting of the first edition, published in 1952 by Hafner Publishing Company, New York, pages 147–8
6. *Ibid.*, pages 96–97.
7. *Ibid., page 208.*
8. *Ibid., page 210.*
9. *Ibid., page 454.*
10. *Ibid., page 456.*
11. *Ibid., page 466.*
12. *Ibid., page 469.*
13. Darwin, F. (ed.), 1893, *Charles Darwin: his life told in an autobiographical chapter and in a selected series of his published letters*, D. Appleton and Company, New York, page 252.
14. Darwin, F. (ed.) 1887. *The life and letters of Charles Darwin*, John Murray, London, volume 1, page 267.
15. See reference in note 5, page 474.
16. Darwin, C., 1845. *Journal of researches into the natural history and geology of the countries visited during the voyage of the H.M.S. "Beagle" round the world*, Minerva Library of Famous Books, edited by G.T. Bettany, 1889, Ward, Lock and Co., London, page 275.
17. *Ibid.*, page 276.
18. Darwin, F. (ed.) 1887, *Life and Letters*, Volume 1, page 83.
19. *Ibid.*, volume 2, page 85.
20. Eldredge, N., and Gould, S.J., 1972. "Punctuated equilibrium: an alternative to phyletic gradualism," in: *Models in Paleobiology,* Schopf, T.J.M. (ed.), Freeman and Cooper, San Francisco, pages 82–115.
21. Darwin, C., 1859. *The origin of species by means of natural selection or the preservation of favoured races in the struggle for life*, facsimile of the first edition, 1964, Harvard University Press, Cambridge, Massachusetts, page 280.
22. Rowe, A.W., 1899. "An analysis of the genus *Micraster,* as determined by rigid zonal collecting from the zone of *Rhynchonella Cuvieri* to that of *Micraster cor-anguinum,*" *Quarterly Journal of the Geological Society of London*, volume 55, pages 494–547.
23. Truemen, A.E., 1922. "The use of *Gryphaea* in the correlation of the Lower Lias," *Geological Magazine*, volume 59, pages 256–68.
24. Gould, S.J., and Eldredge, N., 1977. "Punctuated equilibrium: the tempo and mode of evolution reconsidered," *Paleobiology,* volume 3, pages 115–51.
25. For example, see Stanley, S.M., 1979. *Macroevolution, pattern and process*. W.H. Freeman, San Francisco.
26. Greenwood, P.H., 1974. "The cichlid fishes of Lake Victoria, East Africa: the biology and evolution of a species flock," *Bulletin of the British Museum (Natural History)*, Zoology, Supplement 6
27. Darwin, C., 1859. *op.cit.*, page 295.
28. *Ibid.*, page 298.
29. See reference in note 24. Gould and Eldredge's

punctuational model has not been received without criticism, for example see: Levinton, J.S. and Simon, C.M., 1980. "A critique of the punctuated equilibrium model and implications for the detection of speciation in the fossil record," *Systematic Zoology*, Volume 29, pages 130–142.

Chapter 3 *What Are Fossils?*

1. Ham, A.W., and T.S. Leeson., 1961. *Histology*, Lippincott, Philadelphia. See also: *The biochemistry and physiology of bone*, volume 1, 1972, Academic Press, New York.
2. Galdikas, B.M.F., 1978. "Orangutan death and scavenging by pigs," *Science*, volume 200, pages 68–70.
3. This and many more examples are contained in a useful book which has been extensively drawn upon in this chapter: Wyckoff, R.W.G., 1972. *The biochemistry of animal fossils*, Scientechnica, Bristol.
4. It has been suggested that climatic factors, operating through soil-forming processes, are responsible for the variations in the iron content of fossil bones. See: Houston, R.S., H. Toots, and J.C. Kelley, 1966. "Iron content of fossil bones of Tertiary Age in Wyoming correlated with climatic change," in *Geology*, volume 5, number 2, pages 1–18.
5. Jowsey, J., R.E. Rowland, and J.H. Marshall, 1958. "The deposition of the rare earths in bone," *Radiation Research*, volume 8, pages 490–501.
6. A case has been made that yttrium is taken up by bones after death, and that high levels indicate extensive ground-water circulation through the sediments. See: Parker, R.B., and H. Toots, 1975. "Minor elements in fossil bone: application to Quaternary samples," in *Applied Geology and Archaeology: the Holocene History of Wyoming*, M. Wilson (editor), Geological Survey of Wyoming, Report of Investigation number 10, pages 74–7.
7. Toots, H., and M.R. Voorhies, 1965. "Strontium in fossil bones and the reconstruction of food chains," *Science*, volume 149, pages 854–5.
8. Reported in: Romer, A.S., 1945. *Vertebrate Paleontology*, second edition, University of Chicago Press, Chicago.
9. Moodie, R.C., 1923. *Paleopathology, an introduction to the study of ancient evidences of disease*, University of Illinois Press, Urbana.
10. First reported in: Wyckoff, R.W.G., 1971. "Trace elements and organic constituents in fossil bones and teeth," *Proceedings of the North American Paleontological Convention for 1969*, pages 1514–24, Allen Press, Lawrence.
11. For further details, see page 39 of the reference cited in note 3.

Chapter 4 *Interpreting a Skeleton*

1. Charig, A.J., 1973. "Jurassic and Cretaceous dinosaurs," in *Atlas of Palaeobiogeography*, Elsevier Scientific Publishing Company, Amsterdam, London, and New York.
2. Morris, W.J., 1976. "Mesozoic and Tertiary vertebrates in Baja California, 1968–1971," *National Geographic Society Reports*, 1968 projects, pages 305–16.
3. Galton, P.M., 1970. "The posture of hadrosaurian dinosaurs," Journal of Paleontology, volume 44, pages 464–73.
4. Alexander, R. McNeal., 1976. "Estimates of speeds of dinosaurs," *Nature*, volume 261, pages 129–30.
5. McGowan, C., 1979. "The hind-limb musculature of the Brown Kiew (*Apteryx australis mantelli*)," *Journal of Morphology*, volume 160, page 33–74.
   McGowan, C., 1982. "The wing musculature of the Brown kiwi *Apteryx australis mantelli* and its bearing on ratite affinities," *Journal of Zoology*, volume 197, pages 173–219.
6. Bakker, R.T., 1975. "Experimental and fossil evidence for the evolution of tetrapod bioenergetics," in: *Evolution of tetrapod energetics*, Springer-Verlag, New York.
7. Ostrom. J.H., 1961. "Cranial morphology of the hadrosaurian dinosaurs of North America," *Bulletin of the American Museum of Natural History*, volume 122.
8. Morris, W.J., 1970. "Hadrosaurian dinosaur bills—morphology and function," *Los Angeles County Museum Contributions in Science*, number 193, pages 1–14.
9. Krausel, R., 1922. "Die Nahrung von *Trachodon*," *Palaeontologische Zeitschrift*, volume 4, page 80.
10. Ostrom (1961) estimates that the volume of the crest in *Corythosaurs casuarius* was only about 4 per cent of the total lung capacity.
11. Ostrom, J.H., 1961. *Ibid*.
12. Weishampel, D.B., 1981. "Acoustic analyses of potential vocalization in lambeosaurine dinosaurs (Reptilia:Ornithischia)," *Paleobiology*, volume 7, pages 252–61.
13. Hopson. J.A., 1975. "The evolution of cranial display structures in hadrosaurian dinosaurs," *Paleobiology*, volume 1, pages 21–43.
14. Walls, G.L., 1942. "The vertebrate eye and its

adaptive radiation," *Cranbrook Institute of Science, Bulletin 19.*
The degree of development of binocular vision is not only a matter of eye placement but also involves the relative position and development of the fovea. The fovea is a small depression in the retina, opposite the pupil, which is especially sensitive to light. Most, but not all animals, have a single fovea, and some birds actually have two. Birds that have two foveas have particularly well developed binocular vision. For further information see: Sillman, A.S., 1973. "Avian Vision." Farner, D.S. & J.R. King (eds.) *Avian Biology,* volume 3, Academic Press, New York and London.

15. The cast of the inner ear of *Anatosaurus,* described by Brown in 1914, is discussed in Ostrom (1961), page 127, figures 58–9 and pages 146–7. That of *Lophorhothon* is described in: Langston, W., 1960. "The vertebrate fauna of the Selma Formation of Alabama. Part 6: The dinosaurs," *Fieldiana: Geology Memoirs,* volume 3, pages 315–61.
16. Colbert, E.H., and Ostrom, J.H., 1958. "Dinosaur stapes," *American Museum Novitates,* number 1900, pages 1–20.
17. For a discussion of tooth replacement see; Edmund, A.G., 1960. "Tooth replacement phenomena in the lower vertebrates," *Life Sciences Contributions of the Royal Ontario Museum,* number 52.
18. Russell, D.A., 1969. "A new species of *Stenonychosaurus* from the Oldman Formation (Cretaceous) of Alberta," *Canadian Journal of Earth Sciences,* volume 6, pages 595–612.
19. Osmólska, H., and Roniewicz, E., 1970. "Deinocheiridae, a new family of theropod dinosaurs," *Palaeontologia Polonica,* number 21, pages 5–19.
20. Ostrom, J.H., 1969. "Osteology of *Deinonychus antirrhopus,* an unusual theropod from the Lower Cretaceous of Montana," *Bulletin No. 30,* Peabody Museum of Natural History, Yale University, New Haven, Connecticut.

Chapter 5 *On Being a Giant*

1. The giant hadrosaurs of Baja California must have been considerably heavier than an elephant. Weight estimates for dinosaurs from: Colbert, E.H., 1962. "The weights of dinosaurs," *American Museum Notivates,* number 2076, pages 1–16.
2. Alexander, R. McN. et al., 1979. "Allometry of the limb bones of mammals from shrews *(Sorex)* to elephant *(Loxodonta)," Journal of Zoology,* volume 189, pages 305–14.
See also: Alexander, R. McN., 1977. "Allometry of the limbs of antelopes *(Bovidae)," Journal of Zoology,* volume 183, pages 125–46.
Alexander, R. McN. et al., 1979. "Mechanical stresses in fast locomotion of buffalo *(Syncerus caffer)* and elephant *(Loxodonta africana)," Journal of Zoology,* volume 189, pages 135–44.
3. See the reference given in note 1.
4. For a reference to these experiments see: Bakker, R.T., 1972. "Locomotor energetics of lizards and mammals compared," *Physiologist,* volume 15, page 278.
5. Gregory, W.K., 1912. "Notes on the principles of quadrupedal locomotion," *Annals of the New York Academy of Science,* volume 22, pages 267–94.
6. Sikes, S.F., 1971. *The Natural History of the African Elephant,* Weidenfeld and Nicolson, London. Sikes states that the elephant is naturally amphibious or semi-aquatic, a fact well known to "indigenous Africans or Asiatics but apparently almost totally overlooked or ignored by European and American explorers, settlers, and scientists foreign to these countries."
7. Coombs, W.P., 1975. "Sauropod habits and habitats," *Palaeogeography, Palaeoclimatology, Palaeoecology,* volume 17, pages 1–33.
8. Bird, R.T., 1939. "Thunder in his footsteps," *Natural History,* volume 43, pages 254–61.
9. Bird, R.T., 1944. "Did *Brontosaurus* ever walk on land?" *Natural History,* volume 53, pages 60–67.
10. This illustration of *Barosaurus* first appeared in 1968 in a paper written by A.W. Crompton.
11. See the reference given in note 6.
12. The systolic and diastolic blood pressures for man are about 120 and 80 mm of mercury, respectively. The corresponding pressures of the blood leaving the heart of a giraffe are between 200 and 300, and 100 and 170, respectively. Warren, H.V., 1974. "The physiology of the giraffe," *Scientific American,* volume 231, number 5, pages 96–105.
13. Stanley, S.M., 1973. "An explanation for Cope's Rule," *Evolution,* volume 27, pages 1–26.
14. All data for modern predators were taken from Schaller, B.G., 1972. *The Serengeti Lion,* University of Chicago Press, Chicago.
15. A comparison between growth rates and life spans among modern reptiles has led to the suggestion that the sauropod *Hypselosaurus,* which is known from eggs as well as from adult remains, may have taken between 82 and 118 years to reach maturity. See: Case, T.D., 1978.

"Speculations on the growth rate and reproduction of some dinosaurs," *Paleobiology*, volume 4, pages 320–28.

Chapter 6 *The Hot-Blooded Debate*

1. Desmond, A.J., 1975. *The hot-blooded dinosaurs*, Blond and Briggs, London.
2. Wieland, G.R., 1942. "Too hot for the dinosaurs," *Science*, volume 96, page 359. Russell, L.S., 1965. "Body temperature of dinosaurs and its relationships to their extinction," *Journal of Paleontology*, volume 39, pages 497–501.
3. Bakker, R.T., 1971. "Dinosaur physiology and the origin of mammals," *Evolution*, volume 25, pages 636–58. 1972. "Anatomical and ecological evidence of endothermy in dinosaurs," *Nature*, volume 238, pages 81–5.
4. Bennett, A.F., and B. Dalzell, 1973. "Dinosaur physiology: a critique," *Evolution*, volume 27, pages 170–4.
5. Dodson, P., 1974. "Dinosaurs as Reptiles," *Evolution*, volume 28, pages 494–7. Ostrom, J.H., 1974. "Reply to 'Dinosaurs as Reptiles'," *Evolution*, volume 28, pages 491–3.
6. These data, which are very approximate and serve only as a guide, are from two sources: Brattstrom, B.H., 1970. "Amphibia" (pages 135–66), in: G. Causey Whittow (ed.) *Comparative Physiology of Thermoregulation*, volume 1, Academic Press, New York and London. Dawson, W.R., and J.W. Hudson, 1970. "Birds" (pages 223–310), in the same volume.
7. Bligh, J. and K.G. Johnson, 1973. "Glossary of terms for thermal physiology," *Journal of Applied Physiology*, volume 35, pages 941–61.
8. This is only very approximate. See: Templeton, J.R., 1970. "Reptiles" (pages 167–221), in: *Comparative Physiology of Thermoregulation*, volume 1, Academic Press, New York and London.
9. Heinrich, B., 1974. "Thermoregulation in endothermic insects," *Science*, volume 185, pages 747–56.
10. Somero, G.N., and A.L. De Vries., 1967. "Temperature tolerance of some Antarctic fishes," *Science*, volume 156, pages 257–8. The normal activity range of these fishes is virtually constant at -1.9°C. Raising the temperature to only about 6°C killed half of the fish tested within a week while a temperature of 15°C killed half of the fish within minutes. These temperatures are presumably too low to destroy their enzymes, but probably stop their activities.
11. See, for example, Harlow, H.J., S.S. Hillman, and M. Hoffman, 1976. "The effect of temperature on digestive efficiency in the herbivorous lizard, *Dipsosaurus dorsalis*," *Journal of Comparative Physiology*, volume 111, pages 1–6.
12. De Recqles, A.J., 1976. "On bone histology of fossil and living reptiles, with comments on its functional and evolutionary significance," pages 123–50 in: A. d'A. Bellairs and C.B. Cox (editors), *Morphology and Biology of Reptiles*, Academic Press, London and New York.
13. Bouvier, M., 1977 "Dinosaurian bone and endothermy," *Evolution*, volume 31, pages 449–50.
14. Schaller, G.B., 1972. *The Serengeti Lion*, University of Chicago Press, Chicago.
15. Auffenberg, W., 1970. "A day with number 19, report on a study of the Komodo monitor," *Animal Kingdom*, volume 73, number 6, pages 19–23.
16. Bakker, R.T., 1972, "Anatomical and ecological evidence of endothermy in dinosaurs," *Nature*, volume 238, pages 81–5.
17. Charig, A.J., 1976. "Dinosaur monophyly and a new class of vertebrates: a critical review," pages 65–104 in A. d'A. Bellairs and C.B. Cox (editors), *Morphology and Biology of Reptiles*, Academic Press, London and New York.
18. Torre-Bueno, J.R., 1976. "Temperature regulation and heat dissipation during flight in birds," *Journal of Experimental Biology*, volume 65, pages 471–82.
19. Neilsen, M., 1970. "Heat production and body temperature during rest and work," (pages 205–214), in: Hardy J.D., A.P. Gagge, and J.A.J. Stolwijk, (editors), *Physiological and behavioral temperature regulation*, Charles C. Thomas, Springfield, Illinois.
20. E.D. Stevens (*pers. comm.* 1979) pointed out that certain cold water fish can swim as fast as the (warm blooded) tuna, but that this high level of muscular activity can only be maintained for very short periods. He believes that continuous muscular contraction rather than fast muscular contraction is the significant factor in the maintenance of high body temperatures.
21. McGowan, C., 1979. "Selection pressures for high body temperatures: implications for dinosaurs," *Paleobiology*. volume 5, 285–95.
22. Heinrich, B., 1977. "Why have some animals evolved to regulate a high body temperature?," *American Naturalist*, volume 3, pages 623–40.
23. Crompton, A.W., C.R. Taylor, and J.A. Jagger, 1978. "Evolution of homeothermy in mammals," *Nature*, volume 272, pages 333–36.
24. See the reference given in note 21.
25. Bogert, C.M., 1959. "How reptiles regulate their body temperature," *Scientific American*, volume 200, number 4, pages 105–20.

26. Colbert, E.H., R.B. Cowles, and C.M. Bogert, 1946. "Temperature tolerances in the American alligator and their bearing on the habits, evolution and extinction of the dinosaurs," *Bulletin of the American Museum of Natural History*, volume 86, pages 331–73.
27. Mackay, R.S., 1964. "Galapagos tortoise and marine iguana deep body temperatures measured by radio telemetry," *Nature*, volume 204, pages 355–8.
28. Spotila, J.R., P.W. Lommen, G.S. Bakken, and D.M. Gates, 1973. "A mathematical model for body temperatures of large reptiles: implications for dinosaur ecology," *The American Naturalist*, volume 107, pages 391–404.
29. See the reference cited in note 8.
30. Frair, W., R.G. Ackerman, and N. Mrosovsky, 1972. "Body temperature of *Dermochelys coriacea:* warm turtle from cold water," *Science*, volume 177, pages 791–3.
31. Farlow, J.O., C.V. Thompson, and D.E. Rosner, 1976. "Plátes of the dinosaur *Stegosaurus*: Forced convection heat loss fins?," *Science*, volume 192, pages 1123–5.
32. Hart, J.S., 1971. "Rodents" (pages 1–149), in: G. Causey Whittow (ed.), *Comparative Physiology of Thermoregulation*, volume 2, Academic Press, New York and London.
33. Coombs, W.P. Jr., 1978. "Theoretical aspects of cursorial adaptations in dinosaurs," *The Quarterly Review of Biology*, volume 53, pages 393–418.
34. Galton, P.M., 1970. "The posture of hadrosaurian dinosaurs," *Journal of Paleontology*, volume 44, pages 464–73.
35. McNab, K., and W. Auffenberg, 1976. "The effect of large body size on temperature regulation of the Komodo Dragon, *Varanus komodoensis*," *Comparative Biochemistry and Physiology*, volume 55, pages 345–50.
36. Ostrom, J.H., 1975. "The origin of birds," in *Annual Review of Earth and Planetary Sciences*, volume 3, pages 55–77.
37. Evart, J.C., 1921. "The nestling feathers of the mallard with observations on the composition, origin and history of feathers," *Proceedings of the Zoolological Society of London*, 1921, pages 609–42.
Bock, W.J., 1969. "The origin and radiation of birds," *Annals of the New York Academy of Science*, volume 167, pages 147–55.
Ostrom, J.H., 1974. "*Archaeopteryx* and the origin of flight," *Quarterly Review of Biology*, volume 49, pages 27–47.
38. Regal argues that the presence of complex scales or primitive feathers would not prevent an animal from absorbing solar radiation. For further information see: Regal, P.J., 1975. "The evolutionary origin of feathers," *Quarterly Review of Biology*, volume 50, pages 35–66.
39. Ostrom, J.H., 1978. "The osteology of *Compsognathus longipes* Wagner," *Zitteliana Anhandlungen der Bayerischen Staatssammlung fur Palaeontologie und historische Geologie*, volume 4, pages 73–118.
40. See the reference given in note 21.
41. Colbert, E.H., 1961. *Dinosaurs: Their discovery and their world*, E.P. Dutton and Company, New York.
42. Horner, J.R. and R. Makela, 1979. "Nest of juveniles provides evidence of family structure in dinosaurs," *Nature*, volume 282, pages 296–98.
43. Charig, A.J., 1979. *A new look at the dinosaurs*, Heinemann, London. See photograph on page 113, top right.
44. Coombs, W.P., 1982. "Juvenile specimens of the ornithischian dinosaur *Psittacosaurus*," *Palaeontology*, volume 25, pages 89–107.
45. Dawson, W.R., and J.W. Hudson, 1970. "Birds" (pages 223–310), in: G. Causey Whittow (ed.), *Comparative Physiology of Thermoregulation*, volume 1, Academic Press, New York and London.
46. Hull, D., 1973. "Thermoregulation in young mammals," in: G. Causey Whittow (ed.), *Comparative Physiology of Thermoregulation*, volume 3, pages 167–98, Academic Press, New York and London.
See also: Grant, T.R., and T.J. Dawson, 1978. "Temperature regulation in the platypus, *Ornithorhynchus anatinus*: Maintenance of body temperature in air and water," *Physiological Zoology*, volume 51, pages 1–6.
47. See reference in note 42.
48. See discussion on juvenile dinosaurs and parental care in the reference given in note 44.
49. Broili, F., 1927. "Ein *Ramphorhychus* mit Spuren von Haarbedeckung," *Sitzungsberichte der mathematisch-natur Wissenschaftlichen Abteilung der Bayerischen Akademie der Wissenshaften*, pages 49–67.
50. Sharov, A.G., 1971. "New flying reptiles from the Mesozoic deposits of Kazakhston and Kirgizia," *Akademiia Nauk SSR, Paleontologicheskii Institut, Trudy*, volume 130, pages 104–13.
51. Axelrod, D.I. and H.P. Bailey, 1968. "Cretaceous dinosaur extinction," *Evolution*, volume 22, pages 595–611.

Chapter 7 *Brains and Intellect*

1. McIntyre, J. (ed.), 1974. *Mind in the waters*, McLelland and Stewart Ltd., Toronto
2. Grech, D., R.S. Crutfield, and N. Livson, 1969. *Elements of psychology*. Alfred A. Knopf, New York.

3. Jerison, H.J., 1973. *Evolution of the brain and intelligence*, Academic Press, New York.
4. Burghardt, G.M., 1977. "Learning processes in reptiles," in: *Biology of the Reptiles*, Gans, C. (ed.), pages 555–681, Academic Press, London and New York.
5. Stettner, L.J., and K.A. Matyniak, 1968. "The brain of birds," *Scientific American*, volume 218, number 6, pages 64–76.
6. Edinger, T., 1942. "The pituitary body in giant animals, fossil and living," *Quarterly Review of Biology*, volume 17, page 31.
7. See reference in footnote 3. See also: Hopson, J.A., 1977. "Relative brain size and behavior in archosaurian reptiles," *Annual Review of Ecology and Systematics*, volume 8, pages 429–48.
8. Jerison, H.J., 1973. *op. cit.*, page 28.
9. The logarithm of a number may be obtained from a set of logarithm tables, familiar to those who went to school before pocket calculators were invented.
10. Data used for plotting the graph were from: Crile, G., and Quiring, D.P., 1940. "A record of the body weight and certain organ and gland weights of 3690 animals," *Ohio Journal of Science*, volume 40, number 5, pages 219–59. Jerison plotted data for 198 species (94 mammals, 52 birds, 20 reptiles, and 32 fishes). See: Jerison, H.J., 1969. "Brain evolution and dinosaur brains," *The American Naturalist*, volume 934, pages 575–88.
11. When Jerison (1973, page 61) looked at a broad sample of mammals, he found that the best equation was: brain weight $= 0.12 \times$ (body weight)$^{2/3}$, and if this is used to calculate the brain weight of a 1000 g squirrel monkey, a value of 12 g is obtained.
12. Jerison first published his results in 1969 (ref. note 10) and modified his data in 1973 (ref. note 3). The modified data is included in the text.
13. Pooley, A.C., and C. Gans, 1976. "The Nile Crocodile," *Scientific American*, volume 234, number 4, pages 114–24.
14. The ostrich has a fairly prominent sacral swelling, and we have a slight swelling in our own spinal cord. See: Streeter, G.L., 1904. "The structure of the spinal cord of the Ostrich," *American Journal of Anatomy*, volume 3, pages 1–27.
15. See reference in table on page 129.
16. Jerison (1973) cautions that Marsh's data for the primitive toothed birds of the American west are unreliable.
17. Jerison (1973) gives an estimated brain volume of 0.92 cm^3 while Hopson (1977) gives almost twice this value (1.76 cm^3).
18. Jerison (1973, pages 194–5) compares the size of the endocast of an Eocene species of curlew (*Numenius*) with that of a living species. The Eocene species has an endocast volume of 3.1 cm^3 compared with 3.7 cm^3 for living species. There was therefore an increase of about 20 per cent in brain size between Eocene and modern times, which Jerison interprets as evidence that the brain of birds had not completed its expansion during the Cretaceous period.
19. McGowan, C., 1973. "The cranial morphology of the Lower Liassic latipinnate ichthyosaurs of England," *Bulletin of the British Museum (Natural History)*, volume 24, pages 1–109.
20. Opponents of the concept that dinosaurs may have been endothermic might argue that dinosaurs were inactive at night because, deprived of the sun, their body temperatures were lowered. This might have been true for the smaller dinosaurs but it should be noted that inactivity at night does not necessarily imply ectothermy, because most birds maintain high body temperatures at night but are usually inactive, and many modern (ectothermic) reptiles are active at night.
21. See Jerison (1973), chapter 12.
22. Some mammals, man included, have colour vision, and hence cone cells. But it is believed that these are not homologous with the cone cells of other vertebrates, being instead secondarily derived.
23. Much of the nervous integration of the visual sense occurs at the level of the retina, whereas that for the olfactory and auditory senses occurs mainly in the brain. See Jerison (1973), chapter 12.
24. Crompton, A.W., Taylor, C.R., and Jagger, J.A., 1978. "Evolution of homeothermy in mammals," *Nature*, volume 272, pages 333–6.

Chapter 8 *The Fish-Lizards*

1. Hawkins, T., 1834. *Memoirs of Ichthyosauri and Plesiosauri, extinct monsters of the ancient Earth*, Relfe and Fletcher, London.
2. To be pedantic, Hawkins dined on the eggs of the peahen. See: Owen, R., 1894. *The life of Richard Owen*, John Murray, London, volume 1, page 166.
3. This extract is from pages 25–7 of the reference given in footnote 1. The original spelling and punctuation have been largely retained.
4. According to Sir Everard Home's account (see note 6), most of the specimen was collected in 1812, the remainder the following year. According to Lang, however, the dates were 1810 and 1811. For further information see: Delair,

J.B., 1969. "A history of the early discoveries of Liassic ichthyosaurs in Dorset and Somerset (1779–1835) and the first record of the occurrence of ichthyosaurs in the Purbeck," *Proceedings of the Dorset Natural History and Archaeological Society,* volume 90, pages 115–32.
Lang, W.D., 1959 "Mary Anning's escape from lightning," *Proceedings of the Dorset Natural History and Archaeological Society,* volume 80, pages 91–3.

5. For further information see Delair 1969, *op. cit.*
6. Home, E., 1814. "Some account of the fossil remains of an animal more nearly allied to fishes than any other classes of animals," *Philosophical Transactions of the Royal Society of London,* volume 101, pages 571–6. Home records that the specimen was in the collection of Bullock's museum and that it had been collected from the Henley estate in 1812 and 1813. No mention was made of Mary Anning, and Bullock was credited with supervising the preparation of the material.
7. Home, E., 1819. "Reasons for giving the name *Proteosaurus* to the fossil skeleton which has been described," *Philosophical Transactions of the Royal Society of London,* volume 109, pages 212–6.
8. The name *Ichthyosaurus* was first proposed in 1818 by Charles Koenig who was employed by the British Museum (Natural History) until his untimely death from a fall in 1851. See: Koenig, C., 1818. *Synopsis of the Contents of the British Museum,* edition 13, page 54.
9. Owen, R., 1881. "A monograph of the fossil Reptilia of the Liassic Formations," *Palaeontographical Society,* London, pages 83–4.
10. See: Owen, R., 1894. *op. cit.,* and: Le Fanu, W., 1978. "Natural history drawings collected by John Hunter FRS (1728–1793), at the Royal College of Surgeons of England," *Bibliography of Natural History,* volume 8, pages 329–33.
11. Owen, R., 1861. *Essays and observations in natural history, anatomy, physiology, psychology, and geology, by John Hunter, FRS, London.* This work is cited in the biography of Owen (see note 2).
12. De la Beche, H.T., and Conybeare, W.D., 1821. "Notice of the discovery of a new fossil animal, forming a link between the *Ichthyosaurus* and crocodile, together with general remarks on the osteology of the *Ichthyosaurus,*" *Transactions of the Geological Society of London,* volume 5, pages 559–94.
Conybeare, W.D., 1822. "Additional notices on the fossil genera *Ichthyosaurus* and *Plesiosaurus,*" *Transactions of the Geological Society of London,* volume 5, pages 103–23.
13. Owen, R., 1840 (a). "Report on the British fossil Reptiles," *Report of the ninth meeting of the British Association for the Advancement of Science, held in Birmingham in August 1839,* John Murray, London. Owen, R., 1840 (b). "Notice on the dislocation of the tail at a certain point observable in the skeleton of many ichthyosauri," *Transactions of the Geological Society of London,* volume 5, pages 511–14.
14. Hauff, B., 1954. *Das Holzmadenbuch,* F. Rau, Ohringen.
15. McGowan, C., 1976. "The description and phenetic relationships of a new ichthyosaur genus from the Upper Jurassic of England," *Canadian Journal of Earth Sciences,* volume 13, pages 668–83.
McGowan, C., 1978. "An isolated ichthyosaur coracoid from the Maastrichtian of New Jersey," *Canadian Journal of Earth Sciences,* volume 15, pages 169–71.
16. Kuhn-Schnyder, E., 1963. "Wege der Reptiliensystematik," *Sonderdruck aus Paläontologischen Zeitschrift,* Stuttgart, volume 37, pages 61–87.
17. McGowan, C., 1978. "Further evidence for the wide geographical distribution of ichthyosaur taxa (Reptilia:Ichthyosauria)," *Journal of Paleontology,* volume 52, pages 1155–62.
18. Leidy, J., 1868. "Notice of some reptilian remains from Nevada," *Proceedings of the Philadelphia Academy of Science,* volume 20, pages 177–8.
19. Merriam, C.W., 1908. "Triassic Ichthyosauria, with special reference to the American forms," *Memoirs of the University of California,* volume 1, pages 1–196.
20. Camp, C.L., 1976. "Vorläufige Mitteilung über grosse Ichthyosaurier aus der oberen Trias von Nevada," *Akademie der Wissenschaften Mathematisch-naturwissen-chafliche,* volume 185, pages 125–34. This paper is essentially an abstract of a detailed manuscript which Camp was working on just before his death. This manuscript has now been published: Camp, C.L., 1980. "Large ichthyosaurs from the Upper Triassic of Nevada," *Palaeontographica,* volume 170, pages 139–200.
21. See the reference cited in note 17.
22. McGowan, C., 1974 (b). "A revision of the latipinnate ichthyosaurs of the Lower Jurassic of England (Reptilia: Ichthyosauria)," *Life Sciences Contributions,* Royal Ontario Museum, number 100, pages 1–30.
23. McGowan, C., 1974 (a). "A revision of the longipinnate ichthyosaurs of the Lower Jurassic

of England with descriptions of two new species (Reptilia:Ichthyosauria)," *Life Sciences Contributions*, Royal Ontario Museum, number 97, pages 1–37.

24. See the first reference cited in note 15.

25. For an account of the Holzmaden ichthyosaurs see:
McGowan, C., 1979. "A revision of the Lower Jurassic ichthyosaurs of Germany, with the descriptions of two new species," *Palaeontographica*, volume 166, pages 93–135.

26. See the reference given in note 17.

27. In 1958 an excavator digging a drainage ditch in East Anglia unearthed a large skull which turned out to be a new ichthyosaur genus, subsequently named *Grendelius mordax*. Unlike *Ophthalmosaurus* it had large teeth and a relatively small orbit. See the first reference given in note 15.

28. McGowan, C., 1972. "The systematics of Cretaceous ichthyosaurs with particular reference to the material from North America," *Contributions to Geology*, volume 11, pages 9–29.

29. Webb, P.W., 1977. "Effects of median-fin amputation on fast-start performance of rainbow trout (*Salmo gairdneri*)," *Journal of Experimental Biology*, volume 68, pages 123–35.

30. There is evidence (in the form of a single bone) that *Platypterygius* was not the only ichthyosaur of the late Cretaceous: McGowan, C., 1978. "An isolated ichthyosaur coracoid from the Maastrichtian of New Jersey," *Canadian Journal of Earth Sciences*, volume 15, pages 169–71.

31. Heller, W., 1966. "Untersuchungen zur sogenannten Hauterhaltung bei Ichthyosauriern aus dem Lias epsilon Holzmadens (Schwaben)," *Neues Jahrbuch für Geologie und Paläontologie*, 1966, pages 304–17.

32. The viscosity of water at 10°C. is 1.3037 centipoises which is 0.013 poises, the latter being the c.g.s. (cm,g ,s) unit for viscosity. To convert to SI units (N/m^2) multiply by 10^{-3}. Data from: Kaye, G.W.C., and Laby, T.H., 1966. *Tables of physical and chemical constants*, Longman, London.

33. Fluid flowing over a sphere actually breaks away from the surface before reaching the trailing surface (except beyond the critical Reynolds number, which may be as high as 4×10^5 for a smooth sphere). Therefore spheres derive little or no benefit from pressure drag. See: Kuethe, A.M., and Chow, C. 1976. *Foundations of aerodynamics: Bases of aerodynamic design*. John Wiley and Sons, New York.

34. The fast-swimming bonito and tuna fish, however, have a band of rough scales around the widest part of the body. This causes turbulence, but instead of increasing the drag, it actually reduces it, because at these high Reynolds numbers the turbulent water remains in contact longer with the surface of the body. The beneficial effect of the pressure drag acting on the trailing edge is therefore not lost by the premature separation of the boundary layer. This, incidentally, is why golf balls are dimpled.

35. Hertel, H., 1969. "Hydrodynamics of swimming and wave-riding in dolphins," in: Andersen, H.T., *The biology of marine mammals*, Academic Press, New York.

36. Lang, T.G., and K. Pryor, 1966. "Hydrodynamic performance of porpoises (*Stenella attenuata*)," *Science*, volume 152, pages 531–63.

37. For an account of the possible function of the tail see: McGowan, C., 1973. "Differential growth in three ichthyosaurs: *Ichthyosaurus communis, I. breviceps* and *Stenopterygius quadriscissus* (Reptilia, Ichthyosauria)," *Life Sciences Contributions*, Royal Ontario Museum, number 93, pages 1–21.

38. Thomson, K.S., 1976. "On the heterocercal tail in sharks," *Paleobiology*, volume 2, pages 9–38.
Thomson, K.S., and Simanek, D.E., 1977. "Body form and locomotion in sharks," *American Zoologist*, volume 17, pages 343–54.

39. Pollard, J.E., 1968. "The gastric contents of an ichthyosaur from the Lower Lias of Lyme Regis, Dorset," *Palaeontology*, volume 11, pages 376–88.

40. Pearce, J.C., 1846. "Notice of what appears to be the embryo of an *Ichthyosaurus* (*communis*?)," *Annals and Magazine of Natural History*, volume 17, pages 44–6.

41. Branca, H.W., 1907. "Sind alle im Innern von Ichthyosauren liegenden Jungen ausnahmslos?," *Abhandlungen der Wissenschaften*, Berlin, 1907, pages 1–34.

42. Drevermann, F., 1926. "Eine neue Ichthyosaura mit Jungem in Sendkenberg-Museum," *Bericht der Senckenbergischen Naturforschenden Gesselschaft*, number 56, pages 181–6.

43. Liepmann, W., 1926. "Leichengeburt bei Ichthyosauriern," *Sitzungsberichte der Heidelberger Akademie der Wissenschaften*,1926, pages 1–10.

44. Scott, E.O.G., and Green, R.H., 1975. "Recent whale strandings in Northern Tasmania," *Proceedings of the Royal Society of Tasmania*, volume 109, pages 91–6.

45. McGowan, C., 1973. *op. cit.*

46. Johnson, R., 1977. "Size independent criteria for estimating relative age and the relationships among growth parameters in a group of fossil reptiles (Reptilia:Ichthyosauria)," *Canadian Journal of Earth Sciences*, volume 14, pages 1916–24.

Chapter 9 *The Incredible Flying Machine*

1. See: Seeley, H.G., 1901. *Dragons of the air,* Methuen and Company, London, page 121.
2. See: Schafer, W., 1972. *Ecology and palaeoecology of marine environments,* Oliver and Boyd, Edinburgh.
3. Williston, S.W., 1902. "Winged reptiles," *Popular Science Monthly,* volume 60, pages 314–22.
4. There were many different versions of each aircraft during the war, and the data are based upon the first operational models in each case: the Messerschmitt 109 E-1, and the Spitfire I, which was its contemporary. Data from: Green, W., 1957. *Famous Fighters of the Second World War,* MacDonald, London.
5. For example see: Hildebrand, M., 1974. *Analysis of Vertebrate Structure,* John Wiley and Sons, New York.
6. Hankin, E.H., 1910. *Animal Flight,* Iliffe and Sons Ltd., London, page 346.
7. The condor has a weight of 9–11 kg (20–25 pounds) and a wingspan of 3.3 metres (11 feet). An extinct vulture, *Teratornis incredibilis* from the Pleistocene of Nevada, had a wingspan of 5 metres and probably weighed about 37 kg. It is difficult to visualize the latter becoming airborne under its own power.
8. The usual length measurement of birds is the wingspan. See: Greenewalt, C.H., 1962. "Dimensional relationships for flying animals." *Smithsonian Miscellaneous Collections,* volume 144, pages 1–46.
9. The first *Pteranodon* material was discovered in Kansas by a field party from Yale University, under the direction of Othniel C. Marsh. The party collected giant pterosaur material in 1870, 1871, and 1872. Marsh wrote about these discoveries in the *American Journal of Science,* in 1871, "Note on a new and gigantic species of *Pterodactylus,*" volume 1, page 472; 1872, "Discovery of additional remains of Pterosauria, with descriptions of two new species," volume 3, pages 241–8; and 1876, "Notice of a new Sub-order of Pterosauria," volume 11, pages 507–9. In the first two papers Marsh stated that the bones were very large, and mentioned that teeth were present. In the third paper, he stated that teeth were absent. Presumably he was mistaken in identifying teeth in 1871 and 1872, in which case the date of the discovery of *Pteranodon* material is 1870.
10. Bramwell, C.D., and Whitfield, G.R., 1974. "Biomechanics of *Pteranodon,*" *Philosophical Transactions of the Royal Society of London,* volume 267, pages 503–81. The discussion of *Pteranodon* in this chapter is largely based upon this work.
11. See: Seeley 1901. (reference cited in note 1.)
12. Wellnhofer, P., 1975. "Die Rhamphorhynchoidea (Pterosauria) der Oberjura-Plattenkalke Suddeutschlands, Teil III: Palokologie und Stammesgeschichte," *Palaeontographica,* volume 149, pages 1–30.
13. Eaton, G.F., 1910. "Osteology of *Pteranodon,*" *Memoirs of the Connecticut Academy of Arts and Science,* volume 2, pages 1–38. Eaton was particularly stuck by the avian appearance of the sacrum, which he compared with that of the wild turkey, *Meleagris gallopavo.*
14. Novick, A., 1969. *The World of Bats,* Holt, Rinehart and Winston, New York.
15. See the reference given in note 10.
16. See the reference cited in note 3.
17. Brown, B., 1943. "Flying reptiles," *Natural History,* volume 52 (October), pages 104–11.
18. See reference in note 10.
19. Padian, K., 1979. "The wings of pterosaurs: a new look," *Discovery,* volume 14, pages 20–9.
20. The gliding angle is directly proportional to the sinking speed. For details see pages 554–55 of the reference given in note 10.
21. Force = mass × acceleration. Therefore the force required to keep the animal airborne is the product of its mass (in kilograms) and the acceleration due to gravity (in metres per second per second).

   $\therefore$ force = 16.6 × 9.8 W
   work = force × distance
   power = rate of doing work
   = force × distance/time
   = force × velocity
   $\therefore$ the power required to overcome the sinking velocity of 0.42 m = 16.6 × 9.8 × 0.42
   = 68 W
22. See page 585 of the reference cited in note 10.
23. One of the best accounts of control movements in birds is given in Hankin 1910, *op. cit.*
24. Lawson, D.A., 1975a. "Pterosaur from the Latest Cretaceous of West Texas: discovery of the largest flying creature," *Science,* volume 187, pages 947–8.
25. The name *Quetzalcoatlus* was mentioned in a letter to *Science* (Lawson, D.A., 1975b. *Science,* volume 188). As it was not accompanied by an adequate description, the name cannot yet be formally applied to the material.

Chapter 10 *The End of an Era*

1. Dr. L.S. Russell, himself a collector of long standing as well as one of Canada's senior scientists, gives a detailed history of dinosaur hunting in western Canada: Russell, L.S., 1966. "Dinosaur hunting in western Canada," *Life Sciences Contributions*, Royal Ontario Museum, number 70, pages 1–37.
2. For an excellent account of the park and its dinosaurs see: Dodson, P., 1971. "Sedimentology and taphonomy of the Oldman Formation (Campanian), Dinosaur Provincial Park, Alberta (Canada)," *Palaeogeography, Palaeoclimatology, Palaeoecology*, volume 10, pages 21–74.
3. Russell, D.A., 1967. "A census of dinosaur specimens collected in western Canada," *Natural History Papers*, National Museums of Canada, number 36, pages 1–13. Russell, D.A., and Chamney, T.P., 1967. "Notes on the biostratigraphy of dinosaurian and microfossil faunas in the Edmonton Formation (Cretaceous), of Alberta," *Natural History Papers*, National Museums of Canada, number 35, pages 1–22.
4. Russell (1977) gives upper and lower limits of two million years and 1–100 years, while Van Valen and Sloan (1977) estimate an interval of 400,000 years for the extinction of dinosaurs in Montana: Russell, D.A., 1977. "The biotic crisis at the end of the Cretaceous Period," *Syllogeus Series*, National Museums of Canada, number 12, pages 11–23.
   Van Valen, L., and R.E. Sloan, 1977. "Ecology and the extinction of the dinosaurs," *Evolutionary Theory*, volume 2, pages 37–64.
5. *Syllogeus Series*, National Museums of Canada, number 12, March 1977, Ottawa.
6. Russell, D.A., 1977. *A vanished world: The dinosaurs of western Canada*, National Museums of Canada, Ottawa. This is an excellent account of the environments of Cretaceous dinosaurs, and the present geological setting of the Canadian West.
7. Hays, J.D., 1971. "Faunal extinctions and reversals of the earth's magnetic field," *Bulletin of the Geological Society of America*, volume 82, pages 2433–47.
   Reid, G.C., Isaksen, I.S.A., Holzer, T.E., and Crutzen, P.J., 1976. "Influence of ancient solar-proton events on the evolution of life," *Nature*, volume 250, pages 177–9.
   Ruderman, M.A., 1974. "Possible consequences of nearby supernova explosions for atmospheric ozone and terrestrial life," *Science*, volume 184, pages 1079–81.
8. Alvarez, L.W., Alvarez, W., Asaro, F., and Michel, H.V., 1980. "Extraterrestrial cause for the Cretaceous-Tertiary extinction," *Science*, volume 208, pages 1095–1108.
9. Smit, J., and Hertogen, J., 1980. "An extraterrestrial event at the Cretaceous-Tertiary boundary," *Nature*, volume 285, pages 198–200.
   Orth, C.J. et al. 1981. "An iridium abundance anomaly at the Cretaceous-Tertiary boundary in northern New Mexico," *Science*, volume 214, pages 1341–43.
10. The estimated periodicy for collisions with 10 km asteroids range from 30–100 million years. See references cited in note and 8 and also: Hsü, K.J., 1980. "Terrestrial catastrophe caused by cometary impact at the end of the Cretaceous," *Nature*, volume 285, pages 201–3.
11. See the letter on asteroid extinction hypotheses by Kent, D.V., 1981, *Science*, volume 211, pages 649–50.
12. Pettersson, H., 1960. "Cosmic spherules and meteoritic dust," *Scientific American*, volume 202, pages 123–32.
13. See the article cited in note 11. Another mechanism for concentrating the meteoritic dust, also discussed in this article, is by differential sorting. The meteoritic dust typically occurs as spherules, which have a high density, and these would tend to be concentrated by the winnowing action of water currents. Spherules have actually been described at the Cretaceous-Tertiary boundary for a locality in Spain. See: Smit, J., and Klaver, G., "Sandine spherules at the Cretaceous-Tertiary boundary indicate a large impact event," *Nature*, volume 292, pages 47–9.
14. Hickey, L.J., 1981. "Land plant evidence compatible with gradual, not catastrophic, change at the end of the Cretaceous," *Nature*, volume 292, pages 529–31. See also: Butler, R.F., and Lindsay, E.H., 1980. "Magnetostratigraphy, biostratigraphy and geochronology of the Cretaceous-Tertiary boundary sediments, Red Deer Valley," *Nature*, volume 284, page 375.
15. A hadrosaurian dinosaur has been described from an Argentinian locality that was provisionally dated as the early Paleocene (earliest Tertiary). However, the author of this paper, in a personal communication to D.A. Russell in 1978, reports that this is now believed to be Maestrichtian in age. A supposed ichthyosaur

tooth described from the Miocene of Malta is probably crocodilian. These are just two of a number of reports of post-Cretaceous dinosaurs and other reptiles that are believed to be extinct. See: Casimiquela, R.M., 1964. "Sabre un dinosaurio hadrosaurido de la Argentina," *Ameghiniana*, volume 3, pages 285–312. Lydekker, R., 1889. *Catalogue of the fossil Reptilia and Amphibia in the British Museum (Natural History)*, part 2, London.
See also: Borsuk-Bialynicka, M., 1977. "A new camarasaurid sauropod *Opisthocoelicaudia skarzynskii* gen.n. sp.n. from the Upper Cretaceous of Mongolia," *Palaeontologia Polonica*, volume 37, pages 5–64.

16. Alexander, P., 1959. *Atomic radiation and life.* Harmondsworth, Penguin Books, England.
17. However, D.A. Russell (*pers. comm.* 1978) points out that many marine planktonic organisms are living at the upper limits of their ultra-violet tolerance levels.
18. The data for terrestrial plants are from L. Hickey, reported in: Kerr, R.A., 1980. "Asteroid theory of extinction strengthened," *Science*, volume 210, pages 514–17. This paper gives an excellent review of the evidence for, and against, the asteroid hypothesis.
19. See the first reference given in note 14.
20. Data from: Charig, A.J., 1973. "Jurassic and Cretaceous dinosaurs," in: *Atlas of Palaeobiogeography*, A. Hallum (ed.), Elsevier Scientific Publishing Company, Amsterdam.
21. McGowan, C., 1976. "The description and phenetic relationships of a new ichthyosaur genus from the Upper Jurassic of England," *Canadian Journal of Earth Sciences*, volume 13, pages 668–83.
McGowan, C., 1978. "Further evidence for the wide geographical distribution of ichthyosaur taxa (Reptilia: Ichthyosauria)," *Journal of Paleontology*, volume 52, pages 1155–62.
22. There is some evidence that *Platypterygius* was not the sole ichthyosarian in the Upper Cretaceous seas, because a scrap of material has been found that appears to represent a separate genus. The material, however, is inadequate for the formal recognition of a new genus. See: McGowan, C., 1978. "An isolated ichthyosaur coracoid from the Maastrichtian of New Jersey," *Canadian Journal of Earth Sciences*, volume 15, pages 169–71.
23. Russell, D.A., 1975. "Reptilian diversity and the Cretaceous-Tertiary Transition in North America," *The Geological Association of Canada Special Paper Number 13*, pages 119–35.
24. Raup, D.M., 1978. "Approaches to the extinction problem," *Journal of Paleontology*, volume 52, pages 517–23.
25. Axelrod, D.I., and Bailey, H.P., 1968. "Cretaceous dinosaur extinction," *Evolution*, volume 22, pages 595–611.
26. Hickey (see note 14) argues that the increase in percentage of cooler-climate plants in the latest Cretaceous, the reduction in diversity of dinosaurs, and the lack of synchrony in dinosaur and plant extinctions, all favour a climatic cause for dinosaurian extinction.
27. Sloan, R.E., 1976. "The ecology of the dinosaur extinction," in: *Athlon Essays on palaeontology in honour of Loris Shano Russell*, Churcher, C.S. (ed.), Royal Ontario Museum, Toronto.
28. The floral change that occurred on land at the close of the Cretaceous Period may have been relatively minor. According to the first reference in note 4, only about 10 per cent of the higher plants became extinct, but the floral change was considered to be major by the authors of the second reference.
29. Reported in: Swinton, W.E., 1970. *The dinosaurs*, George Unwin Ltd., London.
30. Koch, N.C., 1967. "Disappearance of the dinosaurs," *Journal of Paleontology*, volume 41, pages 970–2.

Chapter 11 *The King is Dead: Long Live the King*

1. Ostrom, J.H., 1976. "*Archaeopteryx* and the origin of birds," *Biological Journal of the Linnean Society*, volume 8, pages 91–182.
2. Wagner, J.A., 1861. "Ueber ein neues Augenblick mit Vogelfedern versehenes Reptil aus dem Solenhofener lithographischen Schiefer," *Sitzungsberichte bayerische Akademie Wissenschaften*, volume 2, pages 146–54.
3. Owen, R. 1864. "On the *Archaeopteryx* of von Meyer, with a description of the fossil remains of a long-tailed species, from the lithographic stone of Solenhofen," *Philosophical Transactions of the Royal Society of London*, volume 153, pages 33–47. Owen believed that there was probably more than one species of *Archaeopteryx* and that von Meyer's name of *Archaeopteryx lithographica*, based upon the single feather, was not altogether satisfactory. He proposed that the second specimen be referred to a second species, and proposed the name *Archaeopteryx macrura*, because of its long tail.

The current view is that there is only one species, and von Meyer's name has priority.

4. Owen is usually attributed with having been a devout anti-evolutionist, but this does not appear to be entirely true. Owen knew Darwin quite well, they frequently visited and corresponded with one another, and their exchanges were always cordial. When Owen was appointed superintendant of the British Museum (Natural History) and became involved in the planning of a new building that was to be erected in South Kensington (the present building of the museum), he urged that provision be made for exhibits to illustrate the theory of evolution: "The whole intellectual world this year has been excited by a book on the origin of species . . . As to showing you [the public] the varieties of those species, or any of those phenomena that would aid one in getting at that mystery of mysteries, the origin of species, our space does not permit; but surely there ought to be space somewhere, and, if not in the British Museum, where is it to be obtained?" See: Owen, R., 1894. *The Life of Richard Owen*, John Murray, London. (written by his grandson, also named Richard), volume 2, page 39. Owen's subsequent references to his position on the theory of evolution by natural selection are somewhat confusing. See: MacLeod, R.M. 1965. "Evolutionism and Richard Owen, 1830–1868: an episode in Darwin's century." *Isis*, volume 56, pages 259–80.
5. Huxley, T.H., 1868. "On the animals which are most nearly intermediate between the birds and reptiles," *The Annals and Magazine of Natural History*. London, volume 2, pages 66–75.
6. Heilmann, G., 1926. *The Origin of Birds*, H.F. and G. Whitherby, London.
7. There is now some evidence that the avian furcula may not represent fused clavicles, but the problem has not yet been resolved. See: Lansdowne, A.B.G., 1968. "The origin and early development of the clavicle in the quail *Coturnix coturnix japonica*," *Journal of Zoology*, volume 156, pages 307–12.
8. See the reference given in note 1.
9. Ostrom, J.H., 1970. "*Archaeopteryx*, notice of a "new" specimen," *Science*, volume 170, pages 537–8.
10. Gish, D.T., 1973. *Evolution. The fossils say no!* Creation-Life Publishers, San Diego. For a detailed discussion of *Archaeopteryx* and the evolution of birds see, McGowan, C., 1983. *In the beginning.* Macmillan of Canada, Toronto.
11. For a description of these anatomical terms, and further information see the reference given in note 1.
12. Regal, P.J., 1975. "The evolutionary origin of feathers," *Quarterly Review of Biology*, volume 50, pages 35–66.
13. Kollar, E.J., and Fisher, C., 1980. "Tooth induction on chick epithelium: expression of quiescent genes for enamel synthesis," *Science*, volume 207, pages 993–95.
14. Heptonstall, W.B., 1970. "Quantitative assessment of the flight of *Archaeopteryx*," *Nature*, volume 228, pages 185–6. For replies to Heptonstall's article see the letters to *Nature*, 1971, volume 231, pages 127 and 128.
15. *Archaeopteryx* may have had a cartilaginous sternum, like many reptiles, but not a bony sternum. See reference given in note 1.
16. Ostrom, J.H., 1974. "*Archaeopteryx* and the origin of flight," *Quarterly Review of Biology*, volume 49, pages 27–47.
17. Ostrom (1974) argues that this is not a valid objection to his hypothesis because there are several ground-living, predatory birds that have long tails and are not especially good fliers.
18. The centre of lift of an airfoil lies towards the leading edge, and it is important that the main supporting structure (the main spar in an aircraft wing) coincides with this to prevent twisting during flight. The wing feathers of flying birds similarly have the supporting structure (the shaft) offset towards the leading edge. See: Feduccia, A., and H.B. Tordoff, 1979. "Feathers of *Archaeopteryx*: Asymmetric vanes indicate aerodynamic function," *Science*, volume 203, pages 1021–2.
19. For a discussion of the origin of feathers, see Ostrom (1974) (cited in note 16.)
20. Bakker, R.T., and Galton, P.M., 1974. "Dinosaur monophyly and a new class of vertebrates," *Nature*, volume 248, pages 168–72.
21. See the reference given in note 1.

Glossary

Aileron An adjustable plane on the trailing edge of a wing, towards its tip, used to control roll.

Airfoil A body shaped such that it generates a lift when moving through a fluid even when set at a zero angle of attack. Airfoils, such as aircraft wings, typically have a convex upper surface and a flat or concave lower surface.

Air speed The speed of a body, usually an aircraft, relative to the air flowing over it. See also ground speed.

Allopatric Of species or populations of species occupying different geographical areas.

Allopatric speciation A speciation event which entails the geographic separation of one group of individuals of a species from another such group.

Alula The thumb of a bird; has the form of a small wing that often functions as a leading edge slot to delay the onset of separation of the airflow as the wing approaches the stalling condition.

Amino acid One of the component parts of a protein molecule.

Angle of attack The angle between the chord line of an airfoil (or the axis of an inclined plane) and the direction of the flow of the fluid.

Ankylosaur A type of dinosaur; a member of the Suborder Ankylosauria of the Order Ornithischia. Ankylosaurs, which were plant-eaters, were armoured with bony plates that lay flat against the body.

Archosaur A type of reptile; a member of the Subclass Archosauria, which includes dinosaurs and crocodiles.

Arthropod An invertebrate animal belonging to the Phylum Arthropoda. Arthropods, which constitute about 80% of the total number of living species, are characterised by having a hard outer skeleton and jointed limbs.

Aspect ratio The length of a wing, or similar structure, divided by its width.

Bacterium A microscopic single-celled organism, characterised by being without a well-defined nucleus. Many bacteria cause disease.

Behavioral temperature regulator An animal that regulates its body temperature by modifications in the heat produced by its skeletal muscles. Many flying insects and some reptiles are behavioral temperature regulators.

Bipedalism Walking on two legs; man, for example, is bipedal, so too are birds.

Boundary layer The fluid layer that lies in contact with the surface of a moving body. There is a velocity gradient of the particles within the boundary layer, from zero at the surface, to the velocity of the freely moving particles beyond the boundary layer. The thickness of the boundary layer decreases with increasing Reynolds number.

Camber Of an airfoil; the thickness relative to the chord. Thick airfoils have higher cambers than thin airfoils.

Cambrian Period The first geological period, lasting from approximately 570 million years ago to 500 million years ago.

Canadian Shield A large area of land, centred upon Hudson Bay, formed of rock of Precambrian age.

Carboniferous Period The geological period, which lasted from approximately 345 million years ago to 280 million years ago, during which time the major coal deposits were formed.

Carinate Bird that possesses a keeled sternum (breast bone). Flying birds are carinates, as opposed to non-flying birds (the ostrich and its allies) called ratites.

Carnosaur A type of dinosaur; a member of the Infraorder Carnosauria of the Suborder Theropoda. Carnosaurs were all meat-eaters.

Centre of pressure Of an airfoil; the point through which the total reaction acts.

Ceratopsian A type of dinosaur; a member of the Suborder Ceratopsia of Order Ornithischia. Ceratopsians, which were plant eaters, had a bony shield projecting over the neck region from the back of the skull and most of them also had horns.

Chelonia The tortoises or turtles; reptiles belonging to the Order Chelonia of the Subclass Anapsida.

Chord Of an airfoil; a line joining the centres of curvature of the leading and trailing edges.

Coelenterate An invertebrate animal belonging to the Phylum Coelenterata. Coelenterates are characterised by having a relatively simple body that comprises two layers of cells separated by a jelly material called the mesoglea. The group includes jelly fishes, sea anemones and corals.

Conservative Of organs, organisms, or groups of organisms which have tended to remain unchanged from the ancestral condition. Having undergone little or no evolutionary change.

Cretaceous Period The third and last geological period of the Mesozoic Era; lasting from approximately 135 million years ago to 63 million years ago.

Cursorial Having a skeleton adapted for running. One of the features of a cursorial animal, as exemplified by the horse, is that the upper leg bones (femur and humerus) are angled when viewed from the side.

Devonian Period The geological period which lasted from approximately 405 million years ago to 345 million years ago which is often referred to as the Age of Fishes.

Digitigrade Walking on the toes rather than on the whole foot. Cats, for example, are digitigrade, their heels and palms being held clear of the ground when they walk. We are digitigrade only when sprinting.

Diluvial Pertaining to the Biblical flood of Noah. According to the diluvial theory, all geological phenomena can be explained in terms of a worldwide flood that swept the Earth some 10,000 years ago.

Dinosaur A collective term applied to two extinct orders of reptiles, the Saurischia and the Ornithischia.

Drag force The sum total of forces acting on a moving body which act in opposition to its motion.

Ectotherm An animal whose body temperature depends upon the regulated uptake of heat from the environment—usually from the sun. Most reptiles and some amphibians are ectotherms. The term cold-blooded has been used for this thermal strategy.

Elasmosaur A type of plesiosaur, having a long neck and a small head.

Encephalization quotient The ratio of the actual size of an animal's brain compared with the calculated volume. Our encephalization quotient, for example, is about 7.5, which means that our brains are about 7.5 times larger than most other mammals of comparable body size.

Endocast An internal cast of an organ, especially the brain.

Endotherm An animal whose body temperature depends upon a high and controlled rate of metabolism. Birds and mammals are endotherms. The old term for this thermal strategy is warm-blooded. Endotherms are sometimes referred to as homeotherms.

Energy The potential to do work; has the same units as work.

Enzyme A protein which promotes a particular chemical reaction within a living organism.

Evolution The concept that present-day organisms are the modified descendants of organisms that once lived on the Earth. Birds, for example, evolved from reptiles, during the Mesozoic Era.

Extant An organism which is still living.

Extending Moving a segment of the body such that the angle of the joint is increased. When we straighten a bent leg, we are extending the lower leg segment (from the knee down) because the angle of the knee joint is increased.

Fauna A collective term for all animals living in a given place, as opposed to all the plants (flora).

Flapping flight The mode of flying where most of the energy is obtained from the wing muscles. Many birds, including the pigeon, are primarily flapping fliers.

Flexing Moving a segment of the body such that the angle of the joint is decreased. When we bend a straight leg, we are flexing the lower segment (from the knee down) because the angle of the knee joint is decreased.

Force The product of mass and acceleration. The standard unit of force is the Newton (N), defined as the force experienced by a mass of one kilogram accelerated by one metre per second per second. The acceleration due to gravity is 9.81 metres per second per second (written 9.81 ms^{-2}); therefore an average-sized apple, which has a mass of about 0.1 kilogram, would strike the ground with a force of about 1 N when dropped from a height of 1 metre.

Fossil The remains of an organism, such as bones or shell, or evidence of an organism, such as its footprints, which are preserved in rocks, in the ground, in caves, and in similar locations.

Friction drag That part of the drag force acting on a body moving through a fluid that is attributable to the friction, or viscosity, of the fluid particles. Friction drag acts tangentially to the surface of the body.

Gliding angle The angle between the flight path of a gliding aircraft and the horizontal.

Gliding flight The mode of flying where most of the energy is obtained from horizontal air movements. The albatross is primarily a glider and covers many thousands of miles on the wing.

Graviportal Having a skeleton adapted for bearing large weights. One of the features of a graviportal animal, as exemplified by the elephant, is that the leg bones are kept essentially straight-in-line.

Ground speed The speed of a body, usually an aircraft, relative to the ground. See also air speed.

Herbivore A plant eater. Herbivorous animals include cows and sheep as well as most ornithischians, and the sauropod dinosaurs.

Histology The study of the microscopic structure of organs, tissues and cells.

Homeotherm An animal whose body temperature is maintained within small limits ($\pm 2C^{\circ}$). This term is often used interchangeably with the term endotherm, the latter being preferred.

Ichthyosaur An extinct marine reptile that lived during the Mesozoic Era. Ichthyosaurs were so specialised for living in the sea that they bore a superficial resemblance to fishes.

Inertia The tendency for a body to continue in its existing state of rest, or of uniform motion, unless acted upon by an external force. The inertia of a body increases with its mass; it is harder to push a stationary bus than a stationary car.

Inertial homeotherm An animal that maintains an essentially constant body temperature by virtue of its large body mass. Large reptiles, like the Galapagos tortoise, are inertial homeotherms.

Intermediate form An organism or group of organisms which is intermediate in some or all of its features between two other organisms or groups of organisms, either living or extinct. *Archaeopteryx*, for example, is intermediate between reptiles and modern birds.

Invertebrate An animal without a vertebral column (backbone).

Jurassic Period The middle one of the three geological periods comprising the Mesozoic Era; lasting from approximately 180 million years ago to 135 million years ago.

Laminar flow A pattern of flow where the particles of a fluid all move parallel to one another. Laminar flow is characterised by smooth, turbulent-free movements in the fluid. The glossy stream of water from a gently running tap exemplifies laminar flow.

Leading edge slot A device on the leading edge of a wing to delay the onset of the stalling condition. This is achieved by smoothing the airflow over the wing, delaying the onset of separation from the surface of the wing.

Lepidosaur A type of reptile; a member of the Subclass Lepidosauria, which includes lizards and snakes.

Lias The earliest part of the Jurassic Period.

Ligament A tough, flexible, fibrous tissue, often in the form of a short band, used for binding bones together.

Macroevolution The evolutionary processes that result in the appearance of new groups beyond the level of the species. The evolution of mammals from reptiles is an example of macroevolution.

Mandible The lower jaw.

Mass The quantity of matter of a body, usually measured in grams or kilograms. Mass, in contrast to weight, is independent of gravity, therefore a 500 gram brick would still have a mass of 500 grams on the moon.

Mesozoic Era The geological period lasting from approximately 230 million years ago to 63 million years ago, when reptiles were the dominant vertebrate animals. Also know as the Age of Reptiles.

Metabolic rate The rate at which a resting animal expends energy. Metabolic rate varies from one group to another—it is higher in mammals, for example, than in reptiles.

Metabolism The sum total of the chemical processes occurring within a body.

Mollusc An invertebrate animal belonging to the Phylum Mollusca. Molluscs are soft-bodied animals and most, but not all of them, have an outer shell. The group includes snails, slugs, limpets and squids.

Morphology The study of structural features, such as the shape and size of organisms.

Mosasaur An extinct marine lizard that lived during the Cretaceous Period. Mosasaurs were the largest of all lizards.

Mutation A spontaneous change in the genetic material. Changes in genes are called gene mutations, changes in chromosomes are called chromosome mutations.

Natural selection The mechanism of evolution where individuals possessing features that give them an advantage over other individuals of the same species increase their representation in the next generation.

Neontologist One who studies living organisms.

Neontology The study of living organisms.

Neo-Darwinian evolution The modern concept of evolution which combines Darwin's theory of natural selection and modern genetics.

Nocturnal Active at night. Bats, for example, are nocturnal animals.

Ornithischian A type of dinosaur; a member of the Order Ornithischia. The ornithischians were mostly plant-eaters and comprise four suborders: Ornithopoda, Ceratopsia, Stegosauria and Ankylosauria. The ornithischians are sometimes called the bird-hipped dinosaurs for the structure of their pelvic girdles.

Ornithopod A type of dinosaur; a member of the Suborder Ornithopoda of the Order Ornithischia. Ornithopods were plant-eaters and the group includes the hadrosaurs.

Palaeontologist One who studies fossils.

Palaeontology The study of fossils of extinct organisms.

Pectoral girdle The shoulder girdle.

Pelagic Living in the open waters as opposed to living close to the shore, or on the bottom.

Pelvic girdle The pelvis.

Permian Period The geological period immediately preceeding the Mesozoic Era;

lasting from approximately 280 million years ago to 230 million years ago.

Phyletic gradualism The concept that most species are undergoing small but continuous changes and that, over a long period of time, these changes accumulate to the point where the current species is sufficiently different from the original one that it is called a new species. This concept, which was held by Darwin and widely believed, is now challenged by the opposing concept, called punctuated equilibrium.

Physiology The study of living processes which take place inside organisms; includes such subjects as digestion, blood circulation and reproduction.

Pitch Up and down movement about a horizontal axis passing through the centre of gravity of a body, at right angles to its longitudinal axis.

Plantigrade Walking on the whole of the foot. We are plantigrade when we walk, placing our heels on the ground.

Plesiosaur An extinct marine reptile that lived during the Mesozoic Era. Plesiosaurs are characterised by having paddle-shaped fore and hind limbs and large plate-like shoulder and hip girdles. Some plesiosaurs (called elasmosaurs) had long necks and small heads; others (called pliosaurs) had short necks and large heads.

Pliosaur A type of plesiosaur, having a short neck and large head.

Poikilotherm An animal that does not regulate its body temperature, which accordingly varies with ambient temperatures. Most fishes and many amphibians are poikilotherms. The term cold-blooded has been used for this thermal strategy.

Power The rate of doing work; usually expressed in watts (joules per second).

Pressure drag That part of the drag force acting on a body moving through a fluid that is attributable to the inertia of the fluid particles. Pressure drag is therefore directly proportional to the density of the fluid. Pressure drag acts at right angles to the surface of the body.

Protraction Extending a limb, or limb segment, forward during locomotion. When we are walking and our right foot is on the ground, the left foot is being swung forward and is said to be under protraction.

Pterosaur An extinct flying reptile that lived during the Mesozoic Era.

Punctuated equilibrium The concept that most species remain essentially unchanged over long periods of time and that the changes which lead to the formation of a new species occur in a relatively (geological speaking) short time. Long periods of stasis (no change) are therefore interspersed with short bursts of rapid change.

Reproductive isolation Where an organism, or more usually a group of organisms, is isolated from other such groups of the same species such that interbreeding between then can no longer occur.

Reptile A vertebrate animal belonging to the Class Reptilia. Most reptiles live on the land and are characterised by having a dry scaly skin and laying shelled eggs.

Retraction Pulling a limb, or limb segment, backwards during locomotion. When we are walking and our right foot is on the ground, the right leg being drawn back as our left foot swings forward, our right leg is said to be under retraction.

Reynolds number A dimensionless number that expresses the relative magnitudes of the inertial and frictional forces in a fluid system. The product of the length of the body, its speed and the density of the fluid divided by the viscosity of the fluid.

Rhynchocephalia A type of reptile; a member of the Order Rhynchocephalia of the Subclass Lepidosauria. These lizard-like reptiles, which date back to the beginning of the Mesozoic Era, have a single living representative, *Sphenodon* (the Tuatara), found only in New Zealand.

Roll Movement about a horizontal axis passing through the centre of a body, along its longitudinal axis.

Saurischian A type of dinosaur; a member of the Order Saurischia, comprising the sauropods (giant plant-eaters) and the theropods (meat-eaters).

Sauropod A type of dinosaur; a member of the Suborder Sauropoda of the Order Saurischia. Sauropods were plant-eaters, most were large, and the group includes the largest land animals that have ever lived.

Sexual dimorphism Where males and females of a species are morphologically distinct. In many species of birds, for example, including Birds of Paradise, there is a striking dimorphism between the brightly coloured males and the dull females.

Sibling species Two or more species that are so similar to each other that they often cannot be distinguished on morphological features.

Soaring flight The mode of flying where most of the energy is obtained from vertical air movements. Many birds of prey, including vultures, spend much of their time in the air soaring on thermals.

Species An aggregate of interbreeding populations of organisms that are reproductively isolated from any similar group. The yardstick of whether two individuals belong to the same species is whether they freely interbreed when they come into contact in the wild.

Spinal cord The central nerve cord that runs along the length of the vertebral column and which connects with the brain.

Stalling speed The speed at which there is a sudden breaking away of the airflow from a large proportion of the surface of the wing. When the speed of an aircraft falls to the stalling speed, it experiences buffeting and a sudden loss of lift which causes it to sink.

Stegosaur A type of dinosaur; a member of the Suborder Stegosauria of the Order Ornithischia. Stegosaurs, which were plant-eaters, were armoured with bony plates that projected vertically from the body.

Stratigraphy The study of the order and relative position of rock layers (strata).

Streamlined The term used to describe a body whose cross-sectional shape is gently tapering from before to behind, such that the thickest part (the shoulder) occurs about one third of the way back from the front surface. Streamlined bodies, found in structures that move at high Reynolds numbers, reduce the magnitude of the drag force by capitalising on the beneficial effect of the pressure drag acting on the posterior surfaces of the body.

Stress Force per unit area, once measured in pounds per square inch but now measured in Newtons per square metre.

Stride The distance between one footprint and the next footprint made with the same foot.

Synapsid A type of reptile; a member of the Subclass Synapsida, also known as the mammal-like reptiles.

Tendon A tough, flexible, fibrous tissue, often in the form of a cord, used for attaching muscles to bones.

Thecodont A type of reptile; a member of the Order Thecodontia of the Subclass Archosauria. Included within the Thecodontia are the ancestors of the dinosaurs.

Total reaction Of an airfoil; the resultant of lift and drag; the summation of these two vectors.

Triassic Period The first of the three geological periods comprising the Mesozoic Era; lasting from approximately 230 million years ago to 180 million years ago.

Turbulent flow A pattern of flow where the particles of a fluid do not all move parallel to one another. Turbulent flow is characterised by swirling movements in the fluid. The tumbling cascade of water issuing from a fully-opened tap exemplifiies turbulent flow.

Unguligrade Walking on the tips of the toes rather than on the toes or on the whole foot. The horse is unguligrade, and walks on the tips of its middle fingers and middle toes. Ballerinas are unguligrade when they are dancing "on their points."

Uniformity, principle of The concept that past processes, especially geological processes, can be explained in terms of processes that are occurring today. Also knows as uniformitarianism. The opposite concept, catastrophism, explains past processes in terms of unique events that do not happen any more.

Vector A quantity having both magnitude and direction.

Vertebral column The flexible but stiff central supporting structure of vertebrate animals, comprising an articulated series of individual bones called vertebrae.

Vertebrate An animal with a vertebral column (backbone). Vertebrates belong to the Subphylum Craniata of the Phylum Chordata and comprise fishes, amphibians, reptiles, birds and mammals.

Viscosity The property of a fluid which expresses the readiness of the fluid particles to slip past one another. Viscosity is to fluids what friction is to solids. Water has a lower viscosity than syrup because water particles slip past each other more readily than do particles of syrup. Consequently, a body moving through water experiences less drag than it would moving through syrup.

Volume The quantity of matter displaced by a body, or the quantity contained within a vessel, usually measured in litres or millilitres.

Vortex A swirling movement in a fluid. The swirling in the air at the tip of the wings of an aircraft are described as wing-tip vortices.

Weight The force with which a body is attracted towards the Earth or other heavenly body, usually measured in grams or kilograms. Although used interchangeably with mass, the two quantities are not the same because weight varies with gravity whereas mass does not. Therefore a brick which weighs 500 grams on Earth would weigh less on the Moon, but its mass would remain unchanged.

Wing loading The weight of an aircraft divided by its total wing area.

Work The product of force and distance. When a force of one Newton moves its point of application through a distance of one metre, one joule of work has been performed.

Yaw Sideways movement about a vertical axis passing through the centre of gravity of a body, at right angles to its longitudinal axis.

Zygapophyses Paired processes from the anterior and posterior aspects of a vertebra, just above the neural canal. Adjacent zygapophyses articulate with one another, strengthening the inter-vertebral joint, and limiting its movement.

Source of Illustrations and Acknowledgements

(illustrations not listed are courtesy of Royal Ontario Museum or were provided by the author)

Chapter 1
- Largely after Dietz R.S. and Holden, J.C. 1970. "The breakup of Pangaea." *Scientific American*, volume 223. *p* 5
- After Owen, R. 1866. *On the anatomy of vertebrates*, volume 1, Longmans, Green & Co., London. *p*6
- After Eaton, G.F. 1910. "Osteology of *Pteranodon*," *Memoirs of the Connecticut Academy of Arts and Science*, volume 2. *p*6 Courtesy of the Connecticut Academy of Arts and Science.
- After Ewer, R.F. 1965. "The anatomy of the thecodont reptile *Euparkeria capensis* Broom." *Philosophical Transactions of the Royal Society of London*, volume 248. Courtesy of the Royal Society of London. *pp* 7,9
- Marg Sansom *pp* 10, 11
- Jeff Thomason *pp*12, 13

Chapter 2
- Engraving from a photograph by L. Darwin. Darwin, F. (ed.) 1887. *The life and letters of Charles Darwin*, volume 2, John Murray, London. *p* 15
- After Phillips, J. 1855. *The Geology of Yorkshire*. John Murray, London. *p*16
- After Cuvier, G. 1804. "Mémoires sur l'Ibis des anciens Egyptiens." *Annales du Muséum national d'Histoire naturelle*, volume 4. *p* 17
- Darwin, C. 1839. *Journal of researches into the geology and natural history of the various countries visited by H.M.S. Beagle*. John Murray, London. *pp* 19, 21, 22, 25
- After Owen, R. 1851. "On the *Megatherium* (*Megatherium Americanus*, Blumenback)." *Philosophical Transactions of the Royal Society of London*, volume 141. *p*20
- Engraving from *Century Magazine*, January 1883. *p* 27

Chapter 3
- Marg Sansom *p* 43

Chapter 4
- Marg Sansom *pp* 51, 57, 61, 65, 67, 69, 74, 78
- After Marsh, O.C. This is one of many figures which have now been published and which appear in Ostrom, J.H. and McIntosh, J.S. 1966. *Marsh's Dinosaurs*. Yale University Press, New Haven. Courtesy of United States Geological Survey. *p* 54

Chapter 5

- Marg Sansom *pp* 82,84
- After Owen, R. 1866. *On the anatomy of vertebrates*, volume 2, Longmans, Green & Co., London. *pp* 80,86
- After Marsh, O.C. These figures have now been published in Ostrom & McIntosh 1966, *op.cit.* Courtesy of the United States Geological Survey. *pp* 87,88,90
- After Marsh, O.C. 1894. "The dinosaurs of North America," 16th Annual Report of the U.S. Geological Society, Washington. *p* 88
- After Osborn, H.F. and Mook, C.C. 1921 "*Camarasaurus, Amphioelias* and other sauropods of Cope." *Memoirs of the American Museum of Natural History*, volume 3. *p* 91
- After Osborn, H.F. 1912. "Crania of *Tyrannosaurus* and *Allosaurus*." *Memoirs of the American Museum of Natural History*, volume 1.
  Both figures courtesy of the American Museum of Natural History, New York. *p* 91
- Courtesy of the American Museum of Natural History, New York. *p* 93

Chapter 6

- Marg Sansom *p* 101
- Photograph courtesy of Alan Hollet *p* 103
- Photograph courtesy of Allan Baker *p* 109

Chapter 7

- Marg Sansom *p* 119
- After Owen, R.1868. *On the anatomy of vertebrates*, volume 3 Longmans, Green & Co., London. *p* 120
- Modified from Jerison, H.J. 1973. *Evolution of the brain and intelligence*. Academic Press, New York. *p* 125
- After Marsh, O.C. This figure has now been published in Ostrom & McIntosh 1966, *op.cit.* Courtesy of the United States Geological Society. *p* 132
- After Newton, E.T. 1888. "On the skull, brain and auditory organ of a new species of pterosaurian *(Scaphognathus Purdoni)*, from the Upper Lias near Whitby, Yorkshire." *Philosophical Transactions of the Royal Society of London*, volume 179. *p* 133

Chapter 8

- After Hawkins, T. 1834. *Memoirs of Ichthyosauri and Plesiosauri*. Relfe and Fletcher, London.*pp*137, 140
- After Home, E. 1814. "Some account of the fossil remains of an animal more nearly allied to fishes than any other classes of animals." *Philosophical Transactions of the Royal Society of London*, volume 104. *p* 142
- Illustrated London News 1855, volume 26. *p*145
- Marg Sansom *pp* 147, 150, 155, 158, 160, 161, 164, 166
- After Camp, C.L. 1980. "Large ichthyosaurs from the Upper Triassic of Nevada." *Palaeontographica*, volume 170. Courtesy of the Scientific Photographic Laboratory of the University of California at Berkley. *p* 152
- Courtesy of the Director, Institute of Geological Sciences, London. *p* 156
- Courtesy of the Museum National d'Histoire Naturelle, Paris. *p*161
- After Andrews, C.W. 1910. *A descriptive catalogue of the Marine Reptiles of the Oxford Clay*. British Museum, London. Courtesy of the Trustees of the British Museum (Natural History). *p*164
- Jeff Thomason *pp* 173, 180, 181, 183

Chapter 9

- Seeley, H.G.S. 1901. *Dragons of the air*. Methuen, London. *p*190
- After Williston, S.W. 1925. *The osteology of the reptiles*. Harvard University Press, Cambridge. Courtesy of Harvard University Press. *p* 192
- After Eaton, G.F. 1910. "Osteology of *Pteranodon*," *Memoirs of the Connecticut Academy of Arts and Science*, volume 2. Courtesy of the Connecticut Academy of Arts and Science. *pp*200, 20
- Redrawn from Bramwell, C.D. and Whitfield, G.R. 1974. "Biomechanics of *Pteranodon*," *Philosophical Transactions of the Royal Society of London*, volume 267. *p* 201
- Marg Sansom *p*203
- Jeff Thomason *pp* 195, 196, 207, 210

Chapter 10

- Mantell, G.A. 1851. *Petrifications and their teachings*. Henry G. Bohn, London. *p* 213
- Courtesy of Dale Russell *p*216

Index

D

E

F

G

H